PSYCHOPATHOLOGY AND

LITERATURE

PSYCHOPATHOLOGY

AND

LITERATURE

Selected and Edited by

Leslie Y. Rabkin

UNIVERSITY OF ROCHESTER

CHANDLER PUBLISHING COMPANY

124 Spear Street, San Francisco, California 94105

For Karen, who likes to hear it all read aloud.

CONTENTS

vii

II. THE PSYCHOSES

III. CHARACTER AND PERSONALITY DISORDERS

IV. BRAIN DISORDERS

V. THERAPY

SELECTED BIBLIOGRAPHIES

PREFACE

But see the *Madman* rage down right
With furious looks, a ghastly sight.
Naked in chains bound he doth ly,
And roars amain, he knows not why?
Observe him: for as in a glass,
Thine angry portraiture it was.
His picture keep still in thy presence:
Twixt him and thee, there's no difference.

—Robert Burton, *The Anatomy of Melancholy*

It is my hope that *Psychopathology and Literature* will prove a useful resource for the study of the interrelationship between literature and psychology, however this problem is approached. The table of contents reflects the subject matter encountered in a course on abnormal psychology, and the over-all book is intended as an ancilla to a standard text in this subject. Courses in psychology relying heavily or even exclusively on literary materials have been previously described[1] and reported to be successful in arousing and sustaining interest while providing the student with an exciting arena of materials for examining human behavior in all its variegated complexity. The editor has also used this approach with marked success.

A word on the format of the book. The introduction contains a brief commentary on some aspects of the association of literature and psychology and, more specifically, the literary rendering of psychopatho-

---

[1] See A.B. Wood, Psychodynamics through literature. *Amer. Psychologist*, 1955, *10*, 32-33, and E.P. Hollander. Popular literature in the undergraduate social psychology course. *Amer. Psychologist*, 1956, *11*, 95-96.

logical phenomena. As a framework, then, for the selection of readings, the standard psychiatric diagnostic categories have been utilized, focussing on the neuroses, psychoses, character problems, and brain disorders, and including several forms of childhood disturbance under the adult diagnosis to which they are most closely allied. Not every form of disorder subsumed under these general categories has been illustrated, but as wide a range as possible has been included.

Each of the five parts begins with a brief summary of the meaning and content of the generic diagnostic label and every selection is prefaced by a more specific commentary on the disorder represented therein. These prefaces are merely a means of orienting the reader and are not intended as systematic surveys of the pertinent psychological literature nor as literary critiques.

I have tried to utilize selections of intrinsic literary worth and th us provide the reader with something of an aesthetic as well as an intellectual experience. Unfortunately copyright difficulties and similar problems precluded the inclusion of many other items of equal worth. I have deviated from the use of purely fictional selections in only two instances, those of F. Scott Fitzgerald (*The Crack-Up*) and William E. Leonard (*The Locomotive-God*). Both, however, are written in an extremely literary style, and should not represent a jarring intrusion of autobiographical reality.

A book such as this requires many words of thanks to many individuals. I want to single out my good friend Dr. Marvin Goldfried, whose enthusiasm kept me going. A word of sincere appreciation must also go to my secretary, Mrs. Dorothy Gray, who pleasantly provided the seemingly endless pages of copy.

Leslie Y. Rabkin

University of Rochester
Rochester, New York

PSYCHOPATHOLOGY AND LITERATURE

INTRODUCTION

Psychopathology and Literature is an attempt to bring together a collection of literary materials which illuminate, in literature's very special way, a variety of abnormal psychological states. It is offered in the belief that literature can serve an important function in the understanding of personality and, more germane to this volume, the disordered personality.

These writings are not case histories in any clinical sense,[1] but phenomenological portraits of certain conditions, feelings, and situations which are of central focus in the study of the vicissitudes of human behavior. Here the reader will find little concern with the basic causes of the behavior portrayed—the life history and early development are quickly sketched, if mentioned at all—and etiology becomes of secondary importance to the depiction of an individual in a condition of internal crisis or external stress.

What, then, is the value of literature for our explorations into personality and psychopathology? The psychologist Gordon Allport expresses one vital aspect in his commentary on the important role of humanistic thought in personality study:

In literature, personality is never regarded, as it sometimes is in psychology, as a sequence of unrelated actions. Personality is not like a water-skate, darting hither and yon on the surface of a pond, with its several fugitive excursions having no relation to one another. Good literature never makes

---

[1] There are numerous volumes of clinical case studies available and the reader is referred to these to observe how the clinician examines the causes and course of a person's behavior. Examples of such volumes are: A. Burton and R.E. Harris, *Clinical Studies of Personality*. New York: Harper & Row, 1955. and A. Burton, *Case Studies in Counseling and Psychotherapy*. New York: Prentice-Hall, 1960.

the mistake of confusing the personality of man with that of a water-skate. Psychology often does.[2]

Thus, psychology fragments, literature binds; psychology is concerned with part processes, literature is holistic; psychology strives for scientific objectivity, literature seeks for coherence and esthetic truth. In a sense, the very format of this book demonstrates the essence of these distinctions. As the table of contents makes clear, the organizing device employed is the standard psychiatric nosological categories. These diagnostic classifications represent in many ways the epitome of the psychological fragmentation of personality. Specific symptoms are delineated, and the exhibition of these behaviors results in the affixing of a label, while much of the richness and diversity of personality functioning remains ignored. As used here, these categories serve a heuristic purpose in orienting the reader to the many forms of pathological behavior, and demonstrate the wide range of abnormal psychological phenomena portrayed in literature. What the reader will quickly discover, however, is how the subtle delineation of man's behavior in the best of these selections transcends the affixed label; what is depicted is not a mere generalized case, but a complex, multileveled human being.

To the reader accustomed to the usual didactic materials in abnormal psychology, the literary approach may seem at first eccentric. Ordinarily, the study of psychopathology proceeds through three channels—the textbook, the sourcebook or collection of readings, and the volume of case histories. The textbook sketches the basic concepts of the field; the readings add depth to this outline; and the casebook brings in the human element. By the time these varied resources have been tapped, what may have seemed at first exotic and bizarre can be seen as the result of an intense and all-too-human struggle to resolve the stresses of life and achieve some sort of coherent identity, however distorted the end product may be.

It is just this struggle which has been the pivotal concern of great literature—Hamlet and Oedipus, Raskolnikov and Emma Bovary,

---

2 G. Allport, Personality: a problem for science or a problem for art. *Revista de Psihologie*, 1938, *1*, 1-15.

Don Quixote and Stephen Dedalus. The insightful delineation of the inner and outer worlds of these characters is a rich mine for the psychologist. It was Freud himself who asserted, "The poets and philosophers before me discovered the unconscious, what I discovered was the scientific method by which the unconscious can be studied."[3]

The creative artist has always examined the contradictory motivations, the inner unrest, the affects and impulses of man. Endowed with a sometimes painful self-consciousness, the writer has been able to chart the geography of the inner landscape of the mind with a power and precision unmatched by the more objective methods of psychological science.

For so many writers, the most compelling features of this psychological terrain have been the deep-shaded valleys of desire, the hidden caves of fantasy, and the dark abysses of madness. Pathological experience, in its myriad forms, has long obsessed the artist. For some, the key element has been the cathartic effect, the artist's more or less conscious attempt to embody in writing and thus purge himself of the private devils which torment him. Maupassant's anguished tales, Dostoevsky's feverish *Notes from the Underground*, Blake's eerie prophetic visions, Gogol's grotesques, Kafka's gnawing concern with guilt—all have elements of this cathartic aspect in common. Their brooding sensitivity made it possible for them to grasp and confront what Matthew Arnold called "the nameless feelings that course through our breast" and to bring things hidden and unexpressed into the light of our focussed consciousness.

Another of the fascinations of the pathological revolves around the problem of pain. All psychopathology involves pain and suffering, both mental and physical. The torment of the emotionally disturbed person, however, is often scanted in more scientific analyses of mental illness, being attributed to the patient's delusive "imagination." This is a regrettable situation. To deal with the patient's intolerable experience of pain as if it were "all in his mind," is to indicate to him a lack of empathy, of true understanding, and is often a key factor in the disruption of treatment. Anyone who has suffered pain,

---

[3] L. Trilling, *The Liberal Imagination*. Garden City: Doubleday Anchor Books, 1953, p. 32.

no matter what its origin, knows how real the expreience is, yet how difficult to communicate to another person. For the artist, this elusive agony and the helpless feelings which accompany it, provide a special focus of concern. The very thing which makes pain so intractable to scientific investigation is what draws the writer—its subjectivity. Again, it is his ability to brush aside the mask of convention, and to explore the innermost recesses of heart and mind, which makes the artist the true cartographer of pain.

The use of language is another area in which psychopathology and literature, particularly that of the past half-century, meet. The language of the artist, in its emotive richness and its use of resonant imagery, is a far better vehicle than the often dehumanized jargon of science for the description of human experience. As with the affect of pain, the writer can render the nuances of emotion and thought far more compellingly than the psychologist. And his evocative language can find no more dramatic subject than the emotional upheaval of the disordered personality.

The phenomenon known as the "poetry of madness" deserves comment here. The paradoxical, elliptical, and convoluted language of the psychotic has often been likened to that of the poet. Their use of multi-leveled meanings and unexpected juxtapositions of imagery has a formal similarity. However, as Steven Marcuse has correctly pointed out, what so often appears in the language of the psychotic as meaningful and poetic becomes, on closer examination, "merely syntactical elegies for a lost world of intelligible discourse."[4]

In more general terms, the interrelationship of psychology and literature has other dimensions. There are at least four avenues of approach to this broad topic, each independently valid and yet complementary to the others. The first and most comprehensive methodology is to explore the basic psychology of artistic creation with emphasis on writing and literary expression. This type of study might utilize the writings of such an interpreter as Ernst Kris,[5] stressing the psychological, and particularly the psychoanalytic

[4] S. Marcuse, The poetry of madness. *New York Review of Books*, 1964, 2, (9), 7-8.
[5] E. Kris, *Psychoanalytic Explorations in Art*. New York: Internat. Univ. Press, 1952.

insights which concentrate on the motivations and symbolic aspects of artistic creation. Such a study might also make use of the ideas of the Gestalt school of psychology which has conceptualized art as the finest example of the human mind's striving for a well-organized articulated wholeness.

One focus in the examination of the creative process, for example, might be the part played by regression. As Kris has pointed out, some relaxation of conscious control is a necessary condition for the "inspiration" required in artistic production. This regression is different from that which takes place during sleep, in neurosis, or under the influence of drugs. The difference is that the artist deliberately seeks this relaxed state and utilizes it for conscious, productive purposes.

We could, then, attempt to assess the respective roles of conscious control and spontaneity in literary creativity. The final pages of Gogol's *Diary of a Madman*, (see below, *Schizophrenic Reactions*) provide an excellent case in point. The narrator's disintegrating thought processes provide a series of images akin to the verbal transcription of a nightmare. The language is condensed and symbolic, appearing at first glance to be simply fantastic and incoherent. But these verbal wanderings are not merely the end-product of an eruption of spontaneous, unconscious thoughts, which somehow possess their thinker. Closer examination reveals how Gogol controls the pace and utilizes the imagery to delineate the feelings of estrangement and horror of an isolated man's retreat into madness.

A second approach deals with the *effects* of a literary piece on the reader. Here the focus is on the interaction of the psychological field of the reader—his needs, fantasies, wishes—with the structure and content of the world created by the author. Such a study might involve assessment of the effects of certain types of thematic material (for example, incest themes or agression) on varying personalities in whom such conflict areas were of more or less importance, and how each group dealt with the anxieties aroused by these themes.

The "processes of response," as Simon O. Lesser[6] has called them, are a complex amalgam of conscious and unconscious phenomena. As we read a piece of fiction, on the conscious level we attempt to grasp

---

[6] S.O. Lesser, *Fiction and the Unconscious*. Boston: Beacon Press, 1957.

its obvious or manifest meaning and follow the developing story line, while engaging in an unsystematic appraisal of such qualities as honesty and skillfulness. Our unconscious response, as Lesser demonstrates, involves a series of reactions. Most important is the unconscious apprehension of latent anxiety-arousing material, those facets of the story which are reminiscent of past, personal painful experiences. Each individual reader will have a differential response to any single episode depending on his own experiences.

Kafka's powerful story, *The Judgment* (see below, *Anxiety Reactions*), provides a suitable stimulus for such an investigation. The nature of Georg Bendemann's relationship to his father is such as to set off an unconscious resonance in some readers of an anxiety-ridden childhood struggle with a powerful and arbitrary parental authority, the fully conscious recognition of which could produce an intolerable degree of anxiety. Other unconscious elements of our response to such material may involve the phenomenon of identification, or the loss of critical distance from the characters portrayed, leading to a psychological participation in their activities, and day-dreaming behavior fostered by the stories in which we become involved.

A third approach, the biographical, explores the personality of the writer himself and attempts to assess the effect of his experiences on his literary creations, their direct reflection and various mutations and disguises. Here the concern is with the roots of a specific style of literary expression and characterization—what effect, we might ask, did Dostoevsky's epilepsy and gambling compulsion have on his literary style, his depiction of life, and his character portrayals? This technique of study views a literary work as a "personal document," an objectification, however veiled or open, of the artist's inner concerns.

In utilizing literary materials as a form of "projective test" protocol, however, we must be careful not to expect any simple isomorphism between life events and fictional portrayals. Reflections of the author's personality, in all its conscious and unconscious features, will be found in a variety of characters, as well as in the stylistic aspects of his writing.

This reflection is clearly the case in Dostoevsky's *The Idiot* (see below, *Epilepsy*). The selection from this work included here is primarily concerned with depicting the slow development and

eruption of an epileptic seizure. In the novel itself, one is struck by
the complementarity of Myshkin and Rogozhin, the former striving
to maintain control over his impulses, the latter flaunting his sexual
and aggressive behavior. Dualities such as this, whether couched in
terms of repression and license, good and evil, or control and freedom
are an obsessive concern for Dostoevsky and mirror his own inner
psychological struggle. It is important to keep in mind that these
ambivalences may be reflected in a single person or projected into a
series of characters.

The fourth avenue of exploration is the examination of a literary
character as a personality in himself. Under this heading would
appear the countless examinations of the psyche of fictional characters
such as Hamlet, Mann's von Aschenbach, or Lady Chatterley. This
approach often draws heavy critical fire from psychologist and literary critic alike because of the tendency of writers in this area to
erect monolithic psychological structures on quite shaky foundations.
Nevertheless, the intense and finely wrought literary character
study can probe as deeply as the best real-life case history and psycho-
dynamic formulation.

To examine the motivations of the fictional personality, the critic
turns to the tools of clinical psychology and psychoanalysis. The
ambivalences, defenses, and impulses which mark our own personalities are equally as present in a well-drawn literary character. His
world is finite, and we can never discover certain facts about him,
but with our accumulated knowledge concerning personality
functioning we can make some good guesses and elaborate a lucid
and consistent psychological portrait.

For example, the personality of Paul, the unhappy young hero of
Willa Cather's *Paul's Case* (see below, *Schizoid Personality*), can be
subjected to this type of character analysis. We might begin by
assessing the world around him and how he experiences the relationships and events which impinge on him. Drawing on our understanding of the psychology of adolescence, we could extrapolate about
the important relationship of Paul with his father. How, we might
ask, is their interaction different from that of other adolescent-parent
pairs? We could then go on to speculate about Paul's earlier life—the
possible effect on his personality of his mother's death, his developing
sense of isolation, the handling of his childhood fears and anxieties,

and so on. In the end, a portrait as vivid as any case history written about a lonely, frustrated adolescent would emerge. This type of analysis, let it be said, is probably most aptly applied in dealing with a novel in which the author can allow himself greater freedom in sketching the life history and behavior variabilities of his characters.

Literature and psychology thus interpenetrate at many points. For the literary critic, the tools of psychology provide a means of access to new levels of understanding a work of art, the artist who created it, and the audience which responds to it. For the psychologist, the artist's ability to depict delicate shadings of feeling and thought, and to portray the hidden motives of man, makes literature an indispensable resource for the investigation of personality in its most holistic sense.

Anna Sergeyevna was silent for a little. "And so you haven't the least artistic feeling?" she observed, putting her elbow on the table, and by that very action bringing her face nearer to Bazarov. "How can you get on without it?"

"Why, what should I need it for, may I ask?"

"Well, at least to enable you to study and understand men."—Turgenev, *Fathers and Sons*[7]

[7] Quoted in R. N. Wilson, Literature, society and personality. *J. aesth. art Criticism*, 1952, *10*, 297-309.

PART ONE

THE

PSYCHONEUROSES

The neuroses or psychoneuroses represent the most common form of personality maladjustment. Indeed, it has on occasion been estimated that one in every ten people in the United States is suffering from neurotic symptoms severe enough to require some form of psychiatric help. Although the incidence of neuroses appears to be higher in certain segments of the population—primarily the white middle and upper classes—neurotic symptomatology can be found in all spheres of society.

Whatever their particular school of thought concerning etiology, most observers are in agreement about the central aspects of neurotic behavior, or what has been called "the neurotic nucleus." The roots have been found to lie in childhood experiences, in the way the individual learns to cope with anxiety. There are many forms of anxiety, but they share in common a state of tense expectancy and brooding disquiet, what the hero of Maupassant's "He?" calls "that horrible sensation of incomprehensible fear." These experiences, arising early in childhood, have been characterized by Karen Horney as a state of "basic anxiety," a feeling the child develops of being helpless, alone, and afraid in a potentially cruel and dangerous world. The ways learned for coping with these feelings are carried into adulthood where they prove incapable of dealing with new crises; the shaky equilibrium gives way, and ultimately a vicious cycle ensues: anxiety, defensive breakdown, greater anxiety, and the development of neurotic symptom patterns.

Some of the many forms these patterns may take are exemplified below. In most of the selections, although their intensity varies, feelings of anxiety are clearly in evidence; in all of them the final symptom complex is the main focus.

The six symptom patterns presented in these readings are those which have been given official recognition by the American Psychiatric Association. They include the *anxiety reactions*, marked by a persistent state of restless uneasiness and strain; the *dissociative reactions*, exemplified by amnesias and dream states, in which part of the person's life is walled off from consciousness, more or less transiently; the *conversion reactions*, characterized by some form of physical illness which exists without any organic impairment; the *phobic reactions*, or the persistent fear of some life situation or object which offers no real threat to the individual; the *obsessive-compulsive reactions*, in which the person experiences an overwhelming compulsion to repetitively engage in some irrational act or is visited by thoughts which recur and cannot be shaken; and the *depressive reactions*, marked by excessive feelings of sadness, discouragement, lowered self-assurance and loss of initiative, usually precipitated by a current stressful situation.

Anxiety Reactions

Anxiety, that constricting, debilitating fear of everything and nothing is chillingly portrayed in Kafka's "The Judgment" and Maupassant's "He?" The dread and apprehension which Georg Bendemann and the narrator of "He?" experience—Georg in relation to the guilt his father's insane words arouse in him, and the threatened emergence of his own rage towards this overwhelming authority; the anonymous narrator in confronting his isolation—are the key symptoms of the anxiety neurotic. For the neurotic, as for both of these characters, the defensive systems of the personality are inadequate for coping with his current life stresses, and thus the individual is left vulnerable to these feelings of helplessness and loneliness.

It is particularly interesting to observe the vicissitudes of hostility and dependency in Georg Bendemann's relationship with his father. The control of hostile feelings poses great problems to the neurotic who, like Georg, so commonly feels blocked in his strivings for autonomy but cannot express his anger for fear he will be rejected and painfully retaliated against. Despite his overwhelming, childlike fear of his father—note his shrinking into the corner when he feels attacked—Georg's hostility keeps breaking through (" 'You comedian!' Georg could not resist the retort . . .") only to increase his anxiety. Maupassant's narrator succinctly sums up the core of the neurotic's anxiety—"I am not afraid of any danger . . . I am afraid of myself . . . afraid of my own dreadful thoughts, of my reason, which seems as if it were about to leave me, driven away by a mysterious and invisible agony."

Franz Kafka

THE JUDGMENT

It was a Sunday morning in the very height of spring. Georg Bendemann, a young merchant, was sitting in his own room on the first floor of one of a long row of small, ramshackle houses stretching beside the river which were scarcely distinguishable from each other except in height and coloring. He had just finished a letter to an old friend of his who was now living abroad, had put it into its envelope in a slow and dreamy fashion, and with his elbows propped on the writing table was gazing out of the window at the river, the bridge and the hills on the farther bank with their tender green.

He was thinking about his friend, who had actually run away to Russia some years before, being dissatisfied with his prospects at home. Now he was carrying on a business in St. Petersburg, which had flourished to begin with but had long been going downhill, as he always complained on his increasingly rare visits. So he was wearing himself out to no purpose in a foreign country, the unfamiliar full beard he wore did not quite conceal the face Georg had known so well since childhood, and his skin was growing so yellow as to indicate some latent disease. By his own account he had no regular connection with the colony of his fellow countrymen out there and almost no social intercourse with Russian families, so that he was resigning himself to becoming a permanent bachelor.

Franz Kafka, "The Judgment," in The Penal Colony, *tr. by Willa and Edwin Muir. New York: Schocken Books, 1948.*

What could one write to such a man, who had obviously run off the rails, a man one could be sorry for but could not help. Should one advise him to come home, to transplant himself and take up his old friendships again—there was nothing to hinder him—and in general to rely on the help of his friends? But that was as good as telling him, and the more kindly the more offensively, that all his efforts hitherto had miscarried, that he should finally give up, come back home, and be gaped at by everyone as a returned prodigal, that only his friends knew what was what and that he himself was just a big child who should do what his successful and home-keeping friends prescribed. And was it certain, besides, that all the pain one would have to inflict on him would achieve its object? Perhaps it would not even be possible to get him to come home at all—he said himself that he was now out of touch with commerce in his native country—and then he would still be left an alien in a foreign land embittered by his friends' advice and more than ever estranged from them. But if he did follow their advice and then didn't fit in at home—not out of malice, of course, but through force of circumstances—couldn't get on with his friends or without them, felt humiliated, couldn't be said to have either friends or a country of his own any longer, wouldn't it have been better for him to stay abroad just as he was? Taking all this into account how could one be sure that he would make a success of life at home?

For such reasons, supposing one wanted to keep up correspondence with him, one could not send him any real news such as could frankly be told to the most distant acquaintance. It was more than three years since his last visit, and for this he offered the lame excuse that the political situation in Russia was too uncertain, which apparently would not permit even the briefest absence of a small business man while it allowed hundreds of thousands of Russians to travel peacefully abroad. But during these three years Georg's own position in life had changed a lot. Two years ago his mother had died, since when he and his father had shared the household together, and his friend had of course been informed of that and had expressed his sympathy in a letter phrased so dryly that the grief caused by such an event, one had to conclude, could not be realized in a distant country. Since that time, however, Georg had applied

himself with greater determination to the business as well as to
everything else.

Perhaps during his mother's lifetime his father's insistence on
having everything his own way in the business had hindered him
from developing any real activity of his own, perhaps since her death
his father had become less aggressive, although he was still active in
the business, perhaps it was mostly due to an accidental run of good
fortune—which was very probable indeed—but at any rate during
those two years the business had developed in a most unexpected
way, the staff had had to be doubled, the turnover was five times as
great, no doubt about it, farther progress lay just ahead.

But Georg's friend had no inkling of this improvement. In earlier
years, perhaps for the last time in that letter of condolence, he had
tried to persuade Georg to emigrate to Russia and had enlarged
upon the prospects of success for precisely Georg's branch of trade.
The figures quoted were microscopic by comparison with the range
of Georg's present operations. Yet he shrank from letting his friend
know about his business success, and if he were to do it now retro-
spectively that certainly would look peculiar.

So Georg confined himself to giving his friend unimportant
items of gossip such as rise at random in the memory when one is
idly thinking things over on a quiet Sunday. All he desired was to
leave undisturbed the idea of the home town which his friend must
have built up to his own content during the long interval. And so it
happened to Georg that three times in three fairly widely separated
letters he had told his friend about the engagement of an unimportant man to an equally unimportant girl, until indeed, quite
contrary to his intentions, his friend began to show some interest in
this notable event.

Yet Georg preferred to write about things like these rather than
to confess that he himself had got engaged a month ago to a Fräulein
Frieda Brandenfeld, a girl from a well-to-do family. He often
discussed this friend of his with his fiancée and the peculiar relationship that had developed between them in their correspondence.
"So he won't be coming to our wedding," said she, "and yet I have
a right to get to know all your friends." "I don't want to trouble
him," answered Georg, "don't misunderstand me, he would probably
come, at least I think so, but he would feel that his hand had

been forced and he would be hurt, perhaps he would envy me and certainly he'd be discontented and without being able to do anything about his discontent he'd have to go away again alone. Alone—do you know what that means?" "Yes, but may he not hear about our wedding in some other fashion?" "I can't prevent that, of course, but it's unlikely, considering the way he lives." "Since your friends are like that, Georg, you shouldn't ever have got engaged at all." "Well, we're both to blame for that; but I wouldn't have it any other way now." And when, breathing quickly under his kisses, she still brought out: "All the same, I do feel upset," he thought it could not really involve him in trouble were he to send the news to his friend. "That's the kind of man I am and he'll just have to take me as I am," he said to himself, "I can't cut myself to another pattern that might make a more suitable friend for him."

And in fact he did inform his friend, in the long letter he had been writing that Sunday morning, about his engagement, with these words: "I have saved my best news to the end. I have got engaged to a Fräulein Frieda Brandenfeld, a girl from a well-to-do family, who only came to live here a long time after you went away, so that you're hardly likely to know her. There will be time to tell you more about her later, for today let me just say that I am very happy and as between you and me the only difference in our relationship is that instead of a quite ordinary kind of friend you will now have in me a happy friend. Besides that, you will acquire in my fiancée, who sends her warm greetings and will soon write you herself, a genuine friend of the opposite sex, which is not without importance to a bachelor. I know that there are many reasons why you can't come to see us, but would not my wedding be precisely the right occasion for giving all obstacles the go-by? Still, however that may be, do just as seems good to you without regarding any interests but your own."

With this letter in his hand Georg had been sitting a long time at the writing table, his face turned towards the window. He had barely acknowledged, with an absent smile, a greeting waved to him from the street by a passing acquaintance.

At last he put the letter in his pocket and went out of his room across a small lobby into his father's room, which he had not entered for months. There was in fact no need for him to enter it, since he saw his father daily at business and they took their midday meal together at an eating house; in the evening, it was true, each did as he pleased, yet even then, unless Georg—as mostly happened—went out with friends or, more recently, visited his fiancée, they always sat for a while, each with his newspaper, in their common sitting room.

It surprised Georg how dark his father's room was even on this sunny morning. So it was overshadowed as much as that by the high wall on the other side of the narrow courtyard. His father was sitting by the window in a corner hung with various mementoes of Georg's dead mother, reading a newspaper which he held to one side before his eyes in an attempt to overcome a defect of vision. On the table stood the remains of his breakfast, not much of which seemed to have been eaten.

"Ah, Georg," said his father, rising at once to meet him. His heavy dressing gown swung open as he walked and the skirts of it fluttered round him.—"My father is still a giant of a man," said Georg to himself.

"It's unbearably dark here," he said aloud.

"Yes, it's dark enough," answered his father.

"And you've shut the window, too?"

"I prefer it like that."

"Well, it's quite warm outside," said Georg, as if continuing his previous remark, and sat down.

His father cleared away the breakfast dishes and set them on a chest.

"I really only wanted to tell you," went on Georg, who had been vacantly following the old man's movements, "that I am now sending the news of my engagement to St. Petersburg." He drew the letter a little way from his pocket and let it drop back again.

"To St. Petersburg?" asked his father.

"To my friend there," said Georg, trying to meet his father's eye.—In business hours he's quite different, he was thinking, how solidly he sits here with his arms crossed.

"Oh yes. To your friend," said his father, with peculiar emphasis.

"Well, you know, Father, that I wanted not to tell him about my engagement at first. Out of consideration for him, that was the only reason. You know yourself he's a difficult man. I said to myself that someone else might tell him about my engagement, although he's such a solitary creature that that was hardly likely—I couldn't prevent that—but I wasn't ever going to tell him myself."

"And now you've changed your mind?" asked his father, laying his enormous newspaper on the window sill and on top of it his spectacles, which he covered with one hand.

"Yes, I've been thinking it over. If he's a good friend of mine, I said to myself, my being happily engaged should make him happy too. And so I wouldn't put off telling him any longer. But before I posted the letter I wanted to let you know."

"Georg," said his father, lengthening his toothless mouth, "listen to me! You've come to me about this business, to talk it over with me. No doubt that does you honor. But it's nothing, it's worse than nothing, if you don't tell me the whole truth. I don't want to stir up matters that shouldn't be mentioned here. Since the death of our dear mother certain things have been done that aren't right. Maybe the time will come for mentioning them, and maybe sooner than we think. There's many a thing in the business I'm not aware of, maybe it's not done behind my back—I'm not going to say that it's done behind my back—I'm not equal to things any longer, my memory's failing, I haven't an eye for so many things any longer. That's the course of nature in the first place, and in the second place the death of our dear mother hit me harder than it did you.—But since we're talking about it, about this letter, I beg you, Georg, don't deceive me. It's a trivial affair, it's hardly worth mentioning, so don't deceive me. Do you really have this friend in St. Petersburg?"

Georg rose in embarrassment. "Never mind my friends. A thousand friends wouldn't make up to me for my father. Do you know what I think? You're not taking enough care of yourself. But old age must be taken care of. I can't do without you in the business, you know that very well, but if the business is going to undermine your health, I'm ready to close it down tomorrow forever. And that won't do. We'll have to make a change in your way of living. But a radical change. You sit here in the dark, and in the sitting room you would have plenty of light. You just take a bite of breakfast instead of properly keeping up your strength. You sit by a closed window, and the air would be so good for you. No, Father! I'll get the doctor to come, and we'll follow his orders. We'll change your room, you can move into the front room and I'll move in here. You won't notice the change, all your things will be moved with you. But there's time for all that later, I'll put you to bed now for a little, I'm sure you need to rest. Come, I'll help you to take off your things, you'll see I can do it. Or if you would rather go into the front room at once, you can lie down in my bed for the present. That would be the most sensible thing."

Georg stood close beside his father, who had let his head with its unkempt white hair sink on his chest.

"Georg," said his father in a low voice, without moving.

Georg knelt down at once beside his father, in the old man's weary face he saw the pupils, over-large, fixedly looking at him from the corners of the eyes.

"You have no friend in St. Petersburg. You've always been a leg-puller and you haven't even shrunk from pulling my leg. How could you have a friend out there! I can't believe it."

"Just think back a bit, Father," said Georg, lifting his father from the chair and slipping off his dressing gown as he stood feebly enough, "it'll soon be three years since my friend came to see us last. I remember that you used not to like him very much. At least twice I kept you from seeing him, although he was actually sitting with me in my room. I could quite well understand your dislike of him, my friend has his peculiarities. But then, later, you got on with him very well. I was proud because you listened to him and nodded and asked him questions. If you think back you're bound to remember. He used to tell us the most incredible stories of the Russian Revolution. For instance, when he was on a business trip to Kiev and ran into a riot, and saw a priest on a balcony who cut a broad cross in blood on the palm of his hand and held the hand up and appealed to the mob. You've told that story yourself once or twice since."

Meanwhile Georg had succeeded in lowering his father down again and carefully taking off the woollen drawers he wore over his linen underpants and his socks. The not particularly clean appearance of this underwear made him reproach himself for having been neglectful. It should have certainly been his duty to see that his father had clean changes of underwear. He had not yet explicitly discussed with his bride-to-be what arrangements should be made for his father in the future, for they had both of them silently taken it for granted that the old man would go on living alone in the old house. But now he made a quick, firm decision to take him into his own future establishment. It almost looked, on closer inspection, as if the care he meant to lavish there on his father might come too late.

He carried his father to bed in his arms. It gave him a dreadful feeling to notice that while he took the few steps towards the bed the old man on his breast was playing with his watch chain. He could not lay him down on the bed for a moment, so firmly did he hang on to the watch chain.

But as soon as he was laid in bed, all seemed well. He covered himself up and even drew the blankets farther than usual over his shoulders. He looked up at Georg with a not unfriendly eye.

"You begin to remember my friend, don't you?" asked Georg, giving him an encouraging nod.

"Am I well covered up now?" asked his father, as if he were not able to see whether his feet were properly tucked in or not.

"So you find it snug in bed already," said Georg, and tucked the blankets more closely round him.

"Am I well covered up?" asked the father once more, seeming to be strangely intent upon the answer.

"Don't worry, you're well covered up."

"No!" cried his father, cutting short the answer, threw the blankets off with a strength that sent them all flying in a moment and sprang erect in bed. Only one hand lightly touched the ceiling to steady him.

"You wanted to cover me up, I know my young sprig, but I'm far from being covered up yet. And even if this is the last strength I have, it's enough for you, too much for you. Of course I know your friend. He would have been a son after my own heart. That's why you've been playing him false all these years. Why else? Do you think I haven't been sorry for him? And that's why you had to lock yourself up in your office—the Chief is busy, mustn't be disturbed—just so that you could write your lying little letters to Russia. But thank goodness a father doesn't need to be taught how to see through his son. And now that you thought you'd got him down, so far down that you could set your bottom on him and sit on him and he wouldn't move, then my fine son makes up his mind to get married!"

Georg stared at the bogey conjured up by his father. His friend in St. Petersburg, whom his father suddenly knew too well, touched his imagination as never before. Lost in the vastness of Russia he saw him. At the door of an empty, plundered warehouse he saw him. Among the wreckage of his showcases, the slashed remnants of his wares, the falling gas brackets, he was just standing up. Why did he have to go so far away!

"But attend to me!" cried his father, and Georg, almost distracted, ran towards the bed to take everything in, yet came to a stop halfway.

"Because she lifted up her skirts," his father began to flute, "because she lifted her skirts like this, the nasty creature," and mimicking her he lifted his shirt so high that one could see the scar on his thigh from his war wound, "because she lifted her skirts like this and this you made up to her, and in order to make free with her undisturbed you have disgraced your mother's memory, betrayed your friend and stuck your father into bed so that he can't move. But he can move, or can't he?"

And he stood up quite unsupported and kicked his legs out. His insight made him radiant.

Georg shrank into a corner, as far away from his father as possible. A long time ago he had firmly made up his mind to watch closely every least movement so that he should not be surprised by any indirect attack, a pounce from behind or above. At this moment he recalled this long-forgotten resolve and forgot it again, like a man drawing a short thread through the eye of a needle.

"But your friend hasn't been betrayed after all!" cried his father, emphasizing the point with stabs of his forefinger. "I've been representing him here on the spot."

"You comedian!" Georg could not resist the retort, realized at once the harm done and, his eyes starting in his head, bit his tongue back, only too late, till the pain made his knees give.

"Yes, of course I've been playing a comedy! A comedy! That's a good expression! What other comfort was left to a poor old widower? Tell me—and while you're answering me be you still my living son—what else was left to me, in my back room, plagued by a disloyal staff, old to the marrow of my bones? And my son strutting through the world finishing off deals that I had prepared for him, bursting with triumphant glee and stalking away from his father with the closed face of a respectable business man! Do you think I didn't love you, I, from whom you are sprung?"

Now he'll lean forward, thought Georg, what if he topples and smashes himself! These words went hissing through his mind.

His father leaned forward but did not topple. Since Georg did not come any nearer, as he had expected, he straightened himself again.

"Stay where you are, I don't need you! You think you have strength enough to come over here and that you're only hanging back of your own accord. Don't be too sure! I am still much the stronger of us two. All by myself I might have had to give way, but your mother has given me so much of her strength that I've established a fine connection with your friend and I have your customers here in my pocket!"

"He has pockets even in his shirt!" said Georg to himself, and believed that with this remark he could make him an impossible figure for all the world. Only for a moment did he think so, since he kept on forgetting everything.

"Just take your bride on your arm and try getting in my way! I'll sweep her from your very side, you don't know how!"

Georg made a grimace of disbelief. His father only nodded, confirming the truth of his words, towards Georg's corner.

"How you amused me today, coming to ask me if you should tell your friend about your engagement. He knows it already, you stupid boy, he knows it all! I've been writing to him, for you forgot to take my writing things away from me. That's why he hasn't been here for years, he knows everything a hundred times better than you do yourself, in his left hand he crumples your letters unopened while in his right hand he holds up my letters to read through!"

In his enthusiasm he waved his arm over his head. "He knows everything a thousand times better!" he cried.

"Ten thousand times!" said Georg, to make fun of his father, but in his very mouth the words turned into deadly earnest.

"For years I've been waiting for you to come with some such question! Do you think I concern myself with anything else? Do you think I read my newspapers? Look!" and he threw Georg a newspaper sheet which he had somehow taken to bed with him. An old newspaper, with a name entirely unknown to Georg. "How long a time you've taken to grow up! Your mother had to die, she couldn't see the happy day, your friend is going to pieces in Russia, even three years ago he was yellow enough to be thrown away, and as for me, you see what condition I'm in. You have eyes in your head for that!"

"So you've been lying in wait for me!" cried Georg.

His father said pityingly, in an offhand manner: "I suppose you wanted to say that sooner. But now it doesn't matter." And in a louder voice: "So now you know what else there was in the world besides yourself, till now you've known only about yourself! An innocent child, yes, that you were, truly, but still more truly have you been a devilish human being!—And therefore take note: I sentence you now to death by drowning!"

Georg felt himself urged from the room, the crash with which his father fell on the bed behind him was still in his ears as he fled. On the staircase, which he rushed down as if its steps were an inclined plane, he ran into his charwoman on her way up to do the morning cleaning of the room. "Jesus!" she cried, and covered her face with her apron, but he was already gone. Out of the front door he rushed, across the roadway, driven towards the water. Already he was grasping at the railings as a starving man clutches food. He swung himself over, like the distinguished gymnast he had once been in his youth, to his parents' pride. With weakening grip he was still holding on when he spied between the railings a motor-bus coming which would easily cover the noise of his fall, called in a low voice: "Dear parents, I have always loved you, all the same," and let himself drop.

At this moment an unending stream of traffic was just going over the bridge.

Guy de Maupassant

HE?

My dear friend, you cannot understand it by any possible means, you say, and I perfectly believe you. You think I am going mad? It may be so, but not for the reasons which you suppose. Yes, I am going to get married, and I will tell you what has led me to take that step. My ideas and my convictions have not changed at all. I look upon all legalized cohabitation as utterly stupid, for I am certain that nine husbands out of ten are cuckolds; and they get no more than their deserts for having been idiotic enough to fetter their lives and renounce their freedom in love, the only happy and good thing in the world, and for having clipped the wings of fancy which continually drives us on toward all women. You know what I mean. More than ever I feel that I am incapable of loving one woman alone, because I shall always adore all the others too much. I should like to have a thousand arms, a thousand mouths, and a thousand— *temperaments*, to be able to strain an army of these charming creatures in my embrace at the same moment.

And yet I am going to get married!

I may add that I know very little of the girl who is going to become my wife to-morrow; I have only seen her four or five times. I know that there is nothing unpleasing about her, and that is

Guy de Maupassant, "*He?*" in Short Stories of the Tragedy and Comedy of Life, tr. by M. Walter Dunne. Akron, Ohio: St. Dunstan Society, 1903.

enough for my purpose. She is small, fair, and stout; so of course the day after to-morrow I shall ardently wish for a tall, dark, thin woman.

She is not rich, and belongs to the middle clases. She is a girl such as you may find by the gross, well adapted for matrimony, without any apparent faults, and with no particularly striking qualities. People say of her: "Mlle. Lajolle is a very nice girl," and to-morrow they will say: "What a very nice woman Madame Raymon is." She belongs, in a word, to that immense number of girls who make very good wives for us till the moment comes when we discover that we happen to prefer all other women to that particular woman we have married.

"Well," you will say to me, "what on earth do you get married for?"

I hardly like to tell you the strange and seemingly improbable reason that urged me on to this senseless act; the fact, however, is that I am frightened of being alone!

I don't know how to tell you or to make you understand me, but my state of mind is so wretched that you will pity me and despise me.

I do not want to be alone any longer at night; I want to feel that there is some one close to me touching me, a being who can speak and say something, no matter what it be.

I wish to be able to awaken somebody by my side, so that I may be able to ask some sudden question, a stupid question even, if I feel inclined, so that I may hear a human voice, and feel that there is some waking soul close to me, some one whose reason is at work—so that when I hastily light the candle I may see some human face by my side—because—because—I am ashamed to confess it—because I am afraid of being alone.

Oh! you don't understand me yet.

I am not afraid of any danger; if a man were to come into the room I should kill him without trembling. I am not afraid of ghosts, nor do I believe in the supernatural. I am not afraid of dead people, for I believe in the total annihilation of every being that disappears from the face of this earth.

Well,—yes, well, it must be told; I am afraid of myself, afraid of that horrible sensation of incomprehensible fear.

You may laugh, if you like. It is terrible and I cannot get over it.

I am afraid of the walls, of the furniture, of the familiar objects, which are animated, as far as I am concerned, by a kind of animal life. Above all, I am afraid of my own dreadful thoughts of my reason, which seems as if it were about to leave me, driven away by a mysterious and invisible agony.

At first I feel a vague uneasiness in my mind which causes a cold shiver to run all over me. I look round, and of course nothing is to be seen, and I wish there were something there, no matter what, as long as it were something tangible: I am frightened, merely because I cannot understand my own terror.

If I speak, I am afraid of my own voice. If I walk, I am afraid of I know not what, behind the door, behind the curtains, in the cupboard, or under my bed, and yet all the time I know there is nothing anywhere, and I turn round suddenly because I am afraid of what is behind me, although there is nothing there, and I know it.

I get agitated; I feel that my fear increases, and so I shut myself up in my own room, get into bed, and hide under the clothes, and there, cowering down rolled into a ball, I close my eyes in despair and remain thus for an indefinite time, remembering that my candle is alight on the table by my bedside, and that I ought to put it out, and yet—I dare not do it!

It is very terrible, is it not, to be like that?

Formerly I felt nothing of all that; I came home quite comfortably, and went up and down in my rooms without anything disturbing my calmness of mind. Had anyone told me that I should be attacked by a malady—for I can call it nothing else—of most improbable fear, such a stupid and terrible malady as it is, I should have laughed outright. I was certainly never afraid of opening the door in the dark; I used to go to bed slowly without locking it, and never got up in the middle of the night to make sure that everything was firmly closed.

It began last year in a very strange manner, on a damp autumn evening. When my servant had left the room, after I had dined, I asked myself what I was going to do. I walked up and down my room for some time, feeling tired without any reason for it, unable to work, and without enough energy to read. A fine rain was falling, and I felt unhappy, a prey to one of those fits of casual despondency which make us feel inclined to cry, or to talk, no matter to whom, so as to shake off our depressing thoughts. I felt that I was alone and that my rooms seemed to me to be more empty than they had ever been before. I was surrounded by a sensation of infinite and overwhelming solitude. What was I to do? I sat down, but then a kind of nervous impatience agitated my legs, so that I got up and began to walk about again. I was feverish, for my hands, which I had clasped behind me, as one often does when walking slowly, almost seemed to burn one another. Then suddenly a cold shiver ran down my back, and I thought the damp air might have penetrated into my room, so I lit the fire for the first time that year, and sat down again and looked at the flames. But soon I felt that I could not possibly remain quiet. So I got up again and determined to go out, to pull myself together, and to seek a friend to bear me company.

I could not find anyone, so I went on to the boulevards to try and meet some acquaintance or other there.

I was wretched everywhere, and the wet pavement glistened in the gaslight, while the oppressive mist of the almost impalpable rain lay heavily over the streets and seemed to obscure the light from the lamps.

I went on slowly, saying to myself, "I shall not find a soul to talk to."

I glanced into several *cafés*, from the Madeleine as far as the Faubourg Poissonière, and saw many unhappy-looking individuals sitting at the tables, who did not seem even to have enough energy left to finish the refreshments they had ordered.

For a long time I wandered aimlessly up and down, and about midnight I started off for home; I was very calm and very tired. My *concierge* opened the door at once, which was quite unusual for him, and I thought that another lodger had no doubt just come in.

When I go out I always double-lock the door of my room. Now I found it merely closed, which surprised me; but I supposed that some letters had been brought up for me in the course of the evening.

I went in, and found my fire still burning so that it lighted up the room a little. In the act of taking up a candle, I noticed somebody sitting in my armchair by the fire, warming his feet, with his back toward me.

I was not in the slightest degree frightened. I thought very naturally that some friend or other had come to see me. No doubt the porter, whom I had told when I went out, had lent him his own key. In a moment I remembered all the circumstances of my return, how the street door had been opened immediately, and that my own door was only latched, and not locked.

I could see nothing of my friend but his head. He had evidently gone to sleep while waiting for me, so I went up to him to rouse him. I saw him quite clearly; his right arm was hanging down and his legs were crossed, while his head, which was somewhat inclined to the left of the armchair, seemed to indicate that he was asleep. "Who can it be?" I asked myself. I could not see clearly, as the room was rather dark, so I put out my hand to touch him on the shoulder, and it came in contact with the back of the chair. There was nobody there; the seat was empty.

I fairly jumped with fright. For a moment I drew back as if some terrible danger had suddenly appeared in my way; then I turned round again, impelled by some imperious desire to look at the armchair again. I remained standing upright, panting with fear, so upset that I could not collect my thoughts, and ready to drop.

But I am naturally a cool man, and soon recovered myself. I thought: "It is a mere hallucination, that is all," and I immediately began to reflect about this phenomenon. Thoughts fly very quickly at such moments.

I had been suffering from a hallucination, that was an incontestable fact. My mind had been perfectly lucid and had acted regularly and logically, so there was nothing the matter with the brain. It was only my eyes that had been deceived; they had had a vision, one of those visions which lead simple folk to believe in miracles. It was a nervous accident to the optical apparatus, nothing more; the eyes were rather overwrought, perhaps.

I lit my candle, and when I stooped down to the fire in so doing, I noticed that I was trembling, and I raised myself up with a jump, as if somebody had touched me from behind.

I was certainly not by any means reassured.

I walked up and down a little, and hummed a tune or two. Then I double-locked my door, and felt rather reassured; now, at any rate, nobody could come in.

I sat down again, and thought over my adventure for a long time; then I went to bed, and put out my light.

For some minutes all went well; I lay quietly on my back. Then an irresistible desire seized me to look round the room, and I turned on to my side.

My fire was nearly out and the few glowing embers threw a faint light on to the floor by the chair, where I fancied I saw the man sitting again.

I quickly struck a match, but I had been mistaken, for there was nothing there; I got up, however, and hid the chair behind my bed, and tried to get to sleep as the room was now dark. But I had not forgotten myself for more than five minutes when in my dream I saw all the scene which I had witnessed as clearly as if it were reality. I woke up with a start, and, having lit the candle, sat up in bed, without venturing even to try and go to sleep again.

Twice, however, sleep overcame me for a few moments in spite of myself, and twice I saw the same thing again, till I fancied I was going mad. When day broke, however, I thought that I was cured, and slept peacefully till noon.

It was all past and over. I had been feverish, had had the nightmare; I don't know what. I had been ill, in a word, but yet I thought that I was a great fool.

I enjoyed myself thoroughly that evening; I went and dined at a restaurant; afterward I went to the theater, and then started home. But as I got near the house I was seized by a strange feeling of uneasiness once more; I was afraid of *seeing* him again. I was not afraid of him, not afraid of his presence, in which I did not believe; but I was afraid of being deceived again; I was afraid of some fresh hallucination, afraid lest fear should take possession of me.

For more than an hour I wandered up and down the pavement; then I thought that I was really too foolish, and returned home. I panted so that I could scarcely get upstairs, and remained standing outside my door for more than ten minutes; then suddenly I took courage and pulled myself together. I inserted my key into the lock, and went in with a candle in my hand. I kicked open my half-open bedroom door, and gave a frightened look toward the fireplace; there was nothing there. A—h!

What a relief and what a delight! What a deliverance! I walked up and down briskly and boldly, but I was not altogether reassured, and kept turning round with a jump; the very shadows in the corners disquieted me.

I slept badly, and was constantly disturbed by imaginary noises, but I did not see *him;* no, that was all over.

Since that time I have been afraid of being alone at night. I feel that the specter is there, close to me, around me; but it has not appeared to me again. And supposing it did, what would it matter, since I do not believe in it and know that it is nothing?

It still worries me, however, because I am constantly thinking of it: *his right arm hanging down and his head inclined to the left like a man who was asleep*—Enough of that, in Heaven's name! I don't want to think about it!

Why, however, am I so persistently possessed with this idea? His feet were close to the fire!

He haunts me; it is very stupid, but so it is. Who and what is HE? I know that he does not exist except in my cowardly imagination, in my fears, and in my agony! There—enough of that!

Yes, it is all very well for me to reason with myself, *to stiffen myself,* so to say; but I cannot remain at home, because I know he is there. I know I shall not see him again; he will not show himself again; that is all over. But he is there all the same in my thoughts. He remains invisible, but that does not prevent his being there. He is behind the doors, in the closed cupboards, in the wardrobe, under the bed, in every dark corner. If I open the door or the cupboard, if I take the candle to look under the bed and throw a light on to the dark places, he is there no longer, but I feel that he is behind me. I turn round, certain that I shall not see him, that I shall never see him again; but he is, none the less, behind me.

It is very stupid, it is dreadful; but what am I to do? I cannot help it.

But if there were two of us in the place, I feel certain that he would not be there any longer, for he is there just because I am, alone, simply and solely because I am alone!

Dissociative Reactions

The dissociative state is a form of neurosis characterized by the loss of a sense of personal identity. It can extend from the transient situation of a brief amnesia to the more extensive condition of a long-term fugue state in which the individual, amnesic for past events, assumes a totally new identity. The most dramatic form of dissociation is, of course, the multiple personality. These conditions are quite rare but their occurrence provides a fertile field for the examination of the powerful effects of unconscious conflict and repression on the personality. The two most famous descriptions of multiple personality are Morton Prince's *The Dissociation of a Personality* (New York: Longmans, Green & Co., 1905) and Thigpen & Cleckley's *Three Faces of Eve* (New York: McGraw-Hill, 1957). The first of the following excerpts is from a fictional account by Shirley Jackson of the "three faces" of a young woman, Elizabeth Richmond, as observed by her physician Dr. Wright. The differences among these three personalities—"R1," inhibited and frightened; "R2," pleasant and outgoing; and "R3," wanton and pleasure-seeking— suggest the conflicting wishes and needs which remain unintegrated in Elizabeth's personality.

The second selection is taken from Dostoevsky's short novel, *The Double*. Here, in Goldyakin's last feverish encounter with his double, dissociation as it is experienced from within is profoundly portrayed.

Like Elizabeth Richmond's alternate identities, Goldyakin's double represents dissident aspects of his own personality, embodied in an alter ego who lives side-by-side with him.

Shirley Jackson

THE BIRD'S NEST

I myself had already met Miss R. in three personalities: R1, nervous, afflicted by driving pain, ridden by the horrors of fear and embarrassment, modest, self-contained, and reserved to the point of oral paralysis. R2 was, it was assumed, the character Miss R. might have been, the happy girl who smiled and answered truly and with serious thoughtfulness, pretty and relaxed, without the lines of worry which so deformed R1's face; R2 was largely free of pain, and could only sympathize sweetly with R1's torments. R3 was, on the other hand, R2 with a vengeance: where R2 was relaxed, R3 was wanton; where R2 was unreserved, R3 was insolent; where R2 was pleasant and pretty, R3 was coarse and noisy. Moreover, each of the three had a recognizable appearance—R1, of course, the character I had first met, shy and unattractive by reason of her timidity and clumsiness; R2, amiable and charming; R3, the rough, contorted mask. The shy, fleeting smile of R1, the open, merry face of R2, were in R3 a sly grin or an open shout of rude laughter; if it be suspected that I did not particularly love our new friend R3, it can as readily be seen that I had good reason; when my good R2 began to raise her hands to rub her eyes, when her voice grew louder and her expressions freer, when her eyebrows went up sardonically and her mouth twisted, I had perforce to spend a while with a creature who felt and showed me no respect, who attempted enthusiastically

Shirley Jackson, from The Bird's Nest. *New York: Farrar, Straus & Giroux, 1954.*

to undo any good I might have done Miss R., who delighted in
teasing all whom she met, and who, after all, knew no moral sense
and no restrictions to her actions save only those of lack of sight;
who, upon occasion called me a damned old fool! . . .
My immediate attempt must be, I thought, to discover the point
at which the unfortunate Miss R. had subdivided, as it were, and
permitted a creature like Betsy to assume a separate identity; it was
my old teasing analogy of the sewer, but complicated in that I was
now searching for a branch line! (I do most heartily wish that I had
chosen some comparison nearer the stars; a flourishing oak tree, perhaps, but I confess that I misguidedly chose that which seemed most
vivid to me, and most indicative, although ignoble, of the circumstances; I am ashamed to think that without going through and
correcting all of my manuscript, and my notes, too—for this comparison found a place even there—I must abide by it.) It seemed to
me that only a very severe emotional shock could have forced Miss
R. to slough off the greater part of herself into subordinate personalities (until I had, with a magic touch, called them into active life)
and I was fairly certain that their separate existence—although
Betsy claimed a life of her own, in thoughts at any rate, ever since
Miss R. had been born—must date from the patent emotional shock
in Miss R.'s life, the death of her mother. To show what kind of a
problem I was manipulating, let me from my notes present the
reader with the varying descriptions of this event which I received,
first from R1, or Elizabeth, then from R2, the cooperative and
lovely Beth, and then, lastly, from our villain Betsy.
(On May 12, to Elizabeth, in office consultation): Wright: Do
you think you can tell me anything about your mother, my dear?
Elizabeth: I guess so.
W. When did she die?
E. I guess over four years ago. On a Wednesday.
W. Were you at home?
E. (confused) I was upstairs.
W. Did you live then with your aunt?
E. With Aunt Morgen?
W. Do you have any other aunts?
E. No.
W. Then, when your mother died, were you living with your aunt?

E. Yes, with Aunt Morgen.

W. Do you think you can tell me anything more about your mother's death? (She seemed most unwilling, and I thought on the edge of weeping; since I knew I could secure all the information I needed from the other selves, I did not intend to persist in a cruel cross-examination, but I did want as much information as possible for purposes of comparison.)

E. That's all I know. I mean Aunt Morgen came and told me my mother died.

W. Came and told you? You mean, you were not with your mother when she died?

E. No, I was upstairs.

W. Not with your mother?

E. Upstairs.

W. Was your mother downstairs, then?

E. Aunt Morgen was with her. I don't know.

W. Try to stay calm, if you please. This was all very long ago, and I think talking about it will be helpful to you: I know it is a painful subject, but try to believe that I would not ask you unless I felt it to be necessary.

E. No. I mean, I only don't know.

W. Had your mother been ill?

E. I thought she was all right.

W. Then her death was quite sudden, to your mind?

E. It was—(thinking deeply)—a heart attack.

W. But you were not there?

E. I was upstairs.

W. You did not see her?

E. No, I was upstairs.

W. What were you doing?

E. I don't remember. Asleep, I guess. Reading.

W. Were you in your own room?

E. I don't remember. I was upstairs.

W. I beg you to compose yourself, Miss R. This agitation is unnecessary and unbecoming.

E. I have a headache (touching her neck).

And that was, of course, the end of my information from Elizabeth; I knew by now that her headaches, all-enveloping, would obliterate

almost all awareness of myself and my questions. So I pursued my
line of questioning, most pleasantly, by summoning Beth. I longed,
at this time, to chat with Beth informally, and at length, and I
longed to permit her to open her eyes, so that we might seem
friends rather than doctor and patient, but the ever-present fear
of Betsy prevented; since blindness was now the only thing I knew
of which held Betsy in check, I dared not follow my inclinations
and admit Beth as a free personality. I was sad, frequently, to
think that Beth's whole existence had heretofore been passed only
in my office, and that none but I knew this amiable girl; my
conviction that Miss R. must once have been very like Beth was
so far unconfirmed, and yet I deeply wanted to see Beth take her
place in the world and in her family, the place to which my most
unscientific heart told me she was entitled. At any rate, it was
always a great pleasure to me to call Beth, and hear her affectionate greeting. Here are my notes on this conversation, which
followed immediately upon the conversation with Elizabeth which
I have just described.

(On May 12, Beth, or R2, in office consultation): Wright (after
preliminary trance-inducing introduction of name and place identification) My dear, I want to talk about your mother.

B. (smiling wistfully) She was a lovely lady.

W. Much like yourself?

B. Yes. Very lovely and very happy and very sweet to everyone.

W. Do you remember her death?

B. (reluctantly) Not very well. She died that day.

W. Where were you when she died?

B. I was thinking of her.

W. But where?

B. Inside. Hidden.

W. As you usually are?

B. Except when I am with you.

W. I hope we can change that someday, my dear. But you must
help me.

B. I will do anything you ask me to.

W. Splendid. I am most anxious, right now, to learn all I can
about your mother's death.

B. She was very kind to everyone, even Aunt Morgen.

W. You lived with your aunt at the time?

B. Oh, yes, we have lived with *her* for years, ever since my dear father died.

W. And your father died when?

B. When I was two years old, or about that. I don't remember him very well.

W. Were you with your mother when she died?

B. I? I was never allowed to be with her. I am always kept hidden.

W. Compose yourself, Beth dear. We can talk of something else if this disturbs you.

B. No, I am eager to help in any way I can; I don't want you to think badly of me.

W. I assure you, I never shall. Can you tell me, then, precisely what you did after your mother's death?

B. (perplexed) We had lunch. And Aunt Morgen said not to worry.

W. Not to worry? You mean, not to grieve?

B. Not to worry. We had lunch and Aunt Morgen said not to worry, Aunt Morgen said not to cry over spilled milk. Aunt Morgen cried. It was disgusting.

W. (amused) You will not allow your aunt her grief?

B. She cried over spilled milk.

W. (laughing outright) Beth, this is cynicism.

B. Indeed not; I do not think evil of anyone.

A man who has just spoken, however inconclusively, with Beth, does not turn hastily to a conversation with Betsy. Nevertheless, it was obvious that the information which Elizabeth and Beth found themselves unable to give must be mined from Betsy, and so, resolutely, I denied the appeal of Beth's pretty face and dismissed her for Betsy; I made an effort to keep my countenance when Beth's turned head disclosed that grinning face, even though she could not, of course, see me and I forced my voice to remain even and controlled.

(May 12, Betsy, or R3, in office consultation): W. Good afternoon, Betsy. I hope I find you in excellent health.

By. (jeering) The others won't help, so you come and ask *me*.

W. I hoped you might tell me—

By. I know. I was listening. (contemptuously) What do you think *they* can tell you?

W. —about your mother.

By. *My* mother? Do you think I claim that poor dead thing as *my* mother? Perhaps (impudently) I have a mother of my own, question-asker.

W. (Indeed if you had, you demon, I thought, she's a fiend in damnation): Miss R.'s mother, then.

By. As you are her father? (raucous laughter)

W. Miss R.'s mother, who died some years ago. Elizabeth's mother.

By. I know whose mother you mean, old man. The one she— (here she shut her lips, and grinned mysteriously, and put her finger to her mouth in a childlike gesture of secrecy)—Talking about Lizzie when her back is turned, my dear! For shame!

W. Betsy, I would like you to trust me. Believe me, I am only a person who wants to do whatever I can to ensure that you and Elizabeth and Beth will live together peaceably and happily; would you not like to be one person again?

By. I was never one person with her, I have always been her prisoner, and you wouldn't help me if you could. You may want to help Beth, and maybe even Lizzie, but you have no place for me in your pretty world.

W. Indeed, I am truly sorry to see anyone so bitter as to refuse help when it is so badly needed.

By. I have told you hundreds of times that the best way to help me is to let me open my eyes. (gestures of wringing hands, and bringing them up to her eyes.)—May I?—(wheedlingly)—May I open them, dear Doctor Wright? And I will tell you everything you want to know, about Lizzie and about Lizzie's mother and about old Auntie and I will even put in a good word for you with Beth if I may only have my eyes open.— (This was said in a tone of such mockery that I was gravely concerned; I had suddenly the notion that Betsy was teasing me, and might perhaps open her eyes this minute if she chose, and I was genuinely frightened at the thought.)

W. I insist that you keep your eyes closed. Do you realize, young lady, that if I find that you are of no use to me in my investigations, I will surely send you away and never let you come again? (I would have liked to, certainly, and perhaps even then I still could have.)

By. (apprehensive) You will not send me away.

W. I may; it was I who brought you here in the first place.

By. I can come by myself.

W. (not choosing to press *this* point) We shall see. (carelessly) Perhaps you are fond of sweets? (I had thought of this earlier; it occurred to me that a creature so childish might be fairly treated on childish terms; I had as alternatives a doll, and some tawdry jewelry.) Shall I put a candy in your hand?

By. (eagerly) Do you have candy right here?

W. (placing in her outstretched hand a piece of candy which she consumed greedily.) I am glad you begin to find me more friendly. No one would give you candy who did not wish you well.

By. (with satisfaction) If you poisoned me, then Lizzie and Beth would die.

W. I have no intention of poisoning you. I should like to have us friends, you and I.

By. I will be friends with you, old well-wisher. But I want more candy, and I want to open my eyes.

W. I assure you, you will never open your eyes with my permission. But can we not talk together as friends, Betsy?

By. (craftily) You have not given me any more candy yet.

W. (craftier still) When you tell me about your mother.

By. (unexpectedly gentle) Elizabeth's mother? She was always nice. She danced around the kitchen one day when she had a new dress and she said "Nonsense" to Morgen and she curled her hair. I liked to watch her.

W. Where were you?

By. A prisoner, always a prisoner, inside with Beth, only no one knew I was there.

W. Were you ever free? Outside, I mean?

By. (nodding, dreamy) Sometimes, when Lizzie is sleeping or when she turns her head away for a minute, I can get out, but only for a small time, and then she puts me back. (recollecting herself suddenly) But I am not going to tell you, you are not friendly to me.

W. Ridiculous; you know now that we are friends. Were you inside when Elizabeth's mother died?

By. Surely, and I made her scream even louder, and beat on the door.

W. Why did she beat on the door?

By. Why, to get out, Doctor Wrong.

W. To get out of what?

By. To get out of her room, Doctor Wrong.

W. What in heaven's name was Elizabeth doing shut in her room while her mother was dying?

By. Now, see, Doctor Wrong I did not say that her mother was dying, although she surely was, and yet it was not in heaven's name —(laughs wildly)—and as for what Lizzie was doing in her room, why, she was beating on the door.

W. Will you explain it to me?

By. Now certainly not, Doctor Wrong; we all went together to seek a bird's nest; do you remember the man who was wondrous wise and jumped into a bramble bush and scratched out both his eyes . . . may I open my eyes *now?*

W. No.

By.—put her in a pumpkin shell, and there she kept her very well. And so Lizzie's mother died, and it was a good thing, too. She wouldn't have cared for our Lizzie now.

W. Did Elizabeth change after her mother died?

By. (tormenting) I only said that to tease you, eye-closer. I can tell you wonderful stories about your dear. Ask Lizzie about the box of letters in her closet. Ask Beth about Aunt Morgen. (laughing wildly again) Ask Aunt Morgen about Lizzie's mother.

W. That will do, please. I am going to send you away now.

By. (suddenly sober) Please, may I stay a minute longer? I have decided to tell you why Aunt Morgen locked Lizzie in her room.

W. Very well. But no more nonsense.

By. First, you promised me more candy.

W. One more, only. We should not care to make Elizabeth sick.

By. (carelessly) She is always sick, anyway. I never thought of a stomachache, though.

W. Do you make her head ache?

By. Why would I tell you that? (impudently) If I told you every-thing I know, then you would be as wise as I am.

W. Then tell me why Elizabeth was locked in her room.

By. (emphatically) Because she frightened her mother and Aunt Morgen said they all went together to find a bird's nest.

W. I beg your pardon?

By. May I open my eyes *now?*

W. How did she frighten her mother?

By. She put her in a pumpkin shell. Silly silly silly silly. . .

Fyodor Dostoevsky

THE DOUBLE

It seemed as though the weather meant to change for the better. The wet snow, which had till then been coming down in regular clouds, began by degrees to abate, and at last almost ceased. The sky became visible, and here and there tiny stars sparkled in it. It was only wet, muddy, damp, and stifling, especially for Mr. Golyadkin, who could hardly breathe as it was. His greatcoat, soaked and grown heavy, sent a sort of unpleasant warm dampness all through him and made his weakened legs buckle under its weight. A feverish sensation made him feel creepy all over; he was in a cold sick sweat from utter exhaustion, so much so that Mr. Golyadkin even forgot to repeat on this suitable occasion with his characteristic firmness and resolution his favorite phrase that it would all maybe somehow most likely, certainly turn out for the best. "Still, all this does not matter for the time being," our sturdy and undaunted hero repeated, wiping from his face the cold drops that streamed in all directions from the brim of his round hat, which was so soaked that it could hold no more water. Adding that all this was nothing for the present, our hero tried to sit down on a rather thick stump which was lying near a pile of firewood in Olsufy Ivanovich's yard.

Of course, it was no good thinking of Spanish serenades and silken ladders, but it was quite necessary to think of a modest corner, snug

Fyodor Dostoevsky, from The Double, *in* The Eternal Husband and Other Stories, *tr. by Constance Garnett. New York: Macmillan, 1917.*

and private, if not altogether warm. He felt greatly tempted, we may mention in passing, by that corner in the back entry of Olsufy Ivanovich's flat in which he had once, almost at the beginning of this true story, stood for two hours between a cupboard and an old screen among all sorts of domestic odds and ends and useless rubbish. The fact is that now too Mr. Golyadkin had stood waiting for two whole hours in Olsufy Ivanovich's yard. But as regards that modest and snug little corner, there were now certain drawbacks which had not existed before. The first drawback was the fact it was probably now a marked place and that certain precautionary measures had been taken in regard to it since the scandal at Olsufy Ivanovich's last ball. Secondly, he had to wait for a signal from Klara Olsufyevna, for there was bound to be some such signal. That's how it always was, and, as he said, "It didn't begin with us and it won't end with us."

At this point Mr. Golyadkin very appropriately remembered, by the way, a novel he had read long ago in which the heroine, in precisely similar circumstances, signaled to her Alfred by tying a pink ribbon to her window. But now, at night, in the climate of Petersburg, notorious for its dampness and unreliability, a pink ribbon was hardly appropriate and, in short, utterly out of the question.

"No, this is no time for silk ladders," thought our hero, "and I had better stay here quietly and comfortably. . . . I had better stand right here, for instance."

And he selected a place in the yard exactly opposite the window, near the stack of firewood. Of course, many postilions and coachmen and other people were walking about the yard, and there was besides, the rumbling of wheels and the snorting of horses and so on; yet it was a convenient place, whether he was observed or not; but now, anyway, there was the advantage of being to some extent in the shade, and no one could see Mr. Golyadkin while he himself could see everything. The windows were brightly lit up, there was some sort of grand party at Olsufy Ivanovich's. No music was as yet heard, though.

"So it's not a ball, but a gathering of some other sort," thought our hero, his heart sinking. "Is it today?" flashed through his mind. "Perhaps there is a mistake in the date. It's possible; anything is possible. . . . Perhaps a letter was written yesterday, but it didn't reach me, and perhaps it did not reach me because Petrushka got mixed up in the affair, the rascal! Or it was written tomorrow, that is, that everything was to be done tomorrow, that is—waiting with a carriage. . . ."

At this point our hero turned cold all over and felt in his pocket for the letter, to make sure. But to his surprise the letter was not in his pocket.

"How's this?" whispered Mr. Golyadkin, more dead than alive. "Where did I leave it? Then I must have lost it. That is the last straw!" he moaned at last in conclusion. "What if it falls into evil hands? (Perhaps it already has.) Good Lord! What may it not lead to? It may lead to . . . Oh, my miserable fate!" Here Mr. Golyadkin began trembling like a leaf at the thought that perhaps his indecent twin had thrown the greatcoat over him with the express object of stealing the letter of which he had somehow got wind from Mr. Golyadkin's enemies.

"What's more, he's stolen it," thought our hero, "as evidence . . . but evidence of what?"

After the first shock of horror, the blood rushed to Mr. Golyadkin's head. Moaning and gnashing his teeth, he clutched his burning head, sank down on his block of wood, and relapsed into brooding . . . but he could form no coherent thoughts. Faces kept flitting through his mind, incidents came back to his memory, now vaguely, now distinctly, the tunes of some foolish songs kept ringing in his ears. . . . He was in distress, in unnatural distress!

"My God, my God!" our hero thought, recovering a little, and suppressing a muffled sob, "give me fortitude of spirit in the immeasurable depths of my afflictions! That I am done for, that I have vanished there can be no doubt any longer, and this is all in the natural order of things, since it cannot be otherwise. To begin with, I've lost my berth, I've certainly lost it, I couldn't but lose it. . . . Well, suppose things are set right somehow. Let us assume that my money will suffice for a start. I must have another lodging, furniture of some sort. . . . In the first place, I shan't have Petrushka. I can get on without the rascal . . . perhaps as a lodger. Well, that will be all right! I can come and go when I like, and Petrushka won't grumble at my coming in late—yes, that is so; that's why it's a good thing to be a lodger. . . . Well, all this may be fine, but how is it that I am talking about something irrelevant, completely irrelevant?" Here the thought of his real situation again dawned upon Mr. Golyadkin. He looked around. "Oh, my God, my God! What have I just been talking about?" he thought, growing utterly bewildered and clutching his burning head in his hands. . . . "Won't you soon be going, sir?" a voice sounded above Mr. Golyadkin. Our hero started; before him stood his cabman, who was also drenched through and chilled to the bone; growing impatient, and, having nothing to do, he had thought fit to take a look at Mr. Golyadkin behind the woodstack. "I am all right, my friend . . . I am coming soon, very soon; you wait. . . ."

The cabman walked away, grumbling to himself. "What is he grumbling about?" Mr. Golaydkin wondered through his tears. "Why, I have hired him for the evening, I'm within my rights now . . . that's how it is! I've hired him for the evening, and that's the end of it. Even if he stands still all the time, it's just the same. That's for me to decide. I am free to drive or not to drive. And my standing here behind the woodstack is nothing . . . and don't you dare to say anything; if a gentleman wants to stand behind the woodstack, he stands there . . . and he is not sullying anyone's reputation. So that's how it is! That's how it is! Madam, if you care to know, as for living in a hut, madam, nowadays no one does that. That's how it is! And in our industrial age there's no getting anywhere without good behavior, a fact of which you are a fatal example, madam. . . . You say, work as a court clerk and live in a hut on the seashore. In the first place, madam, there are no court clerks on the seashore, and, in the second place, you can't get a job as a court clerk. For suppose that, for example, I submit an application, present myself, saying, 'Give me the post of a court clerk . . . and defend me from my enemy.' . . . They'll tell you, madam, they'll say that there are lots of court clerks, and here you are not at Madame Falbalas', where you learned the rules of good behavior, of which you are such a fatal example. Good behavior, madam, means staying at home, honoring your father, and not thinking about suitors prematurely. Suitors will come in good time, madam, that's so! Of course, you are bound to have some talents, such as playing the piano a little sometimes, speaking French, have a knowledge of history, geography, scripture, and arithmetic, that's so! And that's all you need. Cooking, too, cooking certainly forms part of the education of a well-behaved girl! But what do we find? In the first place, my fair lady, they won't let you go. They'll chain you, and then they'll play their trump, and lock you up in a nunnery. How will it be then, madam? What will you have me do then? Would you have me, madam, emulate the heroes of some silly novels, and melt into tears on a neighboring hill, gazing at the cold walls of your prisonhouse, and finally die, following the example of some wretched German poets and novelists? Is that it, madam? But, to begin with, allow me to tell you, as a friend, that things are not done like that, and, in the second place, I would have given you and your parents, too, a good thrashing for letting you read French books; for French books teach you no good. There's poison in them . . . pernicious poison, madam! Or do you imagine, allow me to ask you, or do you imagine that we shall elope with impunity, and have a hut on the shore of the sea; and that we shall begin billing and cooing and discussing various feelings, and so spend the rest of our lives in happiness and contentment? Then there will be a little one—so we shall go to our father, the councilor of state, Olsufy Ivanovich, and say, 'We've got a little one, and so, on this propitious occasion, remove your curse and bless the couple.' No, madam, I tell you again, that's not the way things are done, and in the first place there'll be no billing and cooing, please don't reckon on it. Nowadays, madam, the husband is the master and a good, well-brought-up wife must try and please him in every way. And endearments, madam, are not liked, nowadays, in our industrial age; the day of Jean Jacques Rousseau is over. The husband comes home, for instance, hungry from the office, and asks, 'Can't I have something before dinner, my love, a drop of vodka to drink, a bit of herring to eat?' So then, madam, you must have the vodka and the herring ready. Your husband will down the snack with relish, and won't so much as look at you. 'Run into the kitchen, kitten,' he'll say, 'and look after the dinner,' and at most, once a week, he'll kiss you, even then perfunctorily. . . . That's what it will be like, my lady! Yes, even then, perfunctorily. . . . That's how it will be, if it comes to looking at the thing in that way. . . . And how do I come in? Why, madam, have you mixed me up in your caprices? 'To the beneficent man who suffers for my sake and who is in every way dear to my heart,' and so on. But in the first place, madam, I am not suited to you, you know yourself, I'm not a great hand at compliments, I'm not fond of uttering perfumed trifles for the ladies. I don't like lady-killers, and I must own I've never been a good-looker. You won't find any swagger or false shame in me, and I tell you so now in all sincerity. A straight-forward, open character and common sense is all I possess; I have nothing to do with intrigues. I am not one to intrigue, I say so and I'm proud of it—that's a fact! . . . I wear no mask among good people, and to tell you the whole truth . . ."

Suddenly Mr. Golyadkin started. The soaked red beard of his cabman appeared over the woodstack again. . . .

"I am coming directly, my friend. I'm coming at once, you know, at once," Mr. Golyadkin responded in a trembling and weak voice.

The cabman scratched the back of his head, stroked his beard, and moved a step forward . . . then stood still and looked at Mr. Golyadkin.

"I am coming directly, my friend; you see, my friend . . . I . . . just a little, you see, only a second . . . you see, my friend. . . ."

"Won't you be going anywhere at all?" the cabman asked, at last resolutely confronting Mr. Golyadkin.

"I'm coming directly, my friend, I am waiting, you see, my friend. . . ."

"Yes, sir. . . ."

"You see, my friend, I . . . What village do you come from, my friend?"

"We are under a master. . . ."

"And have you a kind master?"

"He's not bad. . . ."

"Yes, my friend; you stay here, my friend, you see. . . . Have you been in Petersburg long, my friend?"

"I've been driving a cab for a year now. . . ."

"And are you getting on all right, my friend?"

"Not bad."

"To be sure, my friend, to be sure. You ought to thank Providence, my friend. You should look for a good man. Good people are none too common nowadays, my friend. A good man would wash you, give you food and drink, my good fellow, a good man would. But sometimes you see tears shed by the wealthy, my friend—a lamentable example; that's how it is, my friend. . . ."

The cabman seemed to feel sorry for Mr. Golyadkin.

"Well, your honor, I'll stay on. Will your honor be waiting long?"

"No, my friend, no; I . . . you know . . . er . . . I won't wait any longer, my good man. . . . What do you think, my friend? I rely upon you. I won't stay here any longer."

"Aren't you going to drive anywhere?"

"No, my friend, no; and I'll make it worth your while, my friend . . . that's how it is. How much do I owe you, my dear fellow?"

"What you hired me for, please, sir. I've been waiting here a long time; you won't wrong a man, sir."

"Well, here, my friend, here."

At this point Mr. Golyadkin gave six whole roubles to the cabman, and made up his mind in earnest to waste no more time, that is, to clear off with a whole skin, especially since the matter had been settled and the cabman dismissed, and there was nothing more to wait for. He walked out of the yard, through the gate, turned left and, without looking around, took to his heels, breathless and rejoicing. "Perhaps it will all be for the best," he thought, "and perhaps in this way I've steered clear of trouble." Indeed, Mr. Golyadkin suddenly, all at once, felt unusually lighthearted. "Oh, if only it could turn out for the best!" thought our hero though he put little faith in his own words. "I know what I'll do . . ." he thought. "No, I'd better try the other tack. . . . Or wouldn't it be better to do this?" In this way, hesitating and seeking for the solution of his doubts, our hero ran as far as Semyonovsky Bridge; but, having reached it, he rationally, prudently, and conclusively decided to return.

"It will be better so," he thought. "I had better try another tack. This is what I'll do: I'll look on simply as an outsider, and that will be the end of it; I am simply an onlooker, an outsider—and nothing more, whatever happens—it's not my fault. That's how it is! That's how it shall be now."

Having decided to return, our hero actually did return, the more readily because with this happy thought of his he considered himself now quite an outsider.

"It's the best thing; you're not responsible for anything, and you'll see all that's necessary . . . that's the fact of the matter!"

It was a safe plan and there was an end to it all. Reassured, he crept back into the peaceful shelter of his soothing and protecting woodstack, and began gazing intently at the windows. This time he was not destined to gaze and wait for long. Suddenly a strange commotion became apparent at all the windows. Figures appeared and vanished, curtains were drawn back, Olsufy Ivanovich's windows were crowded with whole groups of people who peered out and were looking for something in the yard. From the security of his woodstack, our hero, too, began watching the general commotion with curiosity and craning his neck with interest to right and to left, at least as far as the short shadow of the woodstack, which screened him, would allow. Suddenly he started, grew numb, and almost caved in with horror. It seemed to him—in short, he realized, that they were not looking for anything or for anybody, but simply for him, Mr. Golyadkin! Everyone was looking and pointing in his direction. It was impossible to escape; they would see him. . . . Dumbfounded, Mr. Golyadkin huddled as closely as he could to the woodstack, and only then noticed that the treacherous shadow had betrayed him, that it did not cover him completely. Our hero would have been delighted at that moment to creep into a mousehole in the woodstack, and there meekly to remain, if only it had been possible. But it was absolutely impossible. In his agony he began at last staring openly and boldly at the windows; it was the best thing to do. . . . And suddenly he was burned up with shame. He had been seen, had been seen by all at once, everyone, they were all waving their hands, nodding their heads at him, calling to him; then several wickets clicked as they opened, several voices shouted something to him at once. . . .

"I wonder why they don't whip these naughty girls when they are children," our hero muttered to himself, losing his head completely. Suddenly without his hat and greatcoat, breathless, bustling, capering, perfidiously displaying intense joy at seeing Mr. Golyadkin at last, came down the steps *he* (we know who).

"Yakov Petrovich," twittered this individual, so notorious for his worthlessness, "Yakov Petrovich, are you here? You'll catch cold. It's chilly here, Yakov Petrovich. Come indoors." "Yakov Petrovich! No, I'm all right, Yakov Petrovich," our hero muttered in a submissive voice. "No, you must come, Yakov Petrovich; they beg you, they most humbly beg you, they are waiting for us. 'Make us happy,' they say, 'and bring in Yakov Petrovich.' That's how things stand." "No, Yakov Petrovich, you see, I'd better . . . I had better go home, Yakov Petrovich . . ." said our hero, roasting on a slow fire and freezing at the same time with shame and terror. "No—no—no—no!" twittered the loathsome person. "No—no— no, on no account! Come along," he said resolutely, and he dragged Mr. Golyadkin Sr. to the steps. Mr. Golyadkin Sr. did not at all want to go, but, as everyone was looking at them, it would have been stupid to balk and resist; so our hero went—though, indeed, one cannot say that he went, because he did not know in the least what was happening to him. Though it made no difference!

Before our hero had time to recover and come to his senses, he found himself in the drawing room. He was pale, disheveled, harassed; with lusterless eyes he scanned the crowd—horror! The drawing room, all the rooms—were full to overflowing. There were masses of people, a whole galaxy of ladies; and all were crowding around Mr. Golyadkin, all were pressing toward Mr. Golyadkin, all were bearing Mr. Golyadkin on their shoulders, and he perceived clearly that they were all forcing him in one direction.

"Not toward the door," was the thought that flashed through Mr. Golyadkin's mind.

They were, in fact, forcing him not toward the door but straight toward Olsufy Ivanovich's easy chair. On one side of the armchair stood Klara Olsufyevna, pale, languid, melancholy, but gorgeously dressed. Mr. Golyadkin was particularly struck by the wonderful effect of the tiny white flowers on her black hair. On the other side of the armchair stood Vladimir Semyonovich in a black dress coat with his new order in his buttonhole. Mr. Golyadkin was led, as has been stated above, straight up to Olsufy Ivanovich—on one side of him Mr. Golyadkin Jr., who had assumed an air of great decorum and propriety, to the immense relief of our hero, while on the other side was Andrey Filippovich, with a very solemn expression on his face.

"What can it mean?" Mr. Golyadkin wondered. When he saw that he was being led to Olsufy Ivanovich, an idea struck him like a flash of lightning. The thought of the intercepted letter darted through his brain. In great agony our hero stood before Olsufy Ivanovich's chair. "How shall I act now?" he wondered to himself. "Of course, I shall speak boldly and with an honorable frankness; I shall say this and that, and so on."

But what our hero apparently feared did not happen. Olsufy Ivanovich seemed to have received Mr. Golyadkin very warmly, and, though he did not hold out his hand to him, yet as he gazed at our hero, he shook his gray and venerable head—shook it with an air of solemn melancholy and at the same time of goodwill. So, at least, it seemed to Mr. Golyadkin. He even fancied that a tear glittered in Olsufy Ivanovich's lusterless eyes; he raised his eyes and saw that there seemed to be tears, too, on the eyelashes of Klara Olsufyevna, who was standing by—that there seemed to be something of the same sort even in the eyes of Vladimir Semyonovich—that the unruffled and composed dignity of Andrey Filippovich was in harmony with the general tearful sympathy—that even the young man who at one time looked very much like an important councilor, seizing the opportunity, was sobbing bitterly. . . . Though perhaps this was only all Mr. Golyadkin's fancy, because he was so much removed himself, and distinctly felt the hot tears running down his cold cheeks. . . .

Reconciled with mankind and his destiny, and at the moment filled with love, not only for Olsufy Ivanovich, not only for the guests as a whole, but even for his noxious twin (who seemed now to be by no means noxious, and not even to be his twin at all, but a person very agreeable in himself and in no way connected with him), our hero, in a voice broken with sobs, tried to express his feelings to Olsufy Ivanovich, but was too much overcome by all that he had gone through, and could not utter a word; he could only, with an expressive gesture, point silently at his heart. . . .

At last, probably to spare the feelings of the old man, Andrey Filippovich led Mr. Golyadkin a little away, though he seemed to leave him free to do as he liked. Smiling, muttering something to himself, somewhat bewildered, yet almost completely reconciled with fate and his fellow-creatures, our hero began to make his way through the dense crowd of guests. Everyone made way for him, everyone looked at him with strange curiosity and with mysterious, unaccountable sympathy. Our hero went into the next room; he met with the same attention everywhere; he was vaguely conscious of a whole crowd closely following him, noting every step he took, talking in undertones among themselves of something very interesting, shaking their heads, arguing and discussing in whispers. Mr. Golyadkin wanted very much to know what they were discussing in whispers. Looking around, he saw near him Mr. Golyadkin Jr. Feeling it necessary to seize his hand and draw him aside, Mr. Golyadkin begged the other Yakov Petrovich most urgently to assist him in all his future undertakings, and not to abandon him at a critical moment. Mr. Golyadkin Jr. nodded his head gravely and warmly pressed the hand of Mr. Golyadkin Sr. Our hero's heart thrilled with the intensity of his emotion. He was gasping for breath, however; he felt such a weight on his chest; all those eyes fastened upon him were oppressing and crushing him. . . . In passing, Mr. Golyadkin caught a glimpse of the councilor who wore a wig. The latter was looking at him with a stern, searching eye, not in the least softened by the general sympathy. Our hero made up his mind to go straight up to him in order to smile at him and have an immediate explanation, but this somehow did not come off. For one instant Mr. Golyadkin became almost unconscious, losing both memory and sensation.

When he came to himself again he noticed that he was revolving in a large circle formed by the rest of the party around him. Suddenly Mr. Golyadkin's name was called from the next room; the shout was at once taken up by the whole crowd. Excitement and uproar followed; all rushed to the door of the drawing room, almost carrying our hero along with them. The hardhearted councilor in the wig found himself side by side with Mr. Golyadkin. Finally, taking our hero by the hand, he made him sit down beside him opposite Olsufy Ivanovich, at a considerable distance from the latter, however. Arranged in rows around Mr. Golyadkin and Olsufy Ivanovich, all the guests sat down. Everything was hushed; everyone preserved a solemn silence; everyone was watching Olsufy Ivanovich, evidently expecting something rather out of the ordinary. Mr.

Golyadkin noticed that beside Olsufy Ivanovich's chair and directly facing the councilor sat Mr. Golyadkin Jr., with Andrey Filippovich. The silence was prolonged; they were evidently expecting something. "Just as it is in a family when someone is setting off on a long journey. We've only to get up and say a prayer now," thought our hero.

Suddenly there was a general stir which interrupted Mr. Golyadkin's reflections. Something long expected happened. "He is coming, he is coming!" passed from one to another in the crowd. "Who is it that is coming?" flashed through Mr. Golyadkin's mind, and a strange sensation made him shudder. "High time too!" said the councilor, looking intently at Andrey Filippovich. Andrey Filippovich, for his part, glanced at Olsufy Ivanovich gravely and solemnly nodded his head. "Let us stand up," said the councilor, and made Mr. Golyadkin get up. All rose to their feet. Then the councilor took Mr. Golyadkin Sr. by the hand, and Andrey Filippovich took Mr. Golyadkin Jr. by the hand, and they solemnly brought together the two identical persons surrounded by the expectant crowd. Our hero looked about him in perplexity, but was at once checked and his attention was called to Mr. Golyadkin Jr., who was holding out his hand to him.

"They want to reconcile us," thought our hero, and deeply, moved, held out his hand to Mr. Golyadkin Jr., and then—then offered his cheek. The other Mr. Golyadkin did the same. . . .

At this point it seemed to Mr. Golyadkin Sr. that his perfidious friend was smiling, that he gave a sly, hurried wink to the crowd of onlookers, and that there was something sinister in the face of the unseemly Mr. Golyadkin Jr., that he even made a grimace as he gave his Judas kiss. . . .

There was a ringing in Mr. Golyadkin's ears, and darkness before his eyes; it seemed to him that a multitude, a whole series of identical Golyadkins were noisily bursting in at every door of the room; but it was too late. . . . The resounding, treacherous kiss was given, and. . . .

Then something quite unexpected occurred. . . . The door opened noisily, and on the threshold stood a man, the very sight of whom

turned Mr. Golyadkin's heart to ice. He stood rooted to the spot. A
cry of horror died away in his choking throat. Yet, Mr.
Golyadkin had known it all beforehand, and had had a presentiment of something of the sort for a long time. The stranger went up to Mr.
Golyadkin gravely and solemly. Mr. Golyadkin knew this personage
very well. He had seen him before, had seen him very often, had
seen him that day. . . . It was a tall, thick-set man in a black dress
coat, with a good-sized cross about his neck, and was possessed of
thick, very black whiskers; nothing was lacking but the cigar in the
mouth to complete the picture. The stranger's eyes, as we have
mentioned already, sent a chill of horror to Mr. Golyadkin's heart.
With a grave and solemn air this terrible man approached the
pitiable hero of our tale. . . . Our hero held out his hand to him;
the stranger took his hand and drew him along with him. . . .
With a bewildered, crushed air our hero looked about him.
"It's . . . it's Krestyan Ivanovich Rutenspitz, doctor of medicine
and surgery; your old acquaintance, Yakov Petrovich!" a detestable
voice twittered in Mr. Golyadkin's ear. He looked around: it was
Mr. Golyadkin's twin, so revolting in the despicable meanness of
his soul. A malicious, indecent joy shone in his countenance; he was
rubbing his hands with rapture, turning his head from side to side
in ecstasy, mincing around all and sundry in delight, and seemed
ready to dance with glee. At last he pranced forward, took a candle
from one of the servants, and walked in front, lighting the way to
Mr. Golyadkin and Krestyan Ivanovich. Mr. Golyadkin heard the
whole party in the drawing room rush out after him, crowding
and squeezing one another, and all beginning to repeat after Mr.
Golyadkin, "It is all right, don't be afraid, Yakov Petrovich; this
is your old friend and acquaintance, you know, Krestyan Ivanovich
Rutenspitz. . . ."
    At last they came out on the brightly lighted stairs; there was a
crowd of people on the stairs too. The front door was thrown open
noisily, and Mr. Golyadkin found himself on the steps, together with
Krestyan Ivanovich. Standing at the entrance was a carriage with
four horses that were snorting with impatience. The malicious Mr.
Golyadkin Jr. in three bounds flew down the stairs and opened the
carriage door himself. Krestyan Ivanovich, with an admonishing
gesture, asked Mr. Golyadkin to get in. There was no need of the

admonishing gesture, however; there were plenty of people to help him in. . . . Faint with horror, Mr. Golyadkin looked back. The whole of the brightly lighted staircase was crowded with people; inquisitive eyes were looking at him from all sides; Olsufy Ivanovich himself was sitting in his easy chair on the top landing and watching all that took place with deep interest. Everyone was waiting. A murmur of impatience ran through the crowd when Mr. Golyadkin looked back.

"I hope there is nothing here . . . nothing reprehensible . . . or that can call for severity . . . and general attention in regard to my official relations," our hero brought out in his bewilderment. A clamor of talk rose all around him, all were shaking their heads. Tears started from Mr. Golyadkin's eyes.

"In that case I'm ready . . . I have full confidence . . . and I entrust my fate to Krestyan Ivanovich. . . ."

No sooner had Mr. Golyadkin declared that he entrusted his fate to Krestyan Ivanovich than a dreadful, deafening shout of joy came from those around him and was repeated in a sinister echo by the whole of the waiting crowd. Then Krestyan Ivanovich on one side and Andrey Filippovich on the other helped Mr. Golyadkin into the carriage; his double, in his usual nasty way, was helping to get him in from behind. The unhappy Mr. Golyadkin Sr. took his last look at everyone and everything, and, shivering like a kitten that has been drenched with cold water—if the comparison may be permitted—got into the carriage. Krestyan Ivanovich followed him in immediately. The carriage door slammed. There was a swish of the whip on the horses' backs . . . the horses started off. . . . The crowd dashed after Mr. Golyadkin. The shrill, furious shouts of his enemies pursued him by way of farewell. For some time several persons were still flashing around the carriage that bore away Mr. Golyadkin; but by degrees they were left behind, till at last they had all disappeared. Mr. Golyadkin's unseemly twin kept up longer than anyone. With his hands in the side pockets of his green uniform trousers, he ran on with a satisfied air, skipping first to one and then to the other side of the carriage, sometimes catching hold of the windowframe and hanging from it, poking his head in at the window, and throwing farewell kisses to Mr. Golyadkin. But he too began to get tired, he was less and less often to be seen, and at last vanished altogether. There was a dull ache in Mr. Golyadkin's heart; a hot rush of blood set Mr. Golyadkin's head throbbing; he was suffocating, he longed to unbutton himself—to bare his breast, to cover it with snow and pour cold water on it. He fell at last into a doze. . . . When he came to himself, he saw that the horses were taking him along an unfamiliar road. Dark woods wound to the right and the left of it; the place was desolate and deserted. Suddenly he almost swooned: two fiery eyes were staring at him in the darkness, and those two eyes were glittering with malignant, hellish glee. "That's not Krestyan Ivanovich! Who is it? Or is it he? It is. It is Krestyan Ivanovich, but not the old Krestyan Ivanovich, it is another Krestyan Ivanovich! It's a terrible Krestyan Ivanovich!"

"Krestyan Ivanovich, I . . . I believe . . . I'm all right, Krestyan Ivanovich," our hero was beginning timidly in a trembling voice, hoping by his meekness and submissiveness to propitiate the terrible Krestyan Ivanovich a little.

"You will get quarters at public expense, viz. firewood, light, and service, which you don't deserve," Krestyan Ivanovich's answer rang out, stern and terrible as a judge's sentence.

Our hero cried out and clutched his head. Alas! He had had a presentiment of this for a long time.

Conversion Reactions

The conversion reaction, a term which has superseded the appellation of hysteria, is a neurotic disorder characterized by the binding
of anxiety arising out of internal conflicts through the development
of a physical symptom. The conversion patient's symptom is his
method of warding off the direct experience of anxiety and is symbolic of the underlying conflicts in his personality. In these scenes from
Home of the Brave we see Coney, a sensitive Jewish boy whose intolerable feelings of guilt over leaving his friend to die at the hands of
the Japanese have led to the development of amnesia and paralysis
of his legs, being treated by a psychiatrist who utilizes a vast array
of therapeutic techniques—role playing, narcosynthesis, interpretation, and abreaction or emotional catharsis.

Coney's conflict, as portrayed in these scenes from *Home of the
Brave*, appears to revolve around his ambivalent feelings toward
his friend Finch. Confronted by the wounded man, the sensitive
Coney is torn between his desire to save his friend and his hostility
towards him because of Finch's anti-semitic attitudes. The conflict
is resolved most economically by the development of a paralysis of
the legs. Note the psychological purposes served by this symptom:
Coney's guilt over his desire to leave Finch is assuaged as he
cannot get away, and at the same time he is punished for having had
such aggressive impulses by being made a cripple. The psychiatrist,
in his theraputic endeavors, attempts to break through Coney's
amnesia and help him face his conflictual feelings.

Although this brief selection makes the therapeutic process
appear artificially speeded-up and somewhat melodramatic, the
patient's resistance to the recognition of his ambivalent feelings is
well-portrayed.

Arthur Laurents

HOME OF THE BRAVE

ACT TWO

SCENE I

[*Scene: Hospital Room. The Pacific Base.* CONEY *is stretched out on the bed with his head buried in the pillow.* The DOCTOR *is sitting on the bed, patting his shoulder.*]

DOCTOR [*gently*] Coney . . . Coney.

CONEY I shouldn't have left him. I shouldn't have left him. Mingo.

DOCTOR What?

CONEY [*turning*] I should have stayed with him.

DOCTOR If you'd stayed with him the maps would be lost. The maps were your job and the job comes first.

CONEY So to hell with Finch!

DOCTOR Finch knew he had to get those maps. He told you to take them and go, didn't he? Didn't he, Coney?

CONEY He's dead.

DOCTOR Didn't he say: Take the maps and get out of here? [*Pause*]

CONEY I shouldn't've left him.

DOCTOR Coney, take the maps and get out of here!

CONEY No, Finch.

DOCTOR Take them and beat it. Go on, will you?

CONEY Finch—Are you sure—

DOCTOR Go on!

Arthur Laurents, from Home of the Brave. *New York: Random House, 1946.*

[*A slight pause.* CONEY *slowly raises himself up on his arms. The* DOCTOR *watches him tensely.* CONEY *moves as though to get off the bed.*]

Go on!

[CONEY *starts to make the effort to get off the bed. Then slowly, he sinks back, shaking his head pitifully.*]

CONEY [*pathetically*] I can't. I can't.
DOCTOR Coney . . . go on!
CONEY I can't, Doc. I'm sorry.

[*There is a slight pause. The* DOCTOR *takes a new tack now.*]

DOCTOR Coney . . . remember when Finch was shot?
CONEY Yeah. I remember.
DOCTOR When you heard that shot and saw he was hit, what did you think of?
CONEY I—I got a bad feeling.
DOCTOR But what did you think of, Coney? At that moment, what went through your mind?
CONEY I didn't want to leave him.
DOCTOR What did you think of at that instant, Coney?
CONEY He told me to leave him.
DOCTOR Coney. Listen. A shot! You turn. [*Slaps his hands together sharply*] You turn now. You see it's Finch.
CONEY Finch!
DOCTOR What are you thinking of, Coney? [*No answer*] Coney, what just went through your mind?
CONEY I . . . I . . .
DOCTOR What?
CONEY I didn't want to leave him.
DOCTOR Coney—
CONEY But he said to leave him! He said to take the maps and beat it. It wasn't because I was yellow. It was because he said to go. Finch said to go!
DOCTOR You were right to go. You were right to go, Coney.
CONEY They didn't think so.
DOCTOR How do you know?
CONEY I know. I could tell that T. J.—

DOCTOR   Did he say anything?

CONEY   No.

DOCTOR   Did the Major say anything? Did Mingo say anything?

CONEY   No.

DOCTOR   Of course not. Because you were right to leave. You did what you had to do: you saved the maps. That's what you had to do, Coney.

CONEY [*plaintively*]   Was it? Was it really?

DOCTOR   Of course it was, son. It was the only thing you could do. [*Pause*]

CONEY   We did come to get the maps.

DOCTOR   Sure.

CONEY   And I saved them.

DOCTOR   Yes.

CONEY   I saved them . . . But Finch made them and . . . and . . . now . . .

DOCTOR   Coney, you had to leave him, you know that.

CONEY   Yes.

DOCTOR   You can't blame yourself.

CONEY   No . . . Only . . .

DOCTOR   Only what?

CONEY   I still got that feeling.

DOCTOR   What feeling?

CONEY   I don't know. That—that bad feeling.

DOCTOR   Did you first get it when you heard that shot? When you saw it was Finch who was hit?

CONEY   I—I'm not sure.

DOCTOR   Did it come back stronger when you found you couldn't walk?

CONEY   I—think so.

DOCTOR   When was that, Coney? When did you find you couldn't walk?

CONEY   It was . . . It was . . . I don't know.

DOCTOR   Think.

CONEY   I'm trying to.

DOCTOR   Why did it happen? Why couldn't you walk?

CONEY   I—I can't remember.

DOCTOR   Why can't you walk now?

CONEY   I—I don't know. I just can't.
DOCTOR   Why?
CONEY   I don't know. I think it started when—when—
DOCTOR   When what, Coney?
CONEY   When—when—
DOCTOR   When what, Coney?
CONEY   Oh, gee, Doc, I'm afraid I'm gonna cry.
DOCTOR   Go on, son. Cry if you want to.
CONEY   But guys don't cry. You shouldn't cry.
DOCTOR   Let it out, son. Let it all out.
CONEY   No, no, I don't want to. I cried when Finch—
DOCTOR   When Finch what?
CONEY   When he—when . . .
DOCTOR   When you left him?
CONEY   No. No, it was after that. Long after that. I'd been waiting
    for him.
DOCTOR   Where?

[*The lights start to fade.*]

CONEY   In the clearing. The clearing by the beach. We were all
    there. Waiting. Nothing to do but wait and listen to those lousy
    birds. And all the time, I was wondering about Finch, waiting
    for Finch, hoping that . . .

[*The stage is dark now. Through the last, there have been the faint sounds of
crickets and jungle birds.*]

ACT TWO

SCENE III

[*Scene: Hospital Room. The Pacific Base. Before the lights come up, we
hear* CONEY *counting.*]

CONEY   85—84—83—82—81—80—79—
DOCTOR   78.
CONEY   78—77—76—75. [*The lights are up now.* CONEY *is on the
    bed, the* DOCTOR *sitting by him watching the needle.*] 74—73—72—
    73—7—

[*The* DOCTOR *withdraws the needle and gets up.*]

DOCTOR   Coney, do you remember how you got off that island?

CONEY   I think—Mingo. Something about Mingo.

DOCTOR   Yes. Mingo picked you up and carried you out.

CONEY   I—I remember water. Being in the canoe on water. There were bullets.

DOCTOR   Some of the Japs fired machine guns when they realized what was happening.

CONEY   I think maybe I passed out because—it's all kind of dark. Then I'm in the plane.

DOCTOR   T.J. lifted you in.

CONEY   T.J.?

DOCTOR   Yes.

CONEY   But Mingo . . .

DOCTOR   Mingo couldn't lift you in alone. His right arm was no good.

CONEY   Oh, yeah . . . yeah.

DOCTOR   That's all you remember, though?

CONEY   I remember being taken off the plane.

DOCTOR   I mean on the island. That's all you remember of what happened on the island?

CONEY   Yes.

DOCTOR   Then why can't you walk, Coney?

CONEY   What?

DOCTOR   You weren't shot, were you?

CONEY   No.

DOCTOR   You didn't break your legs, did you?

CONEY   No.

DOCTOR   Then why can't you walk, Coney?

CONEY   I don't know. I don't know.

DOCTOR   But you said you remember everything that happened.

CONEY   I—yes. Yes.

DOCTOR   Do you remember waking up in the hospital? Do you remember waking up with that bad feeling?

CONEY   Yes.

[*Slight pause. The* DOCTOR *walks next to the bed.*]

DOCTOR   Coney, when did you first get that bad feeling?

CONEY   It was—I don't know.

DOCTOR   Coney—[*He sits down*] Coney, did you first get it right after Finch was shot?

CONEY   No.

DOCTOR   What did you think of when Finch was shot?

CONEY   I don't know.

DOCTOR   You said you remember everything that happened. And you do. You remember that, too. You remember how you felt when Finch was shot, don't you, Coney? Don't you?

CONEY   [*sitting bolt upright*]   Yes. [*A long pause. His hands twist his robe and then lay still. With dead, flat tones*] When we were looking for the map case, he said—he started to say: You lousy yellow Jew bastard. He only said you lousy yellow jerk, but he started to say you lousy yellow Jew bastard. So I knew. I knew.

DOCTOR   You knew what?

CONEY   I knew he'd lied when—when he said he didn't care. When he said people were people to him. I knew he lied. I knew he hated me because I was a Jew so—I was glad when he was shot.

[*The* DOCTOR *straightens up.*]

DOCTOR   Did you leave him there because you were glad?

CONEY   Oh, no!

DOCTOR   You got over it.

CONEY   I was—I was sorry I felt glad. I was ashamed.

DOCTOR   Did you leave him because you were ashamed?

CONEY   No.

DOCTOR   Because you were afraid?

CONEY   No.

DOCTOR   No. You left him because that was what you had to do. Because you were a good soldier. [*Pause*] You left him and you ran through the jungle, didn't you?

CONEY   Yes.

DOCTOR   And you walked around in the clearing by the beach, didn't you?

CONEY   Yes.

DOCTOR   So your legs were all right.

CONEY   Yes.

DOCTOR   Then if anything did happen to your legs, it happened when Finch crawled back. And you say nothing happened to you then.

CONEY   I don't know.

DOCTOR   Did anything happen?

CONEY   I don't know. Maybe—maybe.

DOCTOR   But if anything did happen, you'd remember?

CONEY   I don't know.

DOCTOR   You *do* remember what happened when Finch crawled back, don't you? Don't you, Coney?

CONEY [*covers his face*]   Finch . . . Finch . . .

DOCTOR   Remember that. Think back to that, Coney. You were alone in the clearing and Finch crawled in.

CONEY   O God . . . O dear God . . .

DOCTOR   Remember. [*He gets up quickly, moves across the room and in a cracked voice calls:*] Coney!

CONEY [*plaintively—he turns sharply*]   Finch? . . . Finch?

DOCTOR [*a cracked whisper*]   Coney . . .

CONEY   Oh, Finch, Finch! Is that you, Finch? [*He cradles an imaginary head in his lap and begins to rock back and forth*] I'm so glad. I'm so glad, Finch! I'm so . . . [*He stops short, waits, then ducks his head down as though to listen to Finch's heart. A moment, then he straightens up and then, with the same decisive, brutal gesture as before, shoves the imaginary body of Finch so that it rolls over. He looks at it in horror.*]

DOCTOR [*calls out*]   Hey, Yank! Come out and fight!

CONEY   They won't get you, Finch. I won't leave you this time, I promise! [*He begins to pantomime digging feverishly.*]

DOCTOR   Come out and fight, Yank.

CONEY   I won't leave you this time!

[*The* DOCTOR *walks over deliberately and grabs* CONEY'*s hand, stopping it in the middle of a digging motion.*]

DOCTOR [*curtly*]   What are you trying to bury him in, Coney?

[CONEY *stops and stares up at him*]

This isn't earth, Coney. This is a bed. Feel it. It's a bed. Underneath is a floor, a wooden floor. Hear? [*He stamps*] You can't bury

Finch, Coney, because he isn't here. You're not on that island. You're in a hospital. You're in a hospital, Coney, and I'm your doctor! [*Pause*]

CONEY Yes, sir.

DOCTOR And you remember now, you remember that nothing happened to your legs at all, did it?

CONEY No, sir.

DOCTOR But you had to be carried here.

CONEY Yes, sir.

DOCTOR Why?

CONEY Because I can't walk.

DOCTOR Why can't you walk?

CONEY I don't know.

DOCTOR *I do*. It's because you didn't want to, isn't it, Coney? Because you knew if you couldn't walk, then you couldn't leave Finch. That's it, isn't it?

CONEY I don't know.

DOCTOR That must be it. Because there's nothing wrong with your legs. They're fine, healthy legs and you can walk. You can walk. You had a shock and you didn't want to walk. But you're over the shock and now you do want to walk, don't you? You do want to walk, don't you, Coney?

CONEY Yes. Yes.

DOCTOR Then get up and walk.

CONEY I—can't.

DOCTOR Yes, you can.

CONEY No.

DOCTOR Try.

CONEY I can't.

DOCTOR Try.

CONEY I can't.

DOCTOR Get up and walk! [*Pause*] Coney, get up and walk! [*Pause*] You lousy, yellow Jew bastard, get up and walk!

[*At that,* CONEY *straightens up in rage. He is shaking, but he grips the edge of the bed and swings his feet over. He is in a white fury, and out of his anger comes this tremendous effort. Still shaking, he stands up; holds for a moment; and glares at the* DOCTOR. *Then, with his hands outstretched before him as though he is going to kill the* DOCTOR, *he starts to walk. First one foot, then the other, left, right, left—but he begins to cry violently and as he sinks to the floor, the* DOCTOR *moves forward swiftly and grabs him.*]

DOCTOR [*triumphantly*]   All right, son! All right!

CURTAIN

Phobic Reactions

A phobia is a special form of fear. It is an irrational, unshakeable fear attached to an object which has come to symbolize an actually feared interpersonal situation or person. However incomprehensible the panic may appear to the observer, and as much as it may constrict the individual's life, this focussing of anxiety on a specific object does serve the purpose of diminishing the subject's subjective experience of anxiety and pain since, unlike the all-encompassing dread of the anxiety neurotic, the phobic person *knows* what he is afraid of and can take precautions against this frightening object. The key dynamic element involved in the development of a phobia is, then, a *displacement* of fear from a meaningful feared object to a new symbolic one.

Leonard's description of his life-long agoraphobia (fear of open places) is a classic autobiographical account of an abnormal condition. As a literary man (he was Professor of English at the University of Wisconsin), Leonard was able skillfully and dramatically to portray the intense panic and helplessness which afflicts the phobic as he confronts his special terrorizing situation.

William E. Leonard

THE LOCOMOTIVE-GOD

The phobic phenomena were not simply infantile clinging to parents and house. The central terror—craving for safety, reducible ultimately to the fear of death—spread over my entire consciousness, over my whole environment. Every fear known to timid childhood was mine—fear of darkness, of thunder-storms, of dogs, of bodily pains, of blood. And many fears that only maturity has the knowledge to fabricate—as of symptoms of imagined diseases. The hideous components of this three months nightmare . . . thereafter mitigated but never entirely eliminated from the abiding core of the distance-phobia . . . were of diverse origins. Some were direct reverberations of my childhood, awakened with the awakening of the Locomotive-God, as, for instance, the fear of dogs (still present, mildly), and of stepping on a trestle-bridge (near the cottage), though curiously I did not repeat the phobias of bells. Some were accretions from the immediate past experience, as, for instance, a most acute fear of razors. The rattle of a box inside Agatha's room on the fatal morning of the poison had flooded my mind, as I shook the door, with the vision of my razor at her throat. I had to shave with a safety-razor; and for a year and a half my father stropped it . . . out of my hearing. Since then I have sharpened my own blades, but, even at this writing, I feel a constriction as the shadow of the old blade seems rasping my neck. But even this accretion from the immediate past

William E. Leonard, from The Locomotive-God. *New York: The Century Co., 1927.*

has some general association with 1878, when the terrified child felt a violent convulsion in his *throat*, and perhaps with a *knife* on the table in the house to which the boy was taken in 1885. Some were new buddings, like new tentacles or processes of the aboriginal phobic Octopus, generated by the frightened mind's hyper-anxiety as well as by memories of Agatha's end. I was afraid of constipation, afraid of poison in food and in sleeping-powders, afraid of swallowing at all, afraid of committing suicide (an aspect of the razor-phobia). And the little boy who fingered so objectively the skeleton had become the man morbidly haunted in hyperimagination by the white and red coil of all his insides under the skin and under or around the bones. The external order of marvelous nature, after a few quiet weeks with the grove and the evening star, became for two years merely an intellectual affair, recognized as beautiful and sublime with as little emotional appeal as when we recognize that one pencil makes a green mark and another a red and that one is longer than the other; but the Marvel was ultimately restored to me with power . . . before I wrote "Two Lives."

Several times, shaking with the organic feeling of imminent death, I lay on the bed with my father and mother sitting on either side, a hand in mine, talking to me in low tones. Several times my father had to sleep with me . . . or to sleep while I lay in unresting terror. My door was always open . . . and theirs . . . and I could not go downstairs alone at night that summer. That summer my father had his seventy-fourth birthday. We three had arranged a little celebration . . . a cake and household jokes. That was the morning the postman brought me a letter from the old lady who had been my neighbor. I read the first page . . . there were four pages . . . that denounced me for cruelty to my wife and for a "grasping disposition" toward my wife's kin. I fell in a heap on the floor, as I had fallen before the attack-motif of the vision in the sky. My father seized the letter and tore it instantly into bits, while my mother's black eyes filled with pain, not tears. He was not angry at the old lady . . . he was trying merely to save my life—from the other three pages. I cite the episode, no less to illustrate how tragically two worlds of honorable life may be asunder. She had accepted in her distress the local myth about me: she had never seen the inside of our cottage, never the inside of my mind, probably never half seen the outside of my face, even when I used to look up laughing as I shoveled the snow from her door-steps; but she was the dowager of Langdon Street, the wise and affectionate friend of all Dr. Greylock's children and of so many young faculty wives, the widow of a famous professor. She acted as an outraged neighbor might well act . . . if she had acted from knowledge. But in her nature was Revelation, Authority, Judgment; not for nothing was she the lineal descendant of Puritan Michael Wigglesworth, author of "The Day of Doom." She is dead. And she was old. Death and Age are two Sanctities. How do I dare violate them with this tale? I do not violate them. My father is dead; and when her letter came, he was older than she.

My brown hair turned to its present gray that summer. Not overnight, as folklore would have it, or many a story in tragic fiction. The laws of pigmentation are suspended as little as other laws of organic nature even under grief and terror. The subtle changes of life take place only where life is; and the life of the human hair, as of the camel's or sheep's, is at the roots. The gray steals up from the roots, as the new hair grows, lacking the pigments of old days. So the brown of my head lasted on into August. . . .

But I did not take to my bed. Too often when I lay down, especially after the noon meal, I suffered from a wildly rapid pulse and accentuation of the frequent attacks of diffused terror. I now know why. The Locomotive-God was in the subconsciousness just under the surface all that summer; and such hypnoidal relaxation brought him still nearer. In my recent clinical probings there came a time . . . two years in extent . . . to date . . . when, in milder form, hypnoidal relaxation produced intermittently a similar access of phobic feelings and rapid pulse, even after I knew they were the doings of the Locomotive-God. So the terror, on lying down, during that summer was essentially a terror without content (an emotional analogue of feeling ugly or erotic without an object), but a terror for which the intellect feigned heart-disease as the object—or (by a still more subtle rationalizing process) invented the idea that by feeling terror over a rapid pulse, in itself merely neurotic, I would infallibly cause the pulse to continue in rapidity so long that the heart would wear out. Much of the ingenuity and alertness of my mind was turned against me that summer: my mind found diabolically cunning ways of rationalizing all my terrors into secondary forms, pseudo-explanations, as plausible as horrific. For, not having the true explanation, the reason still insisted by its own instinctive urge upon some explanation. So it was with the innumerable phobias that beset me. Such is the mechanism in phobias generally, I believe. The real causes are unknown to the sufferer; and he makes up his causes. If he is of low intelligence, he makes up palpably foolish causes; if he is of high, then more plausible causes. Let us say both have a phobia of darkness; in both the real cause is a forgotten childhood trauma, from a fright in a wood; the former will explain it as fear lest some goblin thrust out a white hand from the blackness; the latter as a fear that some disease may attack him, appendicitis or spasm, with no one near to help in the night. But in each, even the pseudo-explanations will take their start in unknown past experience or associations in the subconscious. Six years ago I wrote a manuscript, nearly half as long as this book, in large part analyzing the infinitely varying devices my mind had developed for giving content, pseudo-content, and pseudo-objectivity, to its phobias. I knew then nothing at all as to the real causes, but I recognized that the only rational available causes were factitious. I knew I was not really afraid in the ways my mind devised.

The mechanism in its technique can be made clear to the reader. We start with a state of terror generated by past experience. The past experience itself remains in the subconsciousness. Its emotional effect, terror, bursts into consciousness. At times this emotional effect remains merely a diffused state of terror, in intensity running the whole scale from vague anxiety to intensest feel of impending death; and the agonized mind stands balked of any explanation whatever; except perhaps (as formerly with me) that the state is a premonition of the organic break-up of death. The bottom is knocked out of all security, as when, in an earthquake, chasms suddenly open all about one . . . except that in an earthquake the mind knows the fact *earthquake*, and in my case, it once knew no fact at all. But oftenest the subconscious experience in addition to terror generates in consciousness some specific *form* under which the terror manifests itself, a form of course symbolically, even literally, simulating the original experience. My central, dominating phobia of distance is as good an illustration as one will find. But the *form* of itself will lack adequate motivation for consciousness. So the mind feigns motivation. And so friendly counselors ask, "What is there to be afraid of?"—and add to the grievous burden by laughter or by experiments upon the patient . . . of which a vigorous word later. With the knowledge I now have of the real causes, the spells of diffused terror have apparently become negligible, so long as I am in good physical tone; but "what was I . . . am I . . . afraid of" in going a few blocks from the house, in 1911 . . . and after? . . . I always knew the terror was without adequate motivation. I could only say: as soon as I get a certain distance from home—a distance varying back and forth from yards to miles in the past fifteen years— I am overwhelmed with a feeling of insecurity, of terror that I can't get back. The truest statement of the conscious content is this: I am in terror of the seizure of terror; and I fear the seizure at a given distance. There are then perfectly rational sub-terrors—lest in my panic I make a public spectacle of myself, or run in front of an automobile, or actually collapse from nervous exhaustion.

For the emotion in the distance-phobia, as for the emotion in all others, there have been clearly defined degrees of intensity. Let me assume that I am walking down University Drive by the Lake. I am a normal man for the first quarter of a mile; for the next hundred yards I am in a mild state of dread, controllable and controlled; for the next twenty yards in an acute state of dread, yet controlled; for the next ten, in an anguish of terror that hasn't reached the crisis of explosion; and in a half-dozen steps more I am in as fierce a panic of isolation from help and home and of immediate death as a man overboard in mid-Atlantic or on a window-ledge far up in a sky-scraper with flames lapping his shoulders. The reader who can't understand why I have not merely whistled or laughed or ordered the phobias off my psychic premises, or who thinks that I must be grossly exaggerating a mere normal discomfort, like the initial dread in the dentist's chair, is not the reader for whom I am writing one line of this book. He belongs among the fools, of whom in my phobic career I have met a goodly number already. I would leave him alone. Let him leave me alone: let him, in the future, not meddle again unto worst disaster . . . of which later. It is as scientific a fact as any I know that my phobic seizures at their worst approach any limits of terror that the human mind is capable of in the actual presence of death in its most horrible forms. That I have never fainted away or died under them is due to two factors: first, my physical vitality; and, second, my skill in devising escapes—psychic surrogates, deflections of attention, or actual retreat to safety—before the exhausting surge had torn me to pieces. But more than once the escape has been at all but the last moment. The fools say nothing ever happened from one of these seizures—so why worry. Nothing ever happened? Well, here is what happens always. First, the seizure happens—as well say, nothing happens, if a red-hot iron is run down the throat, even though it should miraculously leave no after-effects. The seizure happens; the acutest agony of the conscious brain happens. Second, the seizure leaves me always far more exposed to phobic seizures for weeks or months; increases my fear of the Fear; and, as in the distance-phobia, robs me of a goodly part of what little freedom of movement on street and hillside I have. "Nothing ever happened." This means simply that to date I've lived through the seizures and continued for fifteen years to teach school, write books, and make jokes at the University Club across the street. . . .

Obsessive-Compulsive Reactions

In interpreting the obsessive-compulsive conditions a differentiation is usually made between the *obsession*, an intrusive, persistent, unshakeable idea and the *compulsion*, an equally intrusive and compelling action. The crux of the feeling state which accompanies these behaviors is the sense of loss of volition. The person is visited by forces which seem out of his control; he is *made* to do or think something quite out of keeping with the way he consciously wants to act or feel. The "style" of the obsessive-compulsive revolves around what Shapiro has called "the sense of 'should'."[1] This subjective experience is described by Shapiro: "When another person may experience, 'I want to,' the compulsive person experiences, in one form or another, 'I should.' By 'I should' the compulsive person does not refer to expediency, but rather to a sense of 'ought,' an experience of duty, propriety, or the like. It will be apparent that certain variations of this subjective experience of 'I should' or 'I must' are manifest in some severe forms of obsessional and compulsive symptoms (for example, 'I must wash') and perhaps implicit in others (for example, tics)."

The concerns of the obsessive-compulsive often revolve around themes of sin, guilt, and pollution. Murderous thoughts are not uncommon. The selections below include examples of both compulsive and obsessive behavior. The former is represented by the famous scene from *Macbeth*, in which Lady Macbeth is seeking to "cleanse"

---

[1] David Shapiro, Aspects of obsessive-compulsive style. *Psychiatry*, 1962, *25,* 46-59.

herself of the guilt arising from the murders. In Andreev's tale the morbid ruminations of the narrator are clearly obsessive in nature, and even the resolution he attempts does not dissolve his endless tormenting doubt.

William Shakespeare

MACBETH

[*Scene: Dunsinane, an anteroom in the Castle. Enter a* DOCTOR OF PHYSIC *and a* WAITING GENTLEWOMAN.]

DOCTOR   I have two nights watch'd with you, but can perceive no truth in your report. When was it she last walk'd?

GENTLEWOMAN   Since his majesty went into the field, I have seen her rise from her bed, throw her nightgown upon her, unlock her closet, take forth paper, fold it, write upon't, read it, afterwards seal it, and again return to bed; yet all this while in a most fast sleep.

DOCTOR   A great perturbation in nature, to receive at once the benefit of sleep, and do the effects of watching! In this slumbery agitation, besides her walking and other actual performances, what, at any time, have you heard her say?

GENTLEWOMAN   That, sir, which I will not report after her.

DOCTOR   You may to me: and 'tis most meet you should.

GENTLEWOMAN   Neither to you nor any one; having no witness to confirm my speech.

[*Enter* LADY MACBETH, *with a taper.*]

Lo you, here she comes! This is her very guise, and, upon my life, fast asleep. Observe her; stand close.

DOCTOR   How came she by that light?

William Shakespeare, from Macbeth, *Act V, Scene i, in* College Entrance Requirements in English: 1901-1905. *New York: American Book Co.,* 1898.

GENTLEWOMAN Why, it stood by her: she has light by her continually; 'tis her command.

DOCTOR You see, her eyes are open.

GENTLEWOMAN Ay, but their sense is shut.

DOCTOR What is it she does now? Look how she rubs her hands.

GENTLEWOMAN It is an accustom'd action with her, to seem thus washing her hands: I have known her continue in this a quarter of an hour.

LADY MACBETH Yet here's a spot.

DOCTOR Hark! she speaks: I will set down what comes from her, to satisfy my remembrance the more strongly.

LADY MACBETH Out, damned spot! out, I say!—One: two: why, then 'tis time to do't.—Hell is murky!—Fie, my lord, fie! a soldier, and afeard? What need we fear who knows it, when none can call our power to account?—Yet who would have thought the old man to have had so much blood in him!

DOCTOR Do you mark that?

LADY MACBETH The Thane of Fife had a wife: where is she now? —What, will these hands ne'er be clean?—No more o' that, my lord, no more o' that: you mar all with this starting.

DOCTOR Go to, go to; you have known what you should not.

GENTLEWOMAN She has spoke what she should not, I am sure of that: Heaven knows what she has known.

LADY MACBETH Here's the smell of the blood still: all the perfumes of Arabia will not sweeten this little hand. Oh, oh, oh!

DOCTOR What a sigh is there! The heart is sorely charg'd.

GENTLEWOMAN I would not have such a heart in my bosom for the dignity of the whole body.[1]

DOCTOR Well, well, well,—

GENTLEWOMAN Pray God it be, sir.

DOCTOR This disease is beyond my practice: yet I have known those which have walk'd in their sleep who have died holily in their beds.

LADY MACBETH Wash your hands, put on your nightgown; look not so pale.—I tell you yet again, Banquo's buried; he cannot come out on's grave.

---

[1] For all the rank and honors of her state.

DOCTOR   Even so?

LADY MACBETH   To bed, to bed! there's knocking at the gate:
   come, come, come, come, give me your hand. What's done cannot
   be undone.—To bed, to bed, to bed! [*Exit*]

DOCTOR   Will she go now to bed?

GENTLEWOMAN   Directly.

DOCTOR   Foul whisperings are abroad: unnatural deeds
   Do breed unnatural troubles: infected minds
   To their deaf pillows will discharge their secrets:
   More needs she the divine than the physician.
   God, God forgive us all! Look after her;
   Remove from her the means of all annoyance,
   And still keep eyes upon her. So, good night:
   My mind she has mated,[2] and amazed my sight.
   I think, but dare not speak.

GENTLEWOMAN   Good night, good doctor.

[*Exeunt.*]

---

[2] Confounded.

Leonid Andreev

THE LIE

I

'You are lying! I know you are lying!'

'Why are you shouting? Is it necessary for every one to hear us?'

Again she lied. I was not shouting, but speaking quite quietly and gently; I held her hand and spoke quietly and gently, and this venomous word 'lie' hissed like a little snake.

'I love you,' she continued, 'and you must believe me. Does not this convince you?' and she kissed me. But when I wanted to press her in my arms, she was no longer there. She went out of the dark passage and I followed her into the room where the gay fête was drawing to an end. How do I know where it was? She had told me to come there and I had come, and seen couples wheeling round and round all night. Nobody came up to me or spoke to me: a stranger to all, I sat in a corner near the musicians. The mouth of a large brass trumpet was directed straight towards me, and there was somebody imprisoned there roaring and every other minute laughing jerkily and coarsely: 'Ho, ho, ho!'

From time to time a white, scented cloud approached me. It was she. I do not know how she managed to caress me unperceived by others, but for one short second her shoulder pressed against my shoulder, for one short second lowering my eyes I could see a white

Leonid Andreev, "The Lie," in Selected Russian Short Stories, *tr. by A E. Chamot* London: Oxford World Classics, *1925.*

neck and a low-cut white frock. When I raised my eyes I saw the profile of a white, severe, placid face, like the face of a pensive angel over the graves of forgotten men. I saw her eyes. They were large, greedy for light, lovely, calm. Surrounded by its blue circle the pupils shone darkly, and whenever I looked in them they were always the same, black, deep, and unfathomable. Perhaps I looked in them too short a time for my heart to beat once, but I never felt so deeply and fearfully the meaning of infinity and never knew its power so forcibly. With fear and pain I felt that my whole life, like a tiny ray of light, was swallowed up by her eyes, until I became a stranger to myself, empty and voiceless—almost dead. Then she went away from me, taking my whole life with her, and again danced with some tall, arrogant, handsome man. I studied every detail of his person, the shape of his shoes, the width of his raised shoulders, the regular wave of an unruly lock of hair, and he seemed to press me to the wall with his indifferent unseeing glance, and I became as flat and insignificant to the eye as the wall itself.

When the candles began to go out I went up to her and said, 'It is time to be going, I will take you home.'

She was surprised. 'But I am going with him,' and she pointed to the tall and handsome stranger, who did not even look at us. Taking me into an empty room she kissed me.

'You lie,' said I, quietly, gently.

'We shall meet to-day. You must come,' she answered.

As I drove home the green frosty morning peeped over the high roofs. In all the whole street we two were alone, my *izvozchik* and I. He sat huddled up, hiding his face from the wind, and I behind him also huddled up in my coat and covering up my face to the eyes. The *izvozchik* had his thoughts and I had mine; there behind the thick walls thousands of people were sleeping, and they too had their dreams and their thoughts. I thought of her and how she had lied; I thought of death, and it appeared to me that these walls, lit up by the morning twilight, already saw me dead, and that was why they were so cold and straight. I do not know what the *izvozchik* was thinking, I do not know what those hidden behind the walls were dreaming. But neither did they know what I was thinking, what I was dreaming.

So we drove through the long, straight streets while morning arose over the roofs and everything around us was white and immovable. A sweet-scented white cloud approached me, and right into my ear some one imprisoned laughed: 'Ho, ho, ho!'

II

She had lied. She did not come, and I waited for her in vain. A grey, cold, congealed half-darkness settled down from the gloomy sky and I did not know when the twilight changed into evening or when evening passed into night; I thought of it all as one long night. Always with the same steps, the same regular, monotonous steps of waiting, I passed backwards and forwards. I did not go any nearer to the high house where my love dwelt nor to the glass front-door, which looked yellow in the shade of its iron roof, but always with the same regular steps I paced up and down the other side of the street—backwards and forwards—backwards and forwards. Going towards it I never took my eyes off the glass door, and going away from it I often stopped and turned my head, and then the snow pricked my face with its sharp needles. They were so long, those cold, sharp needles, that they penetrated into my heart and pierced it with the weary longing and irritation of helpless waiting. From the light north to the dark south the cold wind hurried, whistled, played over the frozen roofs, and tearing itself free from them whipped my face with small, sharp snowflakes and rattled like sand on the glass of the empty street lamps, where the solitary yellow flame shivered with cold and bent before it. I was sorry for the solitary flame that lived only by night, and I thought that soon all life would cease in this street, that I should go away, and only the snowflakes would hurry across the empty space and the yellow flame continue to shiver and bend in the solitude and cold.

I waited for her, and she did not come. It appeared to me that the solitary flame and I were alike, only my lamp was not empty. People appeared from time to time in the space that I measured with my footsteps. Silently they grew up behind me, large and dark, passed by me, and like grey phantoms suddenly disappeared round the corner of a white building. Then again from round the corner they came up to me and slowly melted away into the grey distance that was full of the silent moving snow. Wrapt up in their greatcoats, formless and silent, they were all alike and like me, and I thought that many dozen people were walking backwards and forwards as I was—waiting, shivering in silence, as I was, and thinking their own enigmatic, melancholy thoughts. I waited for her, and she did not come. I do not know why I did not cry out and weep with pain—I do not know why I laughed and was happy. I clenched my fingers together as if they were claws, and seemed to grasp tightly between them the little venomous creature—the snake—the lie. She coiled round my arms and bit at my heart, and I grew giddy with her poison. Everything around was lies. The boundary disappeared between the future and the present, between the present and the past. The boundary disappeared between the time when I was not yet alive and the time when I began to live, and I thought that I had always been alive, or never, and always, before I lived and when I began to live, she was reigning over me. It was strange to me to think that she had a name and a body, that in her existence there was a beginning and an end. She had no name, but she was always the one who lied, and who always made you wait for her and never came. I don't know why it was, but I laughed, and the sharp needles plunged into my heart and some one imprisoned laughed in my ear: 'Ho, ho, ho!'

Opening my eyes I saw the lighted windows of the tall house and they spoke to me quietly with their blue and red tongues.

'She is deceiving you at this moment. While you are wandering about waiting for her and suffering, she, the all-beautiful, all-bright, all-deceitful, is here listening to the whispers of the tall and handsome man who despises you. If you rushed in and killed her you would do a good deed, because you would kill the lie.'

I clenched more closely the hand in which I held a knife; laughing, I answered: 'Yes, I will kill her!'

But the windows looked sadly at me and added sadly, 'You will never kill her, never, because the instrument in your hand is as much a lie as are her kisses!'

All the waiting, silent shadows had long disappeared, and in that cold spot I alone remained—I and the solitary tongues of flame that shivered with cold and despair. Not far from me in the church belfry the clock began to strike the hour, and its dejected, metallic sound quavered and sobbed, flying out into space and losing itself in the madly whirling snowflakes. I began to count the strokes and laughed:

the clock struck fifteen. The belfry was old, and the clock too, and although it went well it struck anyhow, often so many times that the old bell-ringer had to go up the belfry to stop with his hands the spasmodic striking tongue. For whom did they lie, these quavering sad sounds that were seized and strangled by the frosty darkness? So pitiful and absurd was this unnecessary lie! With the last lying sound of the clock the glass door banged and the same tall man came down the steps. I only saw his back but I recognised it, for only yesterday I had seen him, haughty and contemptuous. I recognised his gait, and it was lighter, more assured, than yesterday. I too had often left the house thus: it is the way men walk who have just been kissed by the lying lips of a woman.

III

I threatened, I demanded, I gnashed my teeth!

'Tell me the truth!'

With a face as cold as snow, with surprise and raised eyebrows below which, always passionless and mysterious, shone black unfathomable pupils, she asked me: 'But do I lie to you?'

She knew that I could not prove that she lied and that all the heavy, massive creation of my searching thoughts could be destroyed by one word from her—by one lying word. I waited for it, and it came from her mouth, on the surface sparkling with the colours of truth but in its depths dark: 'I love you! Am I not entirely yours?'

We were far from the town and the snow-covered fields looked through the dark windows. Above them was darkness, and around them darkness, thick, immovable, silent darkness, but they gleamed with their own treasured light like the face of a corpse in the gloom. A single candle lighted the large, well-heated room, and even on its red flame could be seen the pale reflection of the dead fields.

'I want to know the truth, no matter how sad it may be. Perhaps I shall die when I hear it, but to die is better than not to know the truth. I feel there is falsehood in your eyes. Tell me the truth, and I will go away from you for ever,' I said. But she was silent and the look in her eyes, the cold searching look, pierced into my innermost heart, turned out the depths of my soul, and with strange inquisitiveness examined it, and I cried: 'Answer, or I will kill you!'

'Kill me,' she answered calmly; 'sometimes it is so wearisome to live. Can you get truth by threats?'

Then I fell on my knees, pressed her hand, cried and besought her for pity—and the truth!

'Poor fellow,' she said, putting her hand on my hair, 'poor fellow!'

'Have pity on me,' I implored, 'I long for the truth!'

I looked at her smooth brow and thought that truth was there behind this thin partition. Madly I wanted to tear open her skull to see the truth. Here below the white breasts her heart was beating, and madly I wanted to tear open those breasts with my claws and see, if only for once, the naked human heart. The pointed yellow flame of the candle, fast burning away, was motionless; the dark walls stretched away in the gloom; it was so sorrowful, so lonely, so fearful.

'Poor fellow,' she said, 'poor fellow!'

With spasmodic flickerings the yellow flame fell and turned blue and then went out; darkness surrounded us. I could not see her face, or her eyes; her arms clasped my head, and I felt the lie no more. I closed my eyes—I did not think, I did not live, I merely absorbed into myself the touch of her hands, and it seemed to me truthful. Through the darkness faintly the sound of her whisper came—strange and fearful.

'Embrace me. I am afraid!'

Then again silence and again the low whisper of fear.

'You want the truth—but do I know it? Even I, do I want to know it? Protect me—oh, how awful!'

I opened my eyes. The pale darkness of the room ran away from the tall windows, collected at the walls, and hid in the corners, and through the windows looked a thing large and deadly white. It seemed that some one's dead eyes searched for us, as if some one encompassed us in his frozen grasp. Shivering we pressed close together, and she whispered: 'Oh, how awful!'

IV

I killed her.

I killed her, and when she lay a faded and flattened mass at that window, beyond which the white fields stretched out, I put my foot on her body and laughed. It was not the laugh of a madman. No! I laughed because my breast breathed evenly and lightly, because in its depth there was happiness, peace, and emptiness: from my heart had fallen the worm that had gnawed it. Bending down I looked in the dead eyes. Large eyes eager for light, they remained open, and were like the eyes of a wax doll, the same round, dim eyes that seemed to be covered with mica. I could touch them with my finger, shut and open them, and I was not afraid because the demon of lies and doubt no longer lived in those black, unfathomable pupils that so long had thirstily drunk of my blood.

When they arrested me I laughed, and those who took me away thought it dreadful and savage. They turned from me with aversion and drew back; others, strict and terrible, with reproaches on their lips, came straight towards me, but when they saw my joyful, merry look their faces grew pale and their feet were glued to the ground.

'A madman!' they said, and I thought that this word calmed them because it helped them to solve the enigma: how I, a lover, could kill my beloved and yet laugh. Only one, a fat, red-faced, jolly man, called me by another name. It hit me and darkened the light before my eyes.

'Poor man,' he said with sympathy, without bitterness, because he was fat and jolly, 'poor man!'

'Don't,' I cried, 'don't call me that!'

I don't know why I cried out at him. Of course I did not want to kill him nor even touch him, but all these frightened people who saw in me a madman and a criminal became more alarmed and cried out in such a way that I laughed again.

When they led me out of the room in which the corpse lay, I said again in a loud voice, obstinately looking at the jolly, fat man, 'I am happy, I am happy!'

And it was true.

V

Once in my childhood I had seen a panther in the Zoological Gardens that had struck my imagination and long occupied my thoughts. He was not like the other animals, who stupidly slept, or viciously gazed at the visitors. He walked about in a straight line from corner to corner of his cage with mathematical precision, each time turning at the same place, each time rubbing against the same bar of his cage with his golden fur. His sharp, rapacious head was bent down, his eyes looking straight before him, and not once did he turn aside. All day long people crowded before his cage; they talked and made a noise, but he continued his wandering and did not once turn his eyes towards the gazers. Few faces in the crowd smiled; most of them looked seriously, even gloomily, on this living picture of dull, despairing reflection, and turned away with a sigh; going away they would turn again inquiringly to look at him, unable to comprehend, and sigh as if there were something in common between them, free men, and this imprisoned beast. Whenever afterwards men or books mentioned eternity I thought of the panther, and it appeared to me that I knew eternity and its torments.

I became such a panther in my stone cage. I walked about and thought. I walked in one line across my cage from corner to corner, and my thoughts travelled along a short line—such heavy thoughts it seemed that I had not a head but a whole world on my shoulders. They consisted of only one word, but what a large, what a tormenting, what a fatal word!

'Lies' is this word.

Again, hissing, it crawled from all the corners and coiled around my soul, but it had ceased to be a little snake—it had grown into a large, fierce, shining serpent, and it stung me and smothered me with its iron rings. When I cried out with pain out of my open mouth came the same repulsive, whistling, serpent-like sound, as if my whole breast were swarming with reptiles: 'Lies!'

I walked amid my thoughts and the smooth, grey asphalt floor changed before my eyes into a grey, transparent, bottomless abyss. My feet ceased to feel the touch of the stones, and I fancied that I was floating at an immeasurable height above the mist and darkness. When my breast was delivered of the hissing sigh, from there, from the bottom, from this thin but impenetrable wrapper, slowly resounded a horrible echo—so slowly and softly, as if it traversed thousands of years and at each minute and in each atom of mist had lost part of its power. I understood that there, down at the bottom, it whistled like the wind which tears up trees, but to my ears it came like evil news brought in one short word: 'Lies.'

This mean whisper made me indignant. I stamped my feet on the stones and shouted: 'There are no lies! I have killed the lies!'

I purposely turned away, for I knew it would answer, and slowly from the deep bottomless abyss came the answer: 'Lies.'

You see, the matter stands thus. I had made a miserable mistake: I had killed the woman, but had made the lie immortal. Do not kill the woman until by means of entreaty, torture, and fire you have torn the truth from her soul.

Thus I thought as I walked from corner to corner of my cage.

VI

It is dark and dreadful where she has carried the truth and the lie —and there shall I go. At the very throne of Satan I shall catch her and fall on my knees and weeping say, 'Show me the truth!'

My God! My God! this too is a lie. Darkness is there, and the emptiness of centuries and eternity, but she is not there—she is not anywhere. The lie has remained. It is immortal. I feel it in every atom of the air, and when I breathe it comes with hisses into my breast and tears it—and tears it!

Oh! what madness it is for a man to look for truth! What pain! Save me! save me!

Neurotic Depressive Reactions

Of depression, Landis has written: "The shadow that melancholia casts on the mental life of any human being is the oldest concept of psychopathology that is still as current in modern thought as it was at any time in the past. The feelings that characterize this experience are typically sorrow, fear, and hopelessness."[1] These feelings are a more or less transient response to situational factors such as the loss of a loved person, an illness, or a change in status, but also appear primarily in middle-aged people, as a reaction to what might be described as an existential awareness of advancing age, the narrowing of horizons, and the lessening of creative powers. In this manifestation it is a form of *weltschmerz*, a weariness and discomfort with the state of the world and one's own place in it.

Fitzgerald's description of shrinking from the world during his crack-up, is a clear expression of the feelings of the neurotic depressive.

---

[1] Carney Landis, *Varieties of Psychopathological Experience*. New York: Holt Rinehart & Winston, 1964, p. 260.

F. Scott Fitzgerald

THE CRACK-UP

Now a man can crack in many ways—can crack in the head—in
which case the power of decision is taken from you by others! or in
the body, when one can but submit to the white hospital world; or
in the nerves. William Seabrook in an unsympathetic book tells,
with some pride and a movie ending, of how he became a public
charge. What led to his alcoholism or was bound up with it, was a
collapse of his nervous system. Though the present writer was not
so entangled—having at the time not tasted so much as a glass of
beer for six months—it was his nervous reflexes that were giving
way—too much anger and too many tears.

Moreover, to go back to my thesis that life has a varying offensive,
the realization of having cracked was not simultaneous with a blow,
but with a reprieve.

Not long before, I had sat in the office of a great doctor and listened
to a grave sentence. With what, in retrospect, seems some equanim-
ity, I had gone on about my affairs in the city where I was then
living, not caring much, not thinking how much had been left
undone, or what would become of this and that responsibility, like
people do in books; I was well insured and anyhow I had been
only a mediocre caretaker of most of the things left in my hands,
even of my talent.

But I had a strong sudden instinct that I must be alone. I didn't

F. Scott Fitzgerald, from The Crack-Up. New York: New Directions, 1945.

want to see any people at all. I had seen so many people all my life
—I was an average mixer, but more than average in a tendency to
identify myself, my ideas, my destiny, with those of all classes that
I came in contact with. I was always saving or being saved—in a
single morning I would go through the emotions ascribable to Wellington at Waterloo. I lived in a world of inscrutable hostiles and
inalienable friends and supporters.

But now I wanted to be absolutely alone and so arranged a certain
insulation from ordinary cares.

It was not an unhappy time. I went away and there were fewer
people. I found I was good-and-tired. I could lie around and was
glad to, sleeping or dozing sometimes twenty hours a day and in the
intervals trying resolutely not to think—instead I made lists—made
lists and tore them up, hundreds of lists: of cavalry leaders and football players and cities, and popular tunes and pitchers, and happy
times, and hobbies and houses lived in and how many suits since I
left the army and how many pairs of shoes (I didn't count the suit I
bought in Sorrento that shrunk, nor the pumps and dress shirt and
collar that I carried around for years and never wore, because the
pumps got damp and grainy and the shirt and collar got yellow and
starch-rotted). And lists of women I'd liked, and of the times I had let
myself be snubbed by people who had not been my betters in character or ability.

—And then suddenly, surprisingly, I got better.

—And cracked like an old plate as soon as I heard the news.

That is the real end of this story. What was to be done about it
will have to rest in what used to be called the "womb of time."
Suffice it to say that after about an hour of solitary pillow-hugging,
I began to realize that for two years my life had been a drawing on
resources that I did not possess, that I had been mortgaging myself
physically and spiritually up to the hilt. What was the small gift of
life given back in comparison to that?—when there had once been
a pride of direction and a confidence in enduring independence.

I realized that in those two years, in order to preserve something
—an inner hush maybe, maybe not—I had weaned myself from all
the things I used to love—that every act of life from the morning
tooth-brush to the friend at dinner had become an effort. I saw that
for a long time I had not liked people and things, but only followed

the rickety old pretense of liking. I saw that even my love for those closest to me was become only an attempt to love, that my casual relations—with an editor, a tobacco seller, the child of a friend, were only what I remembered I *should* do, from other days. All in the same month I became bitter about such things as the sound of the radio, the advertisements in the magazines, the screech of tracks, the dead silence of the country—contemptuous at human softness, immediately (if secretively) quarrelsome toward hardness—hating the night when I couldn't sleep and hating the day because it went toward night. I slept on the heart side now because I knew that the sooner I could tire that out, even a little, the sooner would come that blessed hour of nightmare which, like a catharsis, would enable me to better meet the new day.

There were certain spots, certain faces I could look at. Like most Middle Westerners, I have never had any but the vaguest race prejudices—I always had a secret yen for the lovely Scandinavian blondes who sat on porches in St. Paul but hadn't emerged enough economically to be part of what was then society. They were too nice to be "chickens" and too quickly off the farmlands to seize a place in the sun, but I remember going round blocks to catch a single glimpse of shining hair—the bright shock of a girl I'd never know. This is urban, unpopular talk. It strays afield from the fact that in these latter days I couldn't stand the sight of Celts, English, Politicians, Strangers, Virginians, Negroes (light or dark), Hunting People, or retail clerks, and middlemen in general, all writers (I avoided writers very carefully because they can perpetuate trouble as no one else can)—and all the classes as classes and most of them as members of their class . . .

Trying to cling to something, I liked doctors and girl children up to the age of about thirteen and well-brought-up boy children from about eight years old on. I could have peace and happiness with these few categories of people. I forgot to add that I liked old men—men over seventy, sometimes over sixty if their faces looked seasoned. I liked Katharine Hepburn's face on the screen, no matter what was said about her pretentiousness, and Miriam Hopkins' face, and old friends if I only saw them once a year and could remember their ghosts.

All rather inhuman and undernourished, isn't it? Well, that, children, is the true sign of cracking up.

It is not a pretty picture. Inevitably it was carted here and there within its frame and exposed to various critics. One of them can only be described as a person whose life makes other people's lives seem like death—even this time when she was cast in the usually unappealing role of Job's comforter. In spite of the fact that this story is over, let me append our conversation as a sort of postscript:

"Instead of being so sorry for yourself, listen—" she said. (She always says "Listen," because she thinks while she talks—*really* thinks.) So she said: "Listen. Suppose this wasn't a crack in you— suppose it was a crack in the Grand Canyon."

"The crack's in me," I said heroically.

"Listen! The world only exists in your eyes—your conception of it. You can make it as big or as small as you want to. And you're trying to be a little puny individual. By God, if I ever cracked, I'd try to make the world crack with me. Listen! The world only exists through your apprehension of it, and so it's much better to say that it's not you that's cracked—it's the Grand Canyon."

"Baby et up all her Spinoza?"

"I don't know anything about Spinoza. I know—" She spoke, then, of old woes of her own, that seemed, in the telling, to have been more dolorous than mine, and how she had met them, overridden them, beaten them.

I felt a certain reaction to what she said, but I am a slow-thinking man, and it occurred to me simultaneously that of all natural forces, vitality is the incommunicable one. In days when juice came into one as an article without duty, one tried to distribute it—but always without success; to further mix metaphors, vitality never "takes." You have it or you haven't it, like health or brown eyes or honor or a baritone voice. I might have asked some of it from her, neatly wrapped and ready for home cooking and digestion, but I could never have got it—not if I'd waited around for a thousand hours with the tin cup of self-pity. I could walk from her door, holding myself very carefully like cracked crockery, and go away into the world of bitterness, where I was making a home with such materials as are found there—and quote to myself after I left her door:

"*Ye are the salt of the earth. But if the salt hath lost its savour, wherewith shall it be salted?*"—*Matt.* 5:13.

PART TWO

THE PSYCHOSES

Apart from their psychological meaning, the psychoses represent a social problem of the first order. The overwhelming majority of the half-million patients in American psychiatric hospitals today are psychotics. This number is greater than all patients hospitalized for all other illnesses put together, and the cost of their care runs into millions of dollars annually.

From a psychological point of view, psychosis represents a severe personality disorganization, characterized by the loss of meaningful contact with other people and objects, and the subsequent development of a compensatory, make-believe world, peopled by figures from fantasy and dreams. Unlike the neurotic who, crippled as he may be by symptoms and general anxiety still maintains social and emotional relationships with real people in a real world, the psychotic, as Harry Stack Sullivan has said, "finds himself surrounded by extraordinary caricatures of other people, engaging in bizarre activities more or less definitely injurious to him, the whole of his interpersonal relations resembling the phantasmagoria of the nightmare."[1] Freud made the essential distinction between psychosis and neurosis in this way: "Neurosis does not deny the existence of reality, it merely tries to ignore it; psychosis denies it and tries to substitute something else for it."[2]

The nightmare aspect of the psychotic's world pervades these

[1] H. S. Sullivan, Schizophrenic individuals as a source of data for comparative investigation of personality. In Helen Swick Perry (ed.), *Schizophrenia as a Human Process*. New York: Norton, 1962, pp. 218, 219.

[2] S. Freud. The loss of reality in neurosis and psychosis. *Collected Papers*. New York: Basic Books, 1959, Vol. II, p. 279.

selections. Gogol, Singer, and Chekhov, in particular, present heroes who feel threatened and tormented by the "caricatures" of other people and the malevolent beings surrounding them. Still other selections, notably those of Rubin, Aiken, and Svevo, clearly show what Freud noted—the psychotic's attempt to substitute a more comfortable wish-fulfilling and protecting fantasy world for the oppressive, frightening, and frustrating real world.

Several different forms of psychotic behavior are recognized, although one or more of the core symptoms of hallucinations, delusions, and disturbances in communication are characteristically present in all these. The functional psychoses (those disorders in which there is no demonstrable brain pathology) are divided into four types: schizophrenia, paranoid reactions, affective psychoses, and involutional reactions.

Schizophrenic reactions are a group of disorders characterized by primary disturbances in thought processes and reality relations in which emotional disharmony, hallucinations, and delusions are quite common. The childhood forms of this disturbance are included below with the selections on schizophrenia.

Paranoid reactions exist in two states: paranoia, marked by a complex and well-structured delusional system; and the paranoid state, a more transient situation characterized by delusions and hallucinations without any particular systematization.

Affective reactions, including manic-depressive and psychotic depressive reactions, are manifested mainly by severe mood disturbances.

Involutional psychotic reactions are marked by the development of a severe depressive state during the involutional or "change of life" period. This category is not represented separately among the readings. The depressive aspects of the involutional disorders, however, make them part of the broad spectrum of affective psychoses.

Schizophrenic Reactions

As a complex of pathological conditions the term schizophrenia includes a wide variety of bizarre and disturbing behavioral experiences, including hallucinations, delusions, extreme apathy, personalized and illogical speech, and the whole gamut of phenomena once classified as madness. The schizophrenic exists apart from the mainstream of life around him. He is literally alienated and divorced from reality, living in a world of uncanny, overpowering terrors and unable to make meaningful contact with those around him. One patient has described the experience as that of "a traveler who's been lost in a land where no one speaks his language. Worst of all, the traveler doesn't know where he should be going."[1]

The key symptoms of schizophrenia are predominantly in the realm of thinking and feeling. Language and thought processes appear distorted and confused, peculiarities variously described as prelogical and paleological, implying cognitive behavior at variance with the normally accepted logic of everyday life. Feeling difficulties have been interpreted as "blunting of affect," implying a state of withdrawal and isolation in the emotional sphere. One often observes in these patients strange and abrupt emotional changes seemingly unconnected with present events, as well as what is called "inappropriate affect," emotional responses unsuitable to the context in which they arise.

---

[1] M.L. Hayward and J.E. Taylor. A schizophrenic patient describes the action of intensive psychotherapy. *Psychiatric Quart.*, 1956, *30*, 211-248.

Despite a somewhat dated style, the gradual development and final flowering of delusional and hallucinatory experience is portrayed with clinical intensity in Charlotte Gilman's "The Yellow Wall-paper," the first selection. The speech which follows, taken from Beckett's *Waiting for Godot*, is presented as an analogy to "schizophrenese," a language of devious and uncertain twists and turns, compounded of bits and pieces of experience and a wealth of inner, often incomprehensible, associations. The resemblance of this speech to schizophrenic language lies both in its paradoxical, involuted style, in which words and images are placed in strange new relationships and the ordinary rules of discourse are flaunted, and in its deeply emotional imagery concerning life and death, heaven and hell, isolation and alienation, all of which so often appear to profoundly concern the schizophrenic. Beckett's language differs from that of the psychotic in its obviously greater aesthetic control and more readily discernible meaning. Poetic and striking in its unconscious resonances as such speech may appear, haunting though its suggested meanings may be, the psychotic's desperate efforts at communication fail so often because of the too private nature of his premises and imagery.

Sartre's "The Room" is a brilliant exploration of the communication patterns of the schizophrenic and their often shattering effect on those who attempt to make contact with him. Pierre's shifting levels of response and his refusal to clarify or define his relationship with Eve (to the point that he even denies he is talking to her by calling her Agatha) make it impossible for her to know what role to take in dealing with him. Pierre's aberrant behavior can be seen, in interpersonal terms, as the natural concomitant of this refusal to indicate the nature or course of his relationship with his wife and the others around him. Finally, Gogol's "Diary of a Madman" examines the dissolution of a man's hold on reality and his ultimate total retreat into a world of madness, a world remarkably like that described by Sullivan, with its bizarre activities and nightmare events.

Charlotte Perkins Gilman

THE YELLOW WALL-PAPER

It is very seldom that mere ordinary people like John and myself secure ancestral halls for the summer.

A colonial mansion, a hereditary estate, I would say a haunted house, and reach the height of romantic felicity—but that would be asking too much of fate!

Still I will proudly declare that there is something queer about it.

Else, why should it be let so cheaply? And why have stood so long untenanted?

John laughs at me, of course, but one expects that in marriage.

John is practical in the extreme. He has no patience with faith, an intense horror of superstition, and he scoffs openly at any talk of things not to be felt and seen and put down in figures.

John is a physician, and *perhaps*—(I would not say it to a living soul, of course, but this is dead paper and a great relief to my mind—) *perhaps* that is one reason I do not get well faster.

You see he does not believe I am sick!

And what can one do?

If a physician of high standing, and one's own husband, assures friends and relatives that there is really nothing the matter with one but temporary nervous depression—a slight hysterical tendency— what is one to do?

Charlotte Perkins Stetson [Gilman], "*The Yellow Wall-paper*," *in* New England Magazine, *1891-1892, New Series 5, pp. 647-659.*

My brother is also a physician, and also of high standing, and he says the same thing.

So I take phosphates or phosphites—whichever it is, and tonics, and journeys, and air, and exercise, and am absolutely forbidden to "work" until I am well again.

Personally, I disagree with their ideas.

Personally, I believe that congenial work, with excitement and change, would do me good.

But what is one to do?

I did write for a while in spite of them; but it *does* exhaust me a good deal—having to be so sly about it, or else meet with heavy opposition.

I sometimes fancy that in my condition if I had less opposition and more society and stimulus—but John says the very worst thing I can do is to think about my condition, and I confess it always makes me feel bad.

So I will let it alone and talk about the house.

The most beautiful place! It is quite alone, standing well back from the road, quite three miles from the village. It makes me think of English places that you read about, for there are hedges and walls and gates that lock, and lots of separate little houses for the gardeners and people.

There is a *delicious* garden! I never saw such a garden—large and shady, full of box-bordered paths, and lined with long grape-covered arbors with seats under them.

There were greenhouses, too, but they are all broken now.

There was some legal trouble, I believe, something about the heirs and co-heirs; anyhow, the place has been empty for years.

That spoils my ghostliness, I am afraid, but I don't care—there is something strange about the house—I can feel it.

I even said so to John one moonlight evening, but he said what I felt was a *draught*, and shut the window.

I get unreasonably angry with John sometimes. I'm sure I never used to be so sensitive. I think it is due to this nervous condition.

But John says if I feel so, I shall neglect proper self-control; so I take pains to control myself—before him, at least, and that makes me very tired.

I don't like our room a bit. I wanted one downstairs that opened on the piazza and had roses all over the window, and such pretty old-fashioned chintz hangings! but John would not hear of it.

He said there was only one window and not room for two beds, and no near room for him if he took another.

He is very careful and loving, and hardly lets me stir without special direction.

I have a schedule prescription for each hour in the day; he takes all care from me, and so I feel basely ungrateful not to value it more.

He said we came here solely on my account, that I was to have perfect rest and all the air I could get. "Your exercise depends on your strength, my dear," said he, "and your food somewhat on your appetite; but air you can absorb all the time." So we took the nursery at the top of the house.

It is a big, airy room, the whole floor nearly, with windows that look all ways, and air and sunshine galore. It was nursery first and then playroom and gymnasium, I should judge; for the windows are barred for little children, and there are rings and things in the walls.

The paint and paper look as if a boys' school had used it. It is stripped off—the paper—in great patches all around the head of my bed, about as far as I can reach, and in a great place on the other side of the room low down. I never saw a worse paper in my life.

One of those sprawling flamboyant patterns committing every artistic sin.

It is dull enough to confuse the eye in following, pronounced enough to constantly irritate and provoke study, and when you follow the lame uncertain curves for a little distance they suddenly commit suicide—plunge off at outrageous angles, destroy themselves in unheard of contradictions.

The color is repellant, almost revolting; a smouldering unclean yellow, strangely faded by the slow-turning sunlight.

It is a dull yet lurid orange in some places, a sickly sulphur tint in others.

No wonder the children hated it! I should hate it myself if I had to live in this room long.

There comes John, I must put this away,—he hates to have me write a word.

*   *   *   *   *

We have been here two weeks, and I haven't felt like writing before, since that first day.

I am sitting by the window now, up in this atrocious nursery, and there is nothing to hinder my writing as much as I please, save lack of strength.

John is away all day, and even some nights when his cases are serious.

I am glad my case is not serious!

But these nervous troubles are dreadfully depressing.

John does not know how much I really suffer. He knows there is no *reason* to suffer, and that satisfies him.

Of course it is only nervousness. It does weigh on me so not to do my duty in any way!

I meant to be such a help to John, such a real rest and comfort, and here I am a comparative burden already!

Nobody would believe what an effort it is to do what little I am able,—to dress and entertain, and order things.

It is fortunate Mary is so good with the baby. Such a dear baby!

And yet I *cannot* be with him, it makes me so nervous.

I suppose John never was nervous in his life. He laughs at me so about this wall-paper!

At first he meant to repaper the room, but afterwards he said that I was letting it get the better of me, and that nothing was worse for a nervous patient than to give way to such fancies.

He said that after the wall-paper was changed it would be the heavy bedstead, and then the barred windows, and then that gate at the head of the stairs, and so on.

"You know the place is doing you good," he said, "and really, dear, I don't care to renovate the house just for a three months' rental."

"Then do let us go downstairs," I said, "there are such pretty rooms there."

Then he took me in his arms and called me a blessed little goose, and said he would go down cellar, if I wished, and have it white-washed into the bargain.

But he is right enough about the beds and windows and things.

It is an airy and comfortable room as any one need wish, and, of course, I would not be so silly as to make him uncomfortable just for a whim.

I'm really getting quite fond of the big room, all but that horrid paper.

Out of one window I can see the garden, those mysterious deep-shaded arbors, the riotous old-fashioned flowers, and bushes and gnarly trees.

Out of another I get a lovely view of the bay and a little private wharf belonging to the estate. There is a beautiful shaded lane that runs down there from the house. I always fancy I see people walking in these numerous paths and arbors, but John has cautioned me not to give way to fancy in the least. He says that with my imaginative power and habit of story-making, a nervous weakness like mine is sure to lead to all manner of excited fancies, and that I ought to use my will and good sense to check the tendency. So I try.

I think sometimes that if I were only well enough to write a little it would relieve the press of ideas and rest me.

But I find I get pretty tired when I try.

It is so discouraging not to have any advice and companionship about my work. When I get really well, John says we will ask Cousin Henry and Julia down for a long visit; but he says he would as soon put fireworks in my pillow-case as to let me have those stimulating people about now.

I wish I could get well faster.

But I must not think about that. This paper looks to me as if it *knew* what a vicious influence it had!

There is a recurrent spot where the pattern lolls like a broken neck and two bulbous eyes stare at you upside down.

I get positively angry with the impertinence of it and the ever-lastingness. Up and down and sideways they crawl, and those absurd, unblinking eyes are everywhere. There is one place where two breadths didn't match, and the eyes go all up and down the line, one a little higher than the other.

I never saw so much expression in an inanimate thing before, and we all know how much expression they have! I used to lie awake as a child and get more entertainment and terror out of blank walls and plain furniture than most children could find in a toy-store.

I remember what a kindly wink the knobs of our big, old bureau used to have, and there was one chair always seemed like a strong friend.

I used to feel that if any of the other things looked too fierce I could always hop into that chair and be safe.

The furniture in this room is no worse than inharmonious, however, for we had to bring it all from downstairs. I suppose when this was used as a playroom they had to take the nursery things out, and no wonder! I never saw such ravages as the children have made here.

The wall-paper, as I said before, is torn off in spots, and it sticketh closer than a brother—they must have had perseverance as well as hatred.

Then the floor is scratched and gouged and splintered, the plaster itself is dug out here and there, and this great heavy bed which is all we found in the room, looks as if it had been through the wars.

But I don't mind it a bit—only the paper.

There comes John's sister. Such a dear girl as she is, and so careful of me! I must not let her find me writing.

She is a perfect and enthusiastic housekeeper, and hopes for no better profession. I verily believe she thinks it is the writing which made me sick!

But I can write when she is out, and see her a long way off from these windows.

There is one that commands the road, a lovely shaded winding road, and one that just looks off over the country. A lovely country, too, full of great elms and velvet meadows.

This wall-paper has a kind of sub-pattern in a different shade, a particularly irritating one, for you can only see it in certain lights, and not clearly then.

But in the places where it isn't faded and where the sun is just so —I can see a strange, provoking, formless sort of figure, that seems to skulk about behind that silly and conspicuous front design.

There's sister on the stairs!

*   *   *   *   *

Well, the Fourth of July is over! The people are all gone and I am tired out. John thought it might do me good to see a little company, so we just had mother and Nellie and the children down for a week.

Of course I didn't do a thing. Jennie sees to everything now.

But it tired me all the same.

John says if I don't pick up faster he shall send me to Weir Mitchell in the fall.

But I don't want to go there at all. I had a friend who was in his hands once, and she says he is just like John and my brother, only more so!

Besides, it is such an undertaking to go so far.

I don't feel as if it was worth while to turn my hand over for anything, and I'm getting dreadfully fretful and querulous.

I cry at nothing, and cry most of the time.

Of course I don't when John is here, or anybody else, but when I am alone.

And I am alone a good deal just now. John is kept in town very often by serious cases, and Jennie is good and lets me alone when I want her to.

So I walk a little in the garden or down that lovely lane, sit on the porch under the roses, and lie down up here a good deal.

I'm getting really fond of the room in spite of the wall-paper. Perhaps *because* of the wall-paper.

It dwells in my mind so!

I lie here on this great immovable bed—it is nailed down, I believe—and follow that pattern about by the hour. It is as good as gymnastics, I assure you. I start, we'll say, at the bottom down in the corner over there where it has not been touched, and I determine for the thousandth time that I *will* follow that pointless pattern to some sort of a conclusion.

I know a little of the principle of design, and I know this thing was not arranged on any laws of radiation, or alternation, or repetition, or symmetry, or anything else that I ever heard of.

It is repeated, of course, by the breadths, but not otherwise.

Looked at in one way each breadth stands alone, the bloated curves and flourishes—a kind of "debased Romanesque" with *delirium tremens*—go waddling up and down in isolated columns of fatuity.

But, on the other hand, they connect diagonally, and the sprawling outlines run off in great slanting waves of optic horror, like a lot of wallowing seaweeds in full chase.

The whole thing goes horizontally, too, at least it seems so, and I exhaust myself in trying to distinguish the order of its going in that direction.

They have used a horizontal breadth for a frieze, and that adds wonderfully to the confusion.

There is one end of the room where it is almost intact, and there, when the crosslights fade and the low sun shines directly upon it, I can almost fancy radiation after all,—the interminable grotesque seem to form around a common centre and rush off in headlong plunges of equal distraction.

It makes me tired to follow it. I will take a nap I guess.

*   *   *   *   *

I don't know why I should write this.

I don't want to.

I don't feel able.

And I know John would think it absurd. But I *must* say what I feel and think in some way—it is such a relief!

But the effort is getting to be greater than the relief.

Half the time now I am awfully lazy, and lie down ever so much.

John says I mustn't lose my strength, and has me take cod liver oil and lots of tonics and things, to say nothing of ale and wine and rare meat.

Dear John! He loves me very dearly, and hates to have me sick. I tried to have a real earnest reasonable talk with him the other day, and tell him how I wish he would let me go and make a visit to Cousin Henry and Julia.

But he said I wasn't able to go, nor able to stand it after I got there; and I did not make out a very good case for myself, for I was crying before I had finished.

It is getting to be a great effort for me to think straight. Just this nervous weakness I suppose.

And dear John gathered me up in his arms, and just carried me upstairs and laid me on the bed, and sat by me and read to me till it tired my head.

He said I was his darling and his comfort and all he had, and that I must take care of myself for his sake, and keep well.

He says no one but myself can help me out of it, that I must use my will and self-control and not let any silly fancies run away with me.

There's one comfort, the baby is well and happy, and does not have to occupy this nursery with the horrid wall-paper.

If we had not used it, that blessed child would have! What a fortunate escape! Why, I wouldn't have a child of mine, an impressionable little thing, live in such a room for worlds.

I never thought of it before, but it is lucky that John kept me here after all, I can stand it so much easier than a baby, you see.

Of course I never mention it to them any more—I am too wise,—but I keep watch of it all the same.

There are things in that paper that nobody knows but me, or ever will.

Behind that outside pattern the dim shapes get clearer every day.

It is always the same shape, only very numerous.

And it is like a woman stooping down and creeping about behind that pattern. I don't like it a bit. I wonder—I begin to think—I wish John would take me away from here!

* * * * *

It is so hard to talk with John about my case, because he is so wise, and because he loves me so.

But I tried it last night.

It was moonlight. The moon shines in all around just as the sun does.

I hate to see it sometimes, it creeps so slowly, and always comes in by one window or another.

John was asleep and I hated to waken him, so I kept still and watched the moonlight on that undulating wall-paper till I felt creepy.

The faint figure behind seemed to shake the pattern, just as if she wanted to get out.

I got up softly and went to feel and see if the paper *did* move, and when I came back John was awake.

"What is it, little girl?" he said. "Don't go walking about like that—you'll get cold."

I thought it was a good time to talk, so I told him that I really was not gaining here, and that I wished he would take me away.

"Why, darling!" said he, "our lease will be up in three weeks, and I can't see how to leave before.

"The repairs are not done at home, and I cannot possibly leave town just now. Of course if you were in any danger, I could and would, but you really are better, dear, whether you can see it or not. I am a doctor, dear, and I know. You are gaining flesh and color, your appetite is better, I feel really much easier about you."

"I don't weigh a bit more," said I, "nor as much; and my appetite may be' better in the evening when you are here, but it is worse in the morning when you are away!"

"Bless her little heart!" said he with a big hug, "she shall be as sick as she pleases! But now let's improve the shining hours by going to sleep, and talk about it in the morning!"

"And you won't go away?" I asked gloomily.

"Why, how can I, dear? It is only three weeks more and then we will take a nice little trip of a few days while Jennie is getting the house ready. Really dear you are better!"

"Better in body perhaps—" I began, and stopped short, for he sat up straight and looked at me with such a stern, reproachful look that I could not say another word.

"My darling," said he, "I beg of you, for my sake and for our child's sake, as well as for your own, that you will never for one instant let that idea enter your mind! There is nothing so dangerous, so fascinating, to a temperament like yours. It is a false and foolish fancy. Can you not trust me as a physician when I tell you so?"

So of course I said no more on that score, and we went to sleep before long. He thought I was asleep first, but I wasn't, and lay there for hours trying to decide whether that front pattern and the back pattern really did move together or separately.

*   *   *   *   *

On a pattern like this, by daylight, there is a lack of sequence, a defiance of law, that is a constant irritant to a normal mind.

The color is hideous enough, and unreliable enough, and infuri-, ating enough, but the pattern is torturing.

You think you have mastered it, but just as you get well underway in following, it turns a back-somersault and there you are. It slaps you in the face, knocks you down, and tramples upon you. It is like a bad dream.

The outside pattern is a florid arabesque, reminding one of a fungus. If you can imagine a toadstool in joints, an interminable string of toadstools, budding and sprouting in endless convolutions—why, that is something like it.

That is, sometimes!

There is one marked peculiarity about this paper, a thing nobody seems to notice but myself, and that is that it changes as the light changes.

When the sun shoots in through the east window—I always watch for that first long, straight ray—it changes so quickly that I never can quite believe it.

That is why I watch it always.

By moonlight—the moon shines in all night when there is a moon—I wouldn't know it was the same paper.

At night in any kind of light, in twilight, candlelight, lamplight, and worst of all by moonlight, it becomes bars! The outside pattern I mean, and the woman behind it is as plain as can be.

I didn't realize for a long time what the thing was that showed behind, that dim sub-pattern, but now I am quite sure it is a woman.

By daylight she is subdued, quiet. I fancy it is the pattern that keeps her so still. It is so puzzling. It keeps me quiet by the hour.

I lie down ever so much now. John says it is good for me, and to sleep all I can.

Indeed he started the habit by making me lie down for an hour after each meal.

It is a very bad habit I am convinced, for you see I don't sleep.

And that cultivates deceit, for I don't tell them I'm awake—O no!

The fact is I am getting a little afraid of John.

He seems very queer sometimes, and even Jennie has an inexplicable look.

It strikes me occasionally, just as a scientific hypothesis,—that perhaps it is the paper!

I have watched John when he did not know I was looking, and come into the room suddenly on the most innocent excuses, and I've caught him several times *looking at the paper!* And Jennie too. I caught Jennie with her hand on it once.

She didn't know I was in the room, and when I asked her in a quiet, a very quiet voice, with the most restrained manner possible, what she was doing with the paper—she turned around as if she had been caught stealing, and looked quite angry—asked me why I should frighten her so!

Then she said that the paper stained everything it touched, that she had found yellow smooches on all my clothes and John's, and she wished we would be more careful!

Did not that sound innocent? But I know she was studying that pattern, and I am determined that nobody shall find it out but myself!

*   *   *   *   *

Life is very much more exciting now than it used to be. You see I have something more to expect, to look forward to, to watch. I really do eat better, and am more quiet than I was.

John is so pleased to see me improve! He laughed a little the other day, and said I seemed to be flourishing in spite of my wall-paper.

I turned it off with a laugh. I had no intention of telling him it was *because* of the wall-paper—he would make fun of me. He might even want to take me away.

I don't want to leave now until I have found it out. There is a week more, and I think that will be enough.

*   *   *   *   *

I'm feeling ever so much better! I don't sleep much at night, for it is so interesting to watch developments; but I sleep a good deal in the daytime.

In the daytime it is tiresome and perplexing.

There are always new shoots on the fungus, and new shades of yellow all over it. I cannot keep count of them, though I have tried conscientiously.

It is the strangest yellow, that wall-paper! It makes me think of all the yellow things I ever saw—not beautiful ones like buttercups, but old foul, bad yellow things.

But there is something else about that paper—the smell! I noticed it the moment we came into the room, but with so much air and sun it was not bad. Now we have had a week of fog and rain, and whether the windows are open or not, the smell is here.

It creeps all over the house.

I find it hovering in the dining-room, skulking in the parlor, hiding in the hall, lying in wait for me on the stairs.

It gets into my hair.

Even when I go to ride, if I turn my head suddenly and surprise it—there is that smell!

Such a peculiar odor, too! I have spent hours in trying to analyze it, to find what it smelled like.

It is not bad—at first, and very gentle, but quite the subtlest, most enduring odor I ever met.

In this damp weather it is awful, I wake up in the night and find it hanging over me.

It used to disturb me at first. I thought seriously of burning the house—to reach the smell.

But now I am used to it. The only thing I can think of that it is like is the *color* of the paper! A yellow smell.

There is a very funny mark on this wall, low down, near the mopboard. A streak that runs round the room. It goes behind every piece of furniture, except the bed, a long, straight, even *smooch*, as if it had been rubbed over and over.

I wonder how it was done and who did it, and what they did it for. Round and round and round—round and round and round—it makes me dizzy!

*   *   *   *   *

I really discovered something at last.

Through watching so much at night, when it changes so, I have finally found out.

The front pattern *does* move—and no wonder! The woman behind shakes it!

Sometimes I think there are a great many women behind, and sometimes only one, and she crawls around fast, and her crawling shakes it all over.

Then in the very bright spots she keeps still, and in the very shady spots she just takes hold of the bars and shakes them hard.

And she is all the time trying to climb through. But nobody could climb through that pattern—it strangles so; I think that is why it has so many heads.

They get through, and then the pattern strangles them off and turns them upside down, and makes their eyes white!

If those heads were covered or taken off it would not be half so bad.

*   *   *   *   *

I think that woman gets out in the daytime!

And I'll tell you why—privately—I've seen her!

I can see her out of every one of my windows!

It is the same woman, I know for she is always creeping, and most women do not creep by daylight.

I see her in that long shaded lane, creeping up and down. I see her in those dark grape arbors, creeping all around the garden.

I see her on that long road under the trees, creeping along, and when a carriage comes she hides under the blackberry vines.

I don't blame her a bit. It must be very humiliating to be caught creeping by daylight!

I always lock the door when I creep by daylight. I can't do it at night, for I know John would suspect something at once.

And John is so queer now, that I don't want to irritate him. I wish he would take another room! Besides, I don't want anybody to get that woman out at night but myself.

I often wonder if I could see her out of all the windows at once.

But, turn as fast as I can, I can only see out of one at one time.

And though I always see her, she *may* be able to creep faster than I can turn!

I have watched her sometimes away off in the open country, creeping as fast as a cloud shadow in a high wind.

*   *   *   *   *

If only that top pattern could be gotten off from the under one! I mean to try it, little by little.

I have found out another funny thing, but I shan't tell it this time! It does not do to trust people too much.

There are only two more days to get this paper off, and I believe John is beginning to notice. I don't like the look in his eyes.

And I heard him ask Jennie a lot of professional questions about me. She had a very good report to give.

She said I slept a good deal in the daytime.

John knows I don't sleep very well at night, for all I'm so quiet!

He asked me all sorts of questions, too, and pretended to be very loving and kind.

As if I couldn't see through him!

Still, I don't wonder he acts so, sleeping under this paper for three months.

It only interests me, but I feel sure John and Jennie are secretly affected by it.

    *   *   *   *   *

Hurrah! This is the last day, but it is enough. John is to stay in town over night, and won't be out until this evening.

Jennie wanted to sleep with me—the sly thing! but I told her I should undoubtedly rest better for a night all alone.

That was clever, for really I wasn't alone a bit! As soon as it was moonlight and that poor thing began to crawl and shake the pattern, I got up and ran to help her.

I pulled and she shook, I shook and she pulled, and before morning we had peeled off yards of that paper.

A strip about as high as my head and half around the room.

And then when the sun came and that awful pattern began to laugh at me, I declared I would finish it to-day!

We go away to-morrow, and they are moving all my furniture down again to leave things as they were before.

Jennie looked at the wall in amazement, but I told her merrily that I did it out of pure spite at the vicious thing.

She laughed and said she wouldn't mind doing it herself, but I must not get tired.

How she betrayed herself that time!

But I am here, and no person touches this paper but me,—not *alive!*

She tried to get me out of the room—it was too patent! But I said it was so quiet and empty and clean now that I believed I would lie down again and sleep all I could; and not to wake me even for dinner—I would call when I woke.

So now she is gone, and the servants are gone, and the things are gone, and there is nothing left but that great bedstead nailed down, with the canvas mattress we found on it.

We shall sleep downstairs to-night, and take the boat home to-morrow.

I quite enjoy the room, now it is bare again.

How those children did tear about here!

This bedstead is fairly gnawed!

But I must get to work.

I have locked the door and thrown the key down into the front path.

I don't want to go out, and I don't want to have anybody come in, till John comes.

I want to astonish him.

I've got a rope up here that even Jennie did not find. If that woman does get out, and tries to get away, I can tie her!

But I forgot I could not reach far without anything to stand on! This bed will *not* move!

I tried to lift and push it until I was lame, and then I got so angry I bit off a little piece at one corner—but it hurt my teeth.

Then I peeled off all the paper I could reach standing on the floor. It sticks horribly and the pattern just enjoys it! All those strangled heads and bulbous eyes and waddling fungus growths just shriek with derision!

I am getting angry enough to do something desperate. To jump out of the window would be admirable exercise, but the bars are too strong even to try.

Besides I wouldn't do it. Of course not. I know well enough that a step like that is improper and might be misconstrued.

I don't like to *look* out of the windows even—there are so many of those creeping women, and they creep so fast.

I wonder if they all come out of that wall-paper as I did?

But I am securely fastened now by my well-hidden rope—you don't get *me* out in the road there!

I suppose I shall have to get back behind the pattern when it comes night, and that is hard!

It is so pleasant to be out in this great room and creep around as I please!

I don't want to go outside. I won't, even if Jennie asks me to.

For outside you have to creep on the ground, and everything is green instead of yellow.

But here I can creep smoothly on the floor, and my shoulder just fits in that long smooch around the wall, so I cannot lose my way.

Why there's John at the door!

It is no use, young man, you can't open it!

How he does call and pound!

Now he's crying for an axe.

It would be a shame to break down that beautiful door!

"John dear!" said I in the gentlest voice, "the key is down by the front steps, under a plantain leaf!"

That silenced him for a few moments.

Then he said—very quietly indeed, "Open the door, my darling!"

"I can't," said I. "The key is down by the front door under a plantain leaf!"

And then I said it again, several times, very gently and slowly, and said it so often that he had to go and see, and he got it of course, and came in. He stopped short by the door.

"What is the matter?" he cried. "For God's sake, what are you doing!"

I kept on creeping just the same, but I looked at him over my shoulder.

"I've got out at last," said I, "in spite of you and Jane?[1] And I've pulled off most of the paper, so you can't put me back!"

Now why should that man have fainted? But he did, and right across my path by the wall, so that I had to creep over him every time!

---

[1] "Jane?" in the original text. The " ?" may have been a printer's effort to warn proofreaders of a possible error. "Jane" may be the narrator. Or "Jennie" may be intended.

Samuel Beckett

WAITING FOR GODOT

LUCKY   Given the existence as uttered forth in the public works of
Puncher and Wattmann of a personal God quaquaquaqua
with white beard quaquaquaqua outside time without extension
who from the heights of divine apathia divine athambia divine
aphasia loves us dearly with some exceptions for reasons unknown
but time will tell and suffers like the divine Miranda with those
who for reasons unknown but time will tell are plunged in torment
plunged in fire whose fire flames if that continues and who can
doubt it will fire the firmament that is to say blast hell to heaven
so blue still and calm so calm with a calm which even though
intermittent is better than nothing but not so fast and considering
what is more that as a result of the labors left unfinished crowned
by the Acacacacademy of Anthropopopometry of Essy-in-Possy
of Testew and Cunard it is established beyond all doubt all other
doubt than that which clings to the labors of men that as a result
of the labors unfinished of Testew and Cunard it is established as
hereinafter but not so fast for reasons unknown that as a result of
the public works of Puncher and Wattmann it is established
beyond all doubt that in view of the labors of Fartov and Belcher
left unfinished for reasons unknown of Testew and Cunard left
unfinished it is established what many deny that man in Possy of
Testew and Cunard that man in Essy that man in short that man
in brief in spite of the strides of alimentation and defecation

Samuel Beckett, from Waiting for Godot. *New York: Grove Press, 1954.*

wastes and pines wastes and pines and concurrently simultaneously what is more for reasons unknown in spite of the strides of
physical culture the practice of sports such as tennis football
running cycling swimming flying floating riding gliding conating
camogie skating tennis of all kinds dying flying sports of all sorts
autumn summer winter winter tennis of all kinds hockey of all
sorts penicilline and succedanea in a word I resume flying gliding
golf over nine and eighteen holes tennis of all sorts in a word for
reasons unknown in Feckham Peckham Fulham Clapham
namely concurrently simultaneously what is more for reasons unknown but time will tell fades away I resume Fulham Clapham
in a word the dead loss per head since the death of Bishop Berkeley
being to the tune of one inch four ounce per head approximately
by and large more or less to the nearest decimal good measure
round figures stark naked in the stockinged feet in Connemara in
a word for reasons unknown no matter what matter the facts are
there and considering what is more much more grave that in the
light of the labors lost of Steinweg and Peterman it appears what
is more much more grave that in the light the light the light of the
labors lost of Steinweg and Peterman that in the plains in the
mountains by the seas by the rivers running water running fire
the air is the same and then the earth namely the air and then the
earth in the great cold the great dark the air and the earth abode
of stones in the great cold alas alas in the year of their Lord six
hundred and something the air the earth the sea the earth abode
of stones in the great deeps the great cold on sea on land and in
the air I resume for reasons unknown in spite of the tennis the facts
are there but time will tell I resume alas alas on on in short in fine
on on abode of stones who can doubt it I resume but not so fast I
resume the skull fading fading fading and concurrently simultaneously what is more for reasons unknown in spite of the tennis on on
the beard the flames the tears the stones so blue so calm alas alas on
on the skull the skull the skull the skull in Connemara in spite of the
tennis the labors abandoned left unfinished graver still abode of
stones in a word I resume alas alas abandoned unfinished the
skull the skull in Connemara in spite of the tennis the skull alas
the stones Cunard (*mêlée, final vociferations*) tennis . . . the
stones . . . so calm . . . Cunard . . . unfinished . . .

Jean Paul Sartre

THE ROOM

Mme. Darbedat held a *rahat-loukoum* between her fingers. She brought it carefully to her lips and held her breath, afraid that the fine dust of sugar that powdered it would blow away. "Just right," she told herself. She bit quickly into its glassy flesh and a scent of stagnation filled her mouth. "Odd how illness sharpens the sensations." She began to think of mosques, of obsequious Orientals (she had been to Algeria for her honeymoon) and her pale lips started in a smile: the *rahat-loukoum* was obsequious too.

Several times she had to pass the palm of her hand over the pages of her book, for in spite of the precaution she had taken they were covered with a thin coat of white powder. Her hand made the little grains of sugar slide and roll, grating on the smooth paper: "That makes me think of Arcachon, when I used to read on the beach." She had spent the summer of 1907 at the seashore. Then she wore a big straw hat with a green ribbon; she sat close to the jetty, with a novel by Gyp or Colette Yver. The wind made swirls of sand rain down upon her knees, and from time to time she had to shake the book, holding it by the corners. It was the same sensation: only the grains of sand were dry while the small bits of sugar stuck a little to the ends of her fingers. Again she saw a band of pearl grey sky above a black sea. "Eve wasn't born yet." She felt herself all weighted

Jean Paul Sartre, "The Room," in Intimacy, *tr. by Lloyd Alexander. New York: New Directions, 1948.*

down with memories and precious as a coffer of sandalwood. The name of the book she used to read suddenly came back to mind: it was called *Petite Madame*, not at all boring. But ever since an unknown illness had confined her to her room she preferred memories and historical works.

She hoped that suffering, heavy readings, a vigilant attention to her memories and the most exquisite sensations would ripen her as a lovely hothouse fruit.

She thought, with some annoyance, that her husband would soon be knocking at her door. On other days of the week he came only in the evening, kissed her brow in silence and read *Le Temps*, sitting in the armchair across from her. But Thursday was M. Darbedat's *day:* he spent an hour with his daughter, generally from three to four. Before going he stopped in to see his wife and both discussed their son-in-law with bitterness. These Thursday conversations, predictable to their slightest detail, exhausted Mme. Darbedat. M. Darbedat filled the quiet room with his presence. He never sat, but walked in circles about the room. Each of his outbursts wounded Mme. Darbedat like a glass splintering. This particular Thursday was worse than usual: at the thought that it would soon be necessary to repeat Eve's confessions to her husband, and to see his great terrifying body convulse with fury, Mme. Darbedat broke out in a sweat. She picked up a *loukoum* from the saucer, studied it for a while with hesitation, then sadly set it down: she did not like her husband to see her eating *loukoums*.

She heard a knock and started up. "Come in," she said weakly.

M. Darbedat entered on tiptoe. "I'm going to see Eve," he said, as he did every Thursday. Mme. Darbedat smiled at him. "Give her a kiss for me."

M. Darbedat did not answer and his forehead wrinkled worriedly: every Thursday at the same time, a muffled irritation mingled with the load of his digestion. "I'll stop in and see Franchot after leaving her, I wish he'd talk to her seriously and try to convince her."

He made frequent visits to Dr. Franchot. But in vain. Mme. Darbedat raised her eyebrows. Before, when she was well, she shrugged her shoulders. But since sickness had weighted down her body, she replaced the gestures which would have tired her by plays of emotion in the face: she said *yes* with her eyes, *no* with the corners of her mouth: she raised her eyebrows instead of her shoulders. "There should be some way to take him away from her by force." "I told you already it was impossible. And besides, the law is very poorly drawn up. Only the other day Franchot was telling me that they have a tremendous amount of trouble with the families: people who can't make up their mind, who want to keep the patient at home; the doctors' hands are tied. They can give their advice, period. That's all. He would," he went on, "have to make a public scandal or else she would have to ask to have him put away herself."

"And that," said Mme. Darbedat, "isn't going to happen tomorrow."

"No." He turned to the mirror and began to comb his fingers through his beard. Mme. Darbedat looked at the powerful red neck of her husband without affection.

"If she keeps on," said M. Darbedat, "she'll be crazier than he is. It's terribly unhealthy. She doesn't leave his side, she only goes out to see you. She has no visitors. The air in their room is simply unbreathable. She never opens the window because Pierre doesn't want it open. As if you should ask a sick man. I believe they burn incense, some rubbish in a little pan, you'd think it was a church. Really, sometimes I wonder . . . she's got a funny look in her eyes, you know."

"I haven't noticed," Mme. Darbedat said. "I find her quite normal. She looks sad, obviously."

"She has a face like an unburied corpse. Does she sleep? Does she eat? But we aren't supposed to ask her about those things. But I should think that with a fellow like Pierre next to her, she wouldn't sleep a wink all night." He shrugged his shoulders. "What I find amazing is that we, her parents, don't have the right to protect her against herself. Understand that Pierre would be much better cared for by Franchot. There's a big park. And besides, I think," he added, smiling a little, "he'd get along much better with people of his own type. People like that are children, you have to leave them alone with each other; they form a sort of freemasonry. That's where he should have been put the first day and for his own good, I'd say. Of course it's in his own best interest."

After a moment, he added, "I tell you I don't like to know she's

alone with Pierre, especially at night. Suppose something happened.
Pierre has a very sly way about him."
"I don't know," Mme. Darbedat said, "if there's any reason to
worry. He always looked like that. He always seemed to be making
fun of the world. Poor boy," she sighed, "to have had his pride and
then come to that. He thought he was cleverer than all of us. He
had a way of saying 'You're right' simply to end the argument . . .
It's a blessing for him that he can't see the state he's in."

She recalled with displeasure the long, ironic face, always turned a
little to the side. During the first days of Eve's marriage, Mme.
Darbedat asked nothing more than a little intimacy with her son-
in-law. But he had discouraged her: he almost never spoke, he
always agreed quickly and absent-mindedly.

M. Darbedat pursued his idea. "Franchot let me visit his place,"
he said. "It was magnificent. The patients have private rooms with
leather armchairs, if you please, and day-beds. You know, they have
a tennis court and they're going to build a swimming pool."

He was planted before the window, looking out, rocking a little
on his bent legs. Suddenly he turned lithely on his heel, shoulders
lowered, hands in his pockets. Mme. Darbedat felt she was going
to start perspiring: it was the same thing every time: now he was
pacing back and forth like a bear in a cage and his shoes squeaked
at every step.

"Please, please won't you sit down. You're tiring me." Hesitating,
she added, "I have something important to tell you."

M. Darbedat sat in the armchair and put his hands on his knees;
a slight chill ran up Mme. Darbedat's spine: the time had come, she
had to speak.

"You know," she said with an embarassed cough, "I saw Eve on
Tuesday."

"Yes."

"We talked about a lot of things, she was very nice, she hasn't been
so confiding for a long time. Then I questioned her a little, I got her
to talk about Pierre. Well, I found out," she added, again embarras-
ses, "that she is *very* attached to him."

"I know that too damned well," said M. Darbedat.

He irritated Mme. Darbedat a little: she always had to explain
things in such detail. Mme. Darbedat dreamed of living in the

company of fine and sensitive people who would understand her slightest word.

"But I mean," she went on, "that she is attached to him *differently* than we imagined."

M. Darbedat rolled furious, anxious eyes, as he always did when he never completely grasped the sense of an allusion or something new.

"What does that all mean?"

"Charles," said Mme. Darbedat, "don't tire me. You should understand a mother has difficulty in telling certain things."

"I don't understand a damned word of anything you say," M. Darbedat said with irritation. "You can't mean . . ."

"Yes," she said.

"They're still . . . now, still . . . ?"

"Yes! Yes! Yes!" she said, in three annoyed and dry little jolts.

M. Darbedat spread his arms, lowered his head and was silent.

"Charles," his wife said, worriedly, "I shouldn't have told you. But I couldn't keep it to myself."

"Our child," he said slowly. "With this madman! He doesn't even recognize her any more. He calls her Agatha. She must have lost all sense of her own dignity."

He raised his head and looked at his wife severely. "You're sure you aren't mistaken?"

"No possible doubt. Like you," she added quickly, "I couldn't believe her and I still can't. The mere idea of being touched by that wretch . . . So . . ." she sighed, "I suppose that's how he holds on to her."

"Do you remember what I told you," M. Darbedat said, "when he came to ask for her hand? I told you I thought he pleased Eve *too much.* You wouldn't believe me." He struck the table suddenly, blushing violently. "It's perversity! He takes her in his arms, kisses her and calls her Agatha, selling her on a lot of nonsense about flying statues and God knows what else! Without a word from her! But what in heaven's name's between those two? Let her be sorry for him, let her put him in a sanitorium and see him every day,— fine. But I never thought . . . I considered her a widow. Listen, Jeannette," he said gravely, "I'm going to speak frankly to you; if she had any sense, I'd rather see her take a lover!"

"Be quiet, Charles!" Mme. Darbedat cried.

M. Darbedat wearily took his hat and the cane he had left on the stool. "After what you've just told me," he concluded, "I don't have much hope left. In any case, I'll have a talk with her because it's my duty."

Mme. Darbedat wished he would go quickly.

"You know," she said to encourage him, "I think Eve is more headstrong than . . . than anything. She knows he's incurable but she's obstinate, she doesn't want to be in the wrong."

M. Darbedat stroked his beard absently.

"Headstrong? Maybe so. If you're right, she'll finally get tired of it. He's not always pleasant and he doesn't have much to say. When I say hello to him he gives me a flabby handshake and doesn't say a word. As soon as they're alone, I think they go back to his obsessions: she tells me sometimes he screams as though his throat were being cut because of his hallucinations. He sees statues. They frighten him because they buzz. He says they fly around and make fishy eyes at him."

He put on his gloves and continued, "She'll get tired of it, I'm not saying she won't. But suppose she goes crazy before that? I wish she'd go out a little, see the world: she'd meet some nice young man—well, someone like Schroeder, an engineer with Simplon, somebody with a future, she could see him a little here and there and she'd get used to the idea of making a new life for herself."

Mme. Darbedat did not answer, afraid of starting the conversation up again. Her husband bent over her.

"So," he said, "I've got to be on my way."

"Goodbye, Papa," Mme. Darbedat said, lifting her forehead up to him. "Kiss her for me and tell her for me she's a poor dear."

Once her husband had gone, Mme. Darbedat let herself drift to the bottom of her armchair and closed her eyes, exhausted. "What vitality," she thought reproachfully. As soon as she got a little strength back, she quietly stretched out her pale hand and took a *loukoum* from the saucer, groping for it without opening her eyes.

Eve lived with her husband on the sixth floor of an old building on the Rue du Bac. M. Darbedat slowly climbed the 112 steps of the stairway. He was not even out of breath when he pushed the bell. He remembered with satisfaction the words of Mlle. Dormoy: "Charles, for your age, you're simply marvelous." Never did he feel himself stronger and healthier than on Thursday, especially after these invigorating climbs.

Eve opened the door: that's right, she doesn't have a maid. No girls *can* stay with her. I can put myself in their place. He kissed her. "Hello, poor darling."

Eve greeted him with a certain coldness.

"You look a little pale," M. Darbedat said, touching her cheek. "You don't get enough exercise."

There was a moment of silence.

"Is Mamma well?" Eve asked.

"Not good, not too bad. You saw her Tuesday? Well, she's just the same. Your Aunt Louise came to see her yesterday, that pleased her. She likes to have visitors, but they can't stay too long. Aunt Louise came to Paris for that mortgage business. I think I told you about it, a very odd sort of affair. She stopped in at the office to ask my advice. I told her there was only one thing to do: sell. She found a taker, by the way: Bretonnel. You remember Bretonnel. He's retired from business now."

He stopped suddenly: Eve was hardly listening. He thought sadly that nothing interested her any more. It's like the books. Before you had to tear them away from her. Now she doesn't even read any more.

"How is Pierre?"

"Well," Eve said. "Do you want to see him?"

"Of course," M. Darbedat said gaily, "I'd like to pay him a little call."

He was full of compassion for this poor young man, but he could not see him without repugnance. *I detest unhealthy people.* Obviously, it was not Pierre's fault: his heredity was terribly loaded down. M. Darbedat sighed: *All the precautions are taken in vain, you find out those things too late.* No, Pierre was not responsible. But still he had always carried that fault in him; it formed the base of his character; it wasn't like cancer or tuberculosis, something you could always put aside when you wanted to judge a man as he is. His nervous grace, the subtlety which pleased Eve so much when he was courting her

were the flowers of madness. He was already mad when he married
her only you couldn't tell.

It makes you wonder, thought M. Darbedat, *where responsibility
begins, or rather, where it ends.* In any case, he was always analysing
himself too much, always turned in on himself. But was it the cause
or effect of his sickness? He followed his daughter through a long,
dim corridor.

"This apartment is too big for you," he said. "You ought to move
out."

"You say that every time, Papa," Eve answered, "but I've
already told you Pierre doesn't want to leave his room."

Eve was amazing. Enough to make you wonder if she realized her
husband's state. He was insane enough to be in a strait-jacket and
she respected his decisions and advice as if he still had good sense.

"What I'm saying is for your own good." M. Darbedat went on,
somewhat annoyed, "It seems to me that if I were a woman I'd be
afraid of these badly lighted old rooms. I'd like to see you in a bright
apartment, the kind they're putting up near Auteuil, three airy
little rooms. They lowered the rents because they couldn't find
any tenants; this would be just the time."

Eve quietly turned the doorknob and they entered the room.
M. Darbedat's throat tightened at the heavy odor of incense. The
curtains were drawn. In the shadows he made out a thin neck
above the back of an armchair: Pierre's back was turned. He was
eating.

"Hello, Pierre," M. Darbedat said, raising his voice. "How are
we today?" He drew near him: the sick man was seated in front of
a small table; he looked sly.

"I see we had soft boiled eggs," M. Darbedat said, raising his
voice higher. "That's good!"

"I'm not deaf," Pierre said quietly.

Irritated, M. Darbedat turned his eyes toward Eve as his witness.
But Eve gave him a hard glance and was silent. M. Darbedat realized he had hurt her. Too bad for her. It was impossible to find just
the right tone for this boy. He had less sense than a child of four and
Eve wanted him treated like a man. M. Darbedat could not keep
himself from waiting with impatience for the moment when all this
ridiculous business would be finished. Sick people always annoyed

him a little—especially madmen because they were wrong. Poor Pierre, for example, was wrong all along the line, he couldn't speak a reasonable word and yet it would be useless to expect the least humility from him, or even temporary recognition of his errors.

Eve cleared away the eggshells and the cup. She put a knife and fork in front of Pierre.

"What's he going to eat now," M. Darbedat said jovially.

"A steak."

Pierre had taken the fork and held it in the ends of his long, pale fingers. He inspected it minutely and then gave slight laugh.

"I can't use it this time," he murmured, setting it down, "I was warned."

Eve came in and looked at the fork with passionate interest.

"Agatha," Pierre said, "give me another one."

Eve obeyed and Pierre began to eat. She had taken the suspect fork and held it tightly in her hands, her eyes never leaving it; she seemed to make a violent effort. How suspicious all their gestures and relationships are! thought M. Darbedat. He was uneasy.

"Be careful, Pierre, take it by the middle because of the prongs." Eve sighed and laid the fork on the serving table. M. Darbedat felt his gall rising. He did not think it well to give in to all this poor man's whims—even from Pierre's viewpoint it was pernicious. Franchot had said: "One must never enter the delirium of a madman." Instead of giving him another fork, it would have been better to have reasoned quietly and made him understand that the first was like all the others.

He went to the serving table, took the fork ostentatiously and tested the prongs with a light finger. Then he turned to Pierre. But the latter was cutting his meat peacefully: he gave his father-in-law a gentle, inexpressive glance.

"I'd like to have a little talk with you," M. Darbedat said to Eve.

She followed him docilely into the salon. Sitting on the couch, M. Darbedat realized he had kept the fork in his hand. He threw it on the table.

"It's much better here," he said.

"I never come here."

"All right to smoke?"

"Of course, Papa," Eve said hurriedly. "Do you want a cigar?"

M. Darbedat preferred to roll a cigarette. He thought eagerly of the discussion he was about to begin. Speaking to Pierre he felt as embarrassed about his reason as a giant about his strength when playing with a child. All his qualities of clarity, sharpness, precision, turned against him; *I must confess it's somewhat the same with my poor Jeannette.* Certainly Mme. Darbedat was not insane, but this illness had . . . stultified her. Eve, on the other hand, took after her father . . . a straight, logical nature; discussion with her was a pleasure; *that's why I don't want them to ruin her.* M. Darbedat raised his eyes. Once again he wanted to see the fine intelligent features of his daughter. He was disappointed with this face; once so reasonable and transparent, there was now something clouded and opaque in it. Eve had always been beautiful. M. Darbedat noticed she was made up with great care, almost with pomp. She had blued her eyelids and put mascara on her long lashes. This violent and perfect makeup made a painful impression on her father.

"You're green beneath your rouge," he told her. "I'm afraid you're getting sick. And the way you make yourself up now! You used to be so discreet."

Eve did not answer and for an embarrassed moment M. Darbedat considered this brilliant, wornout face beneath the heavy mass of black hair. He thought she looked like a tragedian. *I even know who she looks like. That woman . . . that Roumanian who played* Phèdre *in French at the Mur d'Orange.* He regretted having made so disagreeable a remark: *It escaped me! Better not worry her with little things.*

"Excuse me," he said smiling, "you know I'm an old purist. I don't like all these creams and paints women stick on their face today. But I'm in the wrong. You must live in your time."

Eve smiled amiably at him. M. Darbedat lit a cigarette and drew several puffs.

"My child," he began, "I wanted to talk with you: the two of us are going to talk the way we used to. Come, sit down and listen to me nicely; you must have confidence in your old Papa."

"I'd rather stand," Eve said. "What did you want to tell me?"

"I am going to ask you a single question," M. Darbedat said a little more dryly. "Where will all this lead you?"

"All this?" Eve asked astonished.

"Yes . . . all this whole life you've made for yourself. Listen," he went on, "don't think I don't understand you (he had a sudden illumination) but what you want to do is beyond human strength. You want to live solely by imagination, isn't that it? You don't want to admit he's sick. You don't want to see the Pierre of today, do you? You have eyes only for the Pierre of before. My dear, my darling little girl, it's an impossible bet to win," M. Darbedat continued. "Now I'm going to tell you a story which perhaps you don't know. When we were at Sables-d'Olonne—you were three years old —your mother made the acquaintance of a charming young woman with a superb little boy. You played on the beach with this little boy, you were thick as thieves, you were engaged to marry him. A while later, in Paris, your mother wanted to see this young woman again; she was told she had had a terrible accident. That fine little boy's head was cut off by a car. They told your mother, 'Go and see her, but above all don't talk to her about the death of her child, she *will not* believe he is dead.' Your mother went, she found a half-mad creature: she lived as though her boy was still alive; she spoke to him, she set his place at the table. She lived in such a state of nervous tension that after six months they had to take her away by force to a sanitorium where she was obliged to stay three years. No, my child," M. Darbedat said, shaking his head, "these things are impossible. It would have been better if she had recognized the truth courageously. She would have suffered once, then time would have erased with its sponge. There is nothing like looking things in the face, believe me."

"You're wrong," Eve said with effort. "I know very well that Pierre is . . ."

The word did not escape. She held herself very straight and put her hands on the back of the armchair: there was something dry and ugly in the lower part of her face.

"So . . . ?" asked M. Darbedat, astonished.

"So . . . ?"

"You . . . ?"

"I love him as he is," said Eve rapidly and with an irritated look.

"Not true," M. Darbedat said forcefully. "It isn't true: you don't love him, you can't love him. You can only feel that way about a healthy, normal person. You pity Pierre, I don't doubt it, and surely you have the memory of three years of happiness he gave you. But don't tell me you love him. I won't believe you."

Eve remained wordless, staring at the carpet absently.

"You could at least answer me," M. Darbedat said coldly. "Don't think this conversation has been any less painful for me than it has for you."

"More than you think."

"Well then, if you love him," he cried, exasperated, "it is a great misfortune for you, for me and for your poor mother because I'm going to tell you something I would rather have hidden from you: before three years Pierre will be sunk in complete dementia, he'll be like a beast."

He watched his daughter with hard eyes: he was angry at her for having compelled him, by stubbornness, to make this painful revelation.

Eve was motionless; she did not so much as raise her eyes.

"I knew."

"Who told you?" he asked stupefied.

"Franchot. I knew six months ago."

"And I told him to be careful with you," said M. Darbedat with bitterness. "Maybe it's better. But under those circumstances you must understand that it would be unpardonable to keep Pierre with you. The struggle you have undertaken is doomed to failure, his illness won't spare him. If there were something to be done, if we could save him by care, I'd say yes. But look: you're pretty, intelligent, gay, you're destroying yourself willingly and without profit. I know you've been admirable, but now it's over . . . done, you've done your duty and more; now it would be immoral to continue. We also have duties to ourselves, child. And then you aren't thinking about us. You must," he repeated, hammering the words, "send Pierre to Franchot's clinic. Leave this apartment where you've had nothing but sorrow and come home to us. If you want to be useful and ease the sufferings of someone else, you have your mother. The poor woman is cared for by nurses, she needs someone closer to her, and *she*," he added, "can appreciate what you do for her and be grateful."

There was a long silence. M. Darbedat heard Pierre singing in the next room. It was hardly a song, rather a sort of sharp, hasty recitative. M. Darbedat raised his eyes to his daughter.

"It's no then?"

"Pierre will stay with me," she said quietly. "I get along well with him."

"By living like an animal all day long?"

Eve smiled and shot a glance at her father, strange, mocking and almost gay. *It's true*, M. Darbedat thought furiously, *that's not all they do: they sleep together.*

"You are completely mad," he said, rising.

Eve smiled sadly and murmured, as if to herself, "Not enough so."

"Not enough? I can only tell you one thing, my child. You frighten me."

He kissed her hastily and left. Going down the stairs he thought: *we should send out two strong-arm men who'd take the poor imbecile away and stick him under a shower without asking his advice on the matter.*

It was a fine autumn day, calm and without mystery; the sunlight gilded the faces of the passers-by. M. Darbedat was struck with the simplicity of the faces; some weather-beaten, others smooth, but they reflected all the happiness and care with which he was so familiar.

I know exactly what I resent in Eve, he told himself, entering the Boulevard St. Germain. *I resent her living outside the limits of human nature. Pierre is no longer a human being: in all the care and all the love she gives him she deprives human beings of a little. We don't have the right to refuse ourselves to the world; no matter what, we live in society.*

He watched the faces of the passers-by with sympathy; he loved their clear, serious looks. In these sunlit streets, in the midst of mankind, one felt secure, as in the midst of a large family.

A woman stopped in front of an open-air display counter. She was holding a little girl by the hand.

"What's that?" the little girl asked, pointing to a radio set.

"Mustn't touch," her mother said. "It's a radio; it plays music."

They stood for a moment without speaking, in ecstacy. Touched, M. Darbedat bent down to the little girl and smiled.

II

"He's gone." The door closed with a dry snap. Eve was alone in the salon. *I wish he'd die.*

She twisted her hands around the back of the armchair: she had just remembered her father's eyes. M. Darbedat was bent over

Pierre with a competent air; he had said "That's good!" the way someone says when they speak to invalids. He had looked and Pierre's face had been painted in the depths of his sharp, bulging eyes. *I hate him when he looks at him because I think he sees him.* Eve's hands slid along the armchair and she turned to the window. She was dazzled. The room was filled with sunlight, it was everywhere, in pale splotches on the rug, in the air like a blinding dust. Eve was not accustomed to this diligent, indiscreet light which darted from everywhere, scouring all the corners, rubbing the furniture like a busy housewife and making it glisten. However, she went to the window and raised the muslin curtain which hung against the pane. Just at that moment M. Darbedat left the building; Eve suddenly caught sight of his broad shoulders. He raised his head and looked at the sky, blinking, then with the stride of a young man he walked away. *He's straining himself*, thought Eve, *soon he'll have a stitch in the side.* She hardly hated him any longer: there was so little in that head; only the tiny worry of appearing young. Yet rage took her again when she saw him turn the corner of the Boulevard St. Germain and disappear. *He's thinking about Pierre.* A little of their life had escaped from the closed room and was being dragged through the streets, in the sun, among the people. *Can they never forget about us?*

The Rue du Bac was almost deserted. An old lady crossed the street with mincing steps; three girls passed, laughing. Then men, strong, serious men carrying briefcases and talking among themselves. *Normal people*, thought Eve, astonished at finding, such a powerful hatred in herself. A handsome, fleshy woman ran heavily toward an elegant gentleman. He took her in his arms and kissed her on the mouth. Eve gave a hard laugh and let the curtain fall.

Pierre sang no more but the woman on the fourth floor was playing the piano; she played a Chopin Etude. Eve felt calmer; she took a step toward Pierre's room but stopped almost immediately and leaned against the wall in anguish; each time she left the room, she was panic-stricken at the thought of going back. Yet she knew she could live nowhere else: she loved the room. She looked around it with cold curiosity as if to gain a little time: this shadowless, odorless room where she waited for her courage to return. *You'd think it was a dentist's waiting room.* Armchairs of pink silk, the divan, the tabourets were somber and discreet, a little fatherly; man's best friends. Eve imagined those grave gentlemen dressed in light suits, all like the ones she saw at the window, entering the room, continuing a conversation already begun. They did not even take time to reconnoiter, but advanced with firm step to the middle of the room; one of them, letting his hand drag behind him like a wake in passing knocked over cushions, objects on the table, and was never disturbed by their contact. And when a piece of furniture was in their way, these poised men, far from making a detour to avoid it, quietly changed its place. Finally they sat down, still plunged in their conversation, without even glancing behind them. *A living-room for normal people*, thought Eve. She stared at the knob of the closed door and anguish clutched her throat: *I must go back. I never leave him alone so long.* She would have to open the door, then stand for a moment on the threshold, trying to accustom her eyes to the shadow and the room would push her back with all its strength. Eve would have to triumph over this resistance and enter all the way into the heart of the room. Suddenly she wanted violently to see Pierre; she would have liked to make fun of M. Darbedat with him. But Pierre had no need of her; Eve could not foresee the welcome he had in store for her. Suddenly she thought with a sort of pride that she had no place anywhere. *Normal people think I belong with them. But I couldn't stay an hour among them. I need to live out there, on the other side of the wall. But they don't want me out there.*

A profound change was taking place around her. The light had grown old and greying: it was heavy, like the water in a vase of flowers that hasn't been changed since the day before. In this aged light Eve found a melancholy she had long forgotten: the melancholy of an autumn afternoon that was ending. She looked around her, hesitant, almost timid: all that was so far away: there was neither day nor night nor season nor melancholy in the room. She vaguely recalled autumns long past, autumns of her childhood, then suddenly she stiffened: she was afraid of memories.

She heard Pierre's voice. "Agatha! Where are you?"

"Coming!" she cried.

She opened the door and entered the room.

The heavy odor of incense filled her mouth and nostrils as she opened her eyes and stretched out her hands—for a long time the perfume and the gloom had meant nothing more to her than a single element, acrid and heavy, as simple, as familiar as water, air or fire —and she prudently advanced toward a pale stain which seemed to float in the fog. It was Pierre's face: Pierre's clothing (he dressed in black ever since he had been sick) melted in obscurity. Pierre had thrown back his head and closed his eyes. He was handsome. Eve looked at his long, curved lashes, then sat close to him on the low chair. *He seems to be suffering*, she thought. Little by little her eyes grew used to the darkness. The bureau emerged first, then the bed, then Pierre's personal things: scissors, the pot of glue, books, the herbarium which shed its leaves onto the rug near the armchair.

"Agatha?"

Pierre had opened his eyes. He was watching her, smiling. "You know, that fork?" he said. "I did it to frighten that fellow. There was *almost* nothing the matter with it."

Eve's apprehensions faded and she gave a light laugh. "You succeeded," she said, "You drove him completely out of his mind."

Pierre smiled. "Did you see? He played with it a long time, he held it right in his hands. The trouble is," he said, "they don't know how to take hold of things; they grab them."

"That's right," Eve said.

Pierre tapped the palm of his left hand lightly with the index of his right.

"They take with that. They reach out their fingers and when they catch hold of something they crack down on it to knock it out."

He spoke rapidly and hardly moving his lips; he looked puzzled.

"I wonder what they want," he said at last, "that fellow has already been here. Why did they send him to me? If they want to know what I'm doing all they have to do is read it on the screen, they don't even need to leave the house. They make mistakes. They have the power but they make mistakes. I never make any, that's my trump card. *Hoffka!*" he said. He shook his long hands before his forehead. "The bitch Hoffka! Paffka! Suffka! Do you want any more?"

"Is it the bell?" asked Eve.

"Yes. It's gone." He went on severely. "This fellow, he's just a subordinate. You know him, you went into the living-room with him."

Eve did not answer.

"What did he want?" asked Pierre. "He must have told you."

She hesitated an instant, then answered brutally. "He wanted you locked up."

When the truth was told quietly to Pierre he distrusted it. He had to be dealt with violently in order to daze and paralyze his suspicions. Eve preferred to brutalize him rather than lie: when she lied and he acted as if he believed it she could not avoid a very slight feeling of superiority which made her horrified at herself.

"Lock me up!" Pierre repeated ironically. "They're crazy. What can walls do to me. Maybe they think that's going to stop me. I sometimes wonder if there aren't two groups. The real one, the negro—and then a bunch of fools trying to stick their noses in and making mistake after mistake."

He made his hand jump up from the arm of the chair and looked at it happily.

"I can get through walls. What did you tell them?" he asked, turning to Eve with curiosity.

"Not to lock you up."

He shrugged. "You shouldn't have said that. You made a mistake too . . . unless you did it on purpose. You've got to call their bluff."

He was silent. Eve lowered her head sadly: "*They grab things!*" *How scornfully he said that—and he was right. Do I grab things too? It doesn't do any good to watch myself, I think most of my movements annoy him. But he doesn't say anything.* Suddenly she felt as miserable as when she was fourteen and Mme. Darbedat told her "You don't know what to do with your hands." She didn't dare make a move and just at that time she had an irresistible desire to change her position. Quietly she put her feet under the chair, barely touching the rug. She watched the lamp on the table—the lamp whose base Pierre had painted black—and the chess set. Pierre had left only the black pawns on the board. Sometimes he would get up, go to the table and take the pawns in his hands one by one. He spoke to them, called them Robots and they seemed to stir with a mute life under his fingers. When he set them down, Eve went and touched them in her turn (she always felt somewhat ridiculous about it). They had become little bits of dead wood again but something vague and incomprehensible stayed in them, something like understanding. *These are his things*, she thought. *There is nothing of mine in the room.* She had had a few pieces of furniture before; the mirror and the little inlaid dresser handed down from her grandmother and which Pierre jokingly called "*your dresser.*" Pierre had carried them away with him; things showed their true face to Pierre alone. Eve could watch them for hours: they were unflaggingly stubborn and determined to deceive her, offering her nothing but their appearance—as they did to Dr. Franchot and M. Darbedat. *Yet,* she told herself with anguish, *I don't see them quite like my father. It isn't possible for me to see them exactly like him.*

She moved her knees a little: her legs felt as though they were crawling with ants. Her body was stiff and taut and hurt her; she felt it too alive, too demanding. *I would like to be invisible and stay here seeing him without his seeing me. He doesn't need me; I am useless in this room.* She turned her head slightly and looked at the wall above Pierre. Threats were written on the wall. Eve knew it but she could not read them. She often watched the big red roses on the wallpaper until they began to dance before her eyes. The roses flamed in shadow. Most of the time the threat was written near the ceiling, a little to the left of the bed; but sometimes it moved. *I must get up. I can't . . . I can't sit down any longer.* There were also white discs on the wall that looked like slices of onion. The discs spun and Eve's hands began to tremble: *Sometimes I think I'm going mad. But no,* she thought, *I can't go mad. I get nervous, that's all.*

Suddenly she felt Pierre's hand on her's.

"Agatha," Pierre said tenderly.

He smiled at her but he held her hand by the ends of his fingers with a sort of revulsion, as though he had picked up a crab by the back and wanted to avoid its claws.

"Agatha," he said, "I would so much like to have confidence in you."

She closed her eyes and her breast heaved. *I mustn't answer anything, if I do he'll get angry, he won't say anything more.*

Pierre had dropped her hand. "I like you, Agatha," he said, "but I can't understand you. Why do you stay in the room all the time?"

Eve did not answer.

"Tell me why."

"You know I love you," she said dryly.

"I don't believe you," Pierre said. "Why should you love me? I must frighten you: I'm haunted." He smiled but suddenly became serious. "There is a wall between you and me. I see you, I speak to you, but you're on the other side. What keeps us from loving? I think it was easier before. In Hamburg."

"Yes," Eve said sadly. Always Hamburg. He never spoke of their real past. Neither Eve nor he had ever been to Hamburg.

"We used to walk along the canal. There was a barge, remember? The barge was black; there was a dog on the deck."

He made it up as he went along; it sounded false.

"I held your hand. You had another skin. I believed all you told me. Be quiet!" he shouted.

He listened for a moment. "They're coming," he said mournfully.

Eve jumped up. "They're coming? I thought they wouldn't ever come again."

Pierre had been calmer for the past three days; the statues did not come. Pierre was terribly afraid of the statues even though he would never admit it. Eve was not afraid: but when they began to fly, buzzing, around the room, she was afraid of Pierre.

"Give me the ziuthre," Pierre said.

Eve got up and took the ziuthre: it was a collection of pieces of cardboard Pierre had glued together; he used it to conjure the statues. The ziuthre looked like a spider. On one of the cardboards Pierre had written "Power over ambush" and on the other, "Black." On a third he had drawn a laughing face with wrinkled eyes: it was Voltaire.

Pierre seized the ziuthre by one end and looked at it darkly.

"I can't use it any more," he said.

"Why?"

"They turned it upside down."

"Will you make another?"

He looked at her for a long while. "You'd like me to, wouldn't you," he said between his teeth.

Eve was angry at Pierre. *He's warned every time they come: how does he do it? He's never wrong.*

The ziuthre dangled pitifully from the ends of Pierre's fingers. *He always finds a good reason not to use it. Sunday when they came he pretended he'd lost it but I saw it behind the paste pot and he couldn't fail to see it. I wonder if he isn't the one who brings them.* One could never tell if he were completely sincere. Sometimes Eve had the impression that despite himself Pierre was surrounded by a swarm of unhealthy thoughts and visions. But at other times Pierre seemed to invent them. *He suffers. But how much does he* believe *in the statues and the negro. Anyhow, I know he doesn't see the statues, he only hears them: when they pass he turns his head away; but he still says he sees them; he describes them.* She remembered the red face of Dr. Franchot: "But my dear madame, all mentally unbalanced persons are liars; you're wasting your time if you're trying to distinguish between what they really feel and what they pretend to feel." She gave a start. *What is Franchot doing here? I don't want to start thinking like him.*

Pierre had gotten up. He went to throw the ziuthre into the wastebasket: *I want to think like you,* she murmured. He walked with tiny steps, on tiptoe, pressing his elbows against his hips so as to take up the least possible space. He came back and sat down and looked at Eve with a closed expression.

"We'll have to put up black wallpaper," he said. "There isn't enough black in this room."

He was crouched in the armchair. Sadly Eve watched his meagre body, always ready to withdraw, to shrink: the arms, legs and head looked like retractable organs. The clock struck six. The piano downstairs was silent. Eve sighed: the statues would not come right away; they had to wait for them.

"Do you want me to turn on the light?"

She would rather not wait for them in darkness.

"Do as you please," Pierre said.

Eve lit the small lamp on the bureau and a red mist filled the room. Pierre was waiting too.

He did not speak but his lips were moving, making two dark stains in the red mist. Eve loved Pierre's lips. Before, they had been moving and sensual; but they had lost their sensuality. They were wide apart, trembling a little, coming together incessantly, crushing against each other only to separate again. They were the only living things in this blank face; they looked like two frightened animals. Pierre could mutter like that for hours without a sound leaving his mouth and Eve often let herself be fascinated by this tiny, obstinate movement. *I love his mouth.* He never kissed her any more; he was horrified at contacts: at night they touched him—the hands of men, hard and dry, pinched him all over; the long-nailed hands of women caressed him. Often he went to bed with his clothes on but the hands slipped under the clothes and tugged at his shirt. Once he heard laughter and puffy lips were placed on his mouth. He never kissed Eve after that night.

"Agatha," Pierre said, "don't look at my mouth."

Eve lowered her eyes.

"I am not ˌunaware that people can learn to read lips," he went on insolently.

His hand trembled on the arm of the chair. The index finger stretched out, tapped three times on the thumb and the other fingers curled: this was a spell. *It's going to start,* she thought. She wanted to take Pierre in her arms.

Pierre began to speak at the top of his voice in a very sophisticated tone.

"Do you remember Sao Paulo?"

No answer. Perhaps it was a trap.

"I met you there," he said, satisfied. "I took you away from a Danish sailor. We almost fought but I paid for a round of drinks and he let me take you away. All that was only a joke."

He's lying, he doesn't believe a word of what he says. He knows my name isn't Agatha. I hate him when he lies. But she saw his staring eyes and her rage melted. *He isn't lying,* she thought, *he can't stand it any more. He feels them coming; he's talking to keep from hearing them.* Pierre dug both hands into the arm of the chair. His face was pale; he was smiling.

"These meetings are often strange," he said, "but I don't believe it's by chance. I'm not asking who sent you. I know you wouldn't answer. Anyhow, you've been smart enough to bluff me."

He spoke with great difficulty, in a sharp, hurried voice. There were words he could not pronounce and which left his mouth like some soft and shapeless substance.

"You dragged me away right in the middle of the party, between the rows of black automobiles, but behind the cars there was an army with red eyes which glowed as soon as I turned my back. I think you made signs to them, all the time hanging on my arm, but

I didn't see a thing. I was too absorbed by the great ceremonies of the Coronation."

He looked straight ahead, his eyes wide open. He passed his hand over his forehead very rapidly, in one spare gesture, without stopping his talking. He did not want to stop talking.

"It was the Coronation of the Republic," he said stridently, "an impressive spectacle of its kind because of all the species of animals that the colonies sent for the ceremony. You were afraid to get lost among the monkeys. I said among the monkeys," he repeated arrogantly, looking around him, "I could say *among the negroes!* The abortions sliding under the tables, trying to pass unseen, are discovered and nailed to the spot by my Look. The password is silence. To be silent. Everything in place and attention for the entrance of the statues, that's the countersign. Tralala . . ." he shrieked and cupped his hands to his mouth. "Tralalala, tralalalala!"

He was silent and Eve knew that the statues had come into the room. He was stiff, pale and distrustful. Eve stiffened too and both waited in silence. Someone was walking in the corridor: it was Marie the housecleaner, she had undoubtedly just arrived. Eve thought, *I have to give her money for the gas.* And then the statues began to fly; they passed between Eve and Pierre.

Pierre went "Ah!" and sank down in the armchair, folding his legs beneath him. He turned his face away; sometimes he grinned, but drops of sweat pearled his forehead. Eve could stand the sight no longer, this pale cheek, this mouth deformed by a trembling grimace; she closed her eyes. Gold threads began to dance on the red background of her eyelids; she felt old and heavy. Not far from her Pierre was breathing violently. *They're flying, they're buzzing, they're bending over him.* She felt a slight tickling, a pain in the shoulder and right side. Instinctively her body bent to the left as if to avoid some disagreeable contact, as if to let a heavy, awkward object pass. Suddenly the floor creaked and she had an insane desire to open her eyes, to look to her right, sweeping the air with her hand.

She did nothing; she kept her eyes closed and a bitter joy made her tremble: *I am afraid too,* she thought. Her entire life had taken refuge in her right side. She leaned towards Pierre without opening her eyes. The slightest effort would be enough and she would enter this tragic world for the first time. *I'm afraid of the statues,* she thought.

It was a violent, blind affirmation, an incantation. She wanted to believe in their presence with all her strength. She tried to make a new sense, a sense of touch out of the anguish which paralysed her right side. She *felt* their passage in her arm, in her side and shoulder. The statues flew low and gently; they buzzed. Eve knew that they had an evil look and that eyelashes stuck out from the stone around their eyes; but she pictured them badly. She knew, too, that they were not quite alive but that slabs of flesh, warm scales appeared on their great bodies; the stone peeled from the ends of their fingers and their palms were eaten away. Eve could not *see* all that: she simply thought of enormous women sliding against her, solemn and grotesque, with a human look and compact heads of stone. *They are bending over Pierre*—Eve made such a violent effort that her hands began trembling—*they are bending over me.* A horrible cry suddenly chilled her. They had touched him. She opened her eyes: Pierre's head was in his hands, he was breathing heavily. Eve felt exhausted: *a game*, she thought with remorse; *it was only a game. I didn't sincerely believe it for an instant. And all that time he suffered as if it were real.*

Pierre relaxed and breathed freely. But his pupils were strangely dilated and he was perspiring.

"Did you see them?" he asked.

"I can't see them."

"Better for you. They'd frighten you," he said. "I am used to them."

Eve's hands were still shaking and the blood had rushed to her head. Pierre took a cigarette from his pocket and brought it up to his mouth. But he did not light it:

"I don't care whether I see them or not," he said, "but I don't want them to touch me: I'm afraid they'll give me pimples."

He thought for an instant, then asked, "Did you hear them?"

"Yes," Eve said, "it's like an airplane engine." (Pierre had told her this the previous Sunday.)

Pierre smiled with condescension. "You exaggerate," he said. But he was still pale. He looked at Eve's hands. "Your hands are trembling. That made quite an impression on you, my poor Agatha. But don't worry. They won't come back again before tomorrow."

Eve could not speak. Her teeth were chattering and she was afraid Pierre would notice it. Pierre watched her for a long time.

"You're tremendously beautiful," he said, nodding his head. "It's too bad, too bad."

He put out his hand quickly and toyed with her ear. "My lovely devil-woman. You disturb me a little, you are too beautiful: that distracts me. If it weren't a question of recapitulation . . ."

He stopped and looked at Eve with surprise.

"That's not the word . . . it came . . . it came," he said, smiling vaguely. "I had another on the tip of my tongue . . . but this one . . . came in its place. I forget what I was telling you."

He thought for a moment, then shook his head.

"Come," he said, "I want to sleep." He added in a childish voice, "You know, Agatha, I'm tired. I can't collect my thoughts any more."

He threw away his cigarette and looked at the rug anxiously. Eve slipped a pillow under his head.

"You can sleep too," he told her, "they won't be back."

. . . Recapitulation . . .

Pierre was asleep, a candid, half-smile on his face; his head was turned to one side: one might have thought he wanted to caress his cheek with his shoulder. Eve was not sleepy, she was thoughtful: *Recapitulation.* Pierre had suddenly looked stupid and the word had slipped out of his mouth, long and whitish. Pierre had stared ahead of him in astonishment, as if he had seen the word and didn't recognize it; his mouth was open, soft: something seemed broken in it. He stammered. *That's the first time it ever happened to him; he noticed it, too. He said he couldn't collect his thoughts any more.* Pierre gave a voluptuous little whimper and his hand made a vague movement. Eve watched him harshly: *how is he going to wake up.* It gnawed at her. As soon as Pierre was asleep she had to think about it. She was afraid he would wake up wild-eyed and stammering. *I'm stupid,* she thought, *it can't start before a year; Franchot said so.* But the anguish did not leave her; a year: a winter, a springtime, a summer, the beginning of another autumn. One day his features would grow confused, his jaw would hang loose, he would half open his weeping eyes. Eve bent over Pierre's hand and pressed her lips against it: *I'll kill you before that.*

Nikolai Gogol

THE DIARY OF A MADMAN

OCTOBER 3

An extraordinary thing happened today. I got up rather late, and when Marva brought my boots, I asked her the time. Hearing that ten had struck quite a while before, I dressed in a hurry. I must say I'd as soon have skipped the office altogether, knowing the sour look the Chief of my Division would give me. For a long time now he has been telling me: "How come, my man, you're always in such a muddle? Sometimes you dart around like a house on fire, and get your work in such a tangle the Devil himself couldn't put it straight; you're likely to start a new heading with a small letter and give no date or reference number." The vicious old crane! He must envy me for sitting in the Director's room and sharpening his quills. So I wouldn't have gone to the office if not in hopes of seeing the cashier and trying to get even a small advance on my salary out of the Jew. What a creature he is! The Last Judgment will come before you'll get a month's pay out of him in advance. Even if there's a dire emergency, you can beg till something bursts inside you; he won't give in, the hoary monster. Yet at home his own cook slaps him around. Everyone knows that. I see no advantage in working in our department. No side benefits whatever. It's not like working, say, for

Nikolai Gogol, "The Diary of a Madman," in The Diary of a Madman and Other Stories, *tr. by Andrew R. MacAndrew. New York: New American Library of World Literature, 1960.*

the City Administration or in the Justice Department. There you may see someone nesting in a corner and scribbling away. He may be wearing a shabby coat and have a snout that you'd want to spit at. But then, just take a look at the summer house he rents! And don't even think of offering him a gilt china cup: this, he'd say, may be all right for a doctor. But he—he must have a pair of horses maybe, or a carriage, or a beaver fur—300 rubles' worth or so. And he looks so quiet and sounds so deferential and polite: "Would you," he'll say, "be so kind as to lend me your penknife to sharpen my quill, if you please." But he'll strip a petitioner naked, except perhaps for his shirt. On the other hand, though, to work in our department carries more prestige. The people of the City Administration have never dreamt of such cleanliness. Then we have red mahogany tables and our superiors always address us politely. Yes, if it weren't for the prestige, I confess I'd have left the department long ago.

I put on my old overcoat and, as it was pouring rain, took my umbrella. The streets were quite deserted except for some peasant women, their skirts thrown over their heads, a few merchants under umbrellas, and a coachman here and there. As for decent people there was only our kind, the civil-service clerk, squelching along. I saw him at a street crossing. And as soon as I saw him I said to myself: "You're not on your way to the office, my man. You're after that one trotting ahead over there and it's her legs you're staring at." What a rogue your civil servant is! When it comes to such matters, he can take on an army officer any day. He'll try to pick up anything under a bonnet. I was passing by a store, thinking about all this, when a carriage stopped in front of it. I recognized it at once: it belonged to the Director of our Department, himself. But, I thought, he cannot possibly need anything here—it must be his daughter. I pressed myself against the wall. The footman opened the carriage door and she fluttered out like a little bird. Ah, how she looked around, first right, then left, how her eyes and eyebrows flashed past me! . . . Oh God, I'm lost, lost forever. And why did she have to drive out in the pouring rain? Try and deny after that, that women have a passion for clothing. She did not recognize me. Besides, I was trying to hide myself; my coat was quite stained and out of fashion too. Nowadays, they are wearing long collars on their

coats while I had two very short ones, one on top of the other. Her
lap dog was too slow to get into the store while the door was open and
had to stay in the street. I know this little dog. She's called Madgie.
Then, a minute or so later, I heard a thin little voice: "Hello,
Madgie." I'll be damned! Who's that talking? I turned around and
saw two ladies walking under their umbrellas: one old, the other
young and pretty. But they had already passed when I heard again,
just next to me: "You ought to be ashamed, Madgie!" What on
earth was going on? I saw Madgie and a dog that had been following
the two ladies sniffing at one another. "Maybe I'm drunk," I said
to myself, "but it's not likely. It doesn't happen to me very often."
"No, Fidele, you're wrong." With my own eyes I saw Madgie forming the words, "I was, bow-wow, I was, bow-ow-ow, very sick."
Talk about a lap dog! I must say I was quite surprised to hear her
talking. Later, however, when I had properly sized up the situation,
I was no longer surprised. As a matter of fact, the world has seen
many similar occurrences before. I've heard that, in England, a fish
broke surface and uttered a couple of words in such an outlandish
language that scholars have been trying to work out their meaning
for three years—so far in vain. Then, too, I read in the newspapers
about two cows who went into a store and asked for a pound of tea.
But I'll confess that I was much more bewildered when Madgie
said: "I *did* write you, Fidele. Perhaps Fido didn't give you my
letter." Now, I'd be willing to forfeit a month's pay if I've ever heard
of a dog that could write. Only a gentleman can write correctly
anyway. Of course, one finds some scribbling shopkeepers—even
serfs—but that sort of writing is mostly mechanical; no commas,
periods, or spelling. So I was surprised. I'll confess that recently I
have been seeing and hearing things that no one else has ever seen or
heard. "Let's," I said to myself, "follow this little dog and find out
who she is and what her thoughts are." I opened my umbrella and
followed the ladies. We crossed Pea Street, from there on to Tradesman's Avenue, turned into Carpenter's Lane, and finally stopped
before a large building near Cuckoo Bridge. "I know this house,"
I said to myself, "it's the Zverkov house." What a house! Who isn't
to be found there! There are so many cooks, so many Poles! And it
teems with my fellow civil servants; they sit there on top of one
another, like dogs. I have a friend there who can play the trumpet

quite well. The ladies went up to the fifth floor. "Fine," I thought, "I won't go in now. I'll make a note of the place and wait for the first opportunity."

OCTOBER 4

Today is Wednesday and that's why I was in our Director's ,tudy at his home. I purposely came in early, settled down and sharpened all the quills. Our Director must be a very brilliant man. His study is crammed with bookcases. I looked at some of the titles: such erudition all over the place—cuts an ordinary person off completely; they're all in French or German. And just look into his face, good gracious! What a lot of importance shines in his eyes! I've never heard him utter an unnecessary word. Except, perhaps, when one hands him some documents, he may ask: "How's the weather outside?" "It's quite damp, sir." Yes, he's different from our kind. A public figure! Nevertheless, I feel that he has taken a special liking to me. If only his daughter . . . Ah, what a rogue I am! Never mind, never mind . . . Quiet! . . . I was reading the *Bee*. Aren't the French a stupid race? Whatever can they be driving at? I'd like to take them all and give each one of them a good thrashing. In the same journal I also read a very nice description of a ball by a landowner from Kursk. Kursk landowners certainly write well . . . Whereupon I noticed that it was striking twelve-thirty and our Director still hadn't left his bedroom. But then, around one-thirty, a thing happened that no pen can adequately describe. The door opened; I thought it was the Director and jumped up from my desk holding the documents in my hand; but it was her, in person! Holy Fathers, the way she was dressed! Her dress was white, all fluffy, like a swan, and when she looked at me, I swear it was like the sun! She nodded to me and said: "Hasn't Papa been in here?" What a voice! A canary, an absolute canary. "Ma'am," I was on the point of saying, "don't have me put to death. But if you do decide that I must die, let it be by your own aristocratic little hand." But my tongue would not obey me and I only muttered, "No, ma'am." Her glance slid from me to the books and she dropped her handkerchief. I rushed like mad, slipped on the blasted parquet and almost smashed my nose. But somehow I recovered my balance and picked it up. Holy Saints, what a hanky!

Such fine, delicate linen, and amber, sheer amber. It exuded aristocracy. She said, "Thank you" and smiled, but so faintly that her divine lips hardly moved, and then she left. I remained seated there and, after another hour, a footman came in and told me: "You may go home, the master has gone out." The flunky is the one thing I cannot stand. They're always sprawled out in the entrance hall, not even bothering to acknowledge my existence with a little nod. Once, one of those lumps actually offered me snuff, and without even getting up. Don't you know, you stupid flunky, that I am a civil servant and that I come from a respectable family? Still, I picked up my hat and pulled on my overcoat unaided since those gents wouldn't think of helping you, and left. At home, I lay on my bed most of the time. Then I copied an excellent poem:

> Without you one hour crept
>   Slowly like a year.
> "Is my life worth while," I wept,
>   "When you are not near?"

Sounds like Pushkin. In the evening, I put on my overcoat and walked over to the Director's house and waited by the gate for quite a while to see whether she wouldn't come out and get into her carriage. But she didn't.

NOVEMBER 6

Something has got into the Chief of my Division. When I arrived at the office he called me and began as follows: "Now then, tell me. What's the matter with you?" "What do you mean? Nothing," I said. "Come, try to understand; aren't you over forty? Time to be a bit wiser. What do you fancy you are? Don't imagine I can't see what you're up to. I know you're trailing after the Director's daughter. Just look at yourself—what are you? Just nothing. You haven't a penny to your name. Look in the mirror. How can you even think of such things?" The hell with him! Just because he's got a face like a druggist's bottle and that quiff of hair on his head all curled and pomaded, and because he holds his head up in the air like that, he thinks he can get away with anything. I see through his indignation. He's envious; perhaps he's noticed the marks of favor bestowed upon me. A lot I care what he says. So he's a Divisional Chief, so what! So he hangs out his gold watch chain and has custom-made boots at thirty rubles. Let him be damned. Perhaps he imagines I had a shopkeeper or a tailor for a father. I'm a gentleman! And I can be promoted too. I'm only forty-two, an age when one's career is really just beginning. Wait, my friend, I'll go higher than you yet, and, God willing, very, very much higher. Then I'll have a social position beyond your dreams. Do you imagine you're the only one to have dignity? Give me a fashionable new coat, let me wear a tie like yours, and you won't be worthy to shine my shoes. My lack of means—that's the only trouble.

NOVEMBER 8

Went to the theater. The play was about the Russian fool Filatka. Laughed a lot. They had a vaudeville show as well, full of amusing verses lampooning lawyers, so outspoken that I wondered how it got past the censor; as to the merchants, it says plainly that they swindle the people, that their sons wallow in debauchery and elbow their way into society. There was also an amusing couplet which complained about the way newspapermen criticize everything and asked the audience for protection from them. Playwrights write very amusing plays nowadays. I love going to the theater. As soon as I get hold of a few pennies, I can't help myself, I go. But civil servants are such swine . . . you won't catch clods like them going to the theater, not even if they're given free tickets. One actress sang really well. . . . It made me think of . . . What a rogue I am! Never mind, never mind . . . silence!

NOVEMBER 9

Left for the office at eight. The Divisional Chief pretended he hadn't noticed me come in. And I also acted as though nothing had happened between us. I went through the papers and sorted them out. Left at four. On the way home, passed by the Director's house but didn't see anyone. After dinner, mostly lay on my bed.

Today, I sat in the Director's study and sharpened twenty-three quills for him, and four quills for . . . oh-oh . . . her. He likes to have as many quills to hand as possible. My, how brainy he must be! Usually he doesn't say much but I guess he must be weighing everything in that head of his. I'd like to know what he has on his mind most of the time, what's cooking up there. I'd like to have a closer look at these people, how they live, with all their subtle innuendoes and courtly jokes; I wish I knew how they behave and what they do among themselves. I've often tried to engage the Director in conversation but I'm damned if it's ever come off. I've managed to say it's warm or cold outside and that is absolutely as far as I've got. One day I'd like just to step into their drawing room. The door is ajar sometimes and from there I can see another door, leading to another room. That drawing room! You should see how it's decorated. All those mirrors and fine pieces of porcelain. I'd also like to see the part where her rooms are. That's where I'd really like to go! I'd like to peep into her boudoir, and see all those little jars and bottles of hers standing there amidst the sort of flowers one doesn't even dare breathe on; to have a glimpse at the dress she has thrown off, lying there looking more like air than a dress. It would be wonderful to glance into her bedroom. . . . Miracles must happen there. It's a paradise surpassing the heavenly one. What wouldn't I give to see the little stool upon which her delicate foot descends when she gets out of bed and watch how an incredibly fine, immaculate stocking is pulled up her leg. . . . Oh, the roguish thoughts! . . . Never mind . . . never mind . . . silence!

But today something suddenly became clear to me when I recalled the conversation between the two dogs I'd overheard on Nevsky Avenue. Fine, I said to myself, now I'll find out everything. I must get hold of the letters exchanged between those nasty mutts. I'm sure to find out something. Now I'll confess that, at one point, I almost called Madgie and said to her: "Listen, Madgie, we are alone now. If you wish, I'll even lock the door so that no one'll see us. Tell me everything you know about your mistress: what she's like and all that. And don't worry, I swear I'll not repeat a thing to anyone." But the sly little mutt just sort of shrank into herself, put her tail between her legs, and left the room in silence, as though she hadn't heard a thing. For a long time I've suspected that dogs are much more intelligent than men; I was even certain that they could speak and simply chose not to out of a peculiar stubbornness. A dog is an extraordinary politician and notices everything, every step a human takes. Still, whatever happens, tomorrow I'll go to the Zverkov house and question Fidele and, if possible, I'll lay my hand on Madgie's letters to her.

NOVEMBER 12

At 2:00 P.M. I went out determined to find Fidele and question her. I can't stand the smell of cabbage which comes pouring out of all the greengrocers along Tradesman's Avenue. This, and the infernal stench from under the gates of every house, sent me scurrying, holding my nose. And all the soot and smoke that they let pour out of the vile workshops make it a quite unsuitable place for a person of breeding to take a stroll. When I reached the sixth floor and rang the bell, out came a girl with little freckles and not too bad-looking at that. I recognized her at once. She was the one I had seen walking with the old woman. She blushed a little and I immediately saw through her: what you need, my dear, is a husband. "What do you want?" she asked. "I want to have a talk with your doggie."

The girl was stupid. I could see from the start how stupid she was! At that moment the mutt ran in yapping furiously and as I was trying to grab her, the repulsive creature almost caught my nose between her teeth. But then I saw her basket in the corner—which was just what I was looking for! I went over to it and felt under the straw and, to my great joy, I found a small bundle of papers. Seeing what I was doing, the nasty little cur first took a bite out of my calf; then, when upon further sniffing she found that I had taken her letters, she began whining and making up to me, but I told her, "Oh no, my dear. See you later!" And off I went. I believe the girl mistook me for a madman—she seemed very frightened indeed.

Once home, I wanted to get down to work immediately, to have those letters sorted before dark, since I can't see too well by candlelight. But for some reason Marva decided to scrub the floor just then. Those stupid Finns always succumb to their obsession for cleanliness at the worst moments. So I went out for a walk to think it all over. Now, finally, I'll find out everything about these intrigues and plots; I'll understand all the little wheels and springs and get to the bottom of the matter. These letters will explain. Dogs are a clever race. They know all about intrigue and so it's all bound to be in their letters: all there is to know about the Director's character and actions. And she, she too is sure to be mentioned . . . but never mind that . . . silence! I came home toward evening. Most of the time, I lay on my bed.

NOVEMBER 13

Let's see now. This letter looks quite legible, though there *is* something canine about the handwriting:

Dear Fidele, I still find it difficult to get accustomed to the commonness of your name. Couldn't they find a better one for you? Fidele, like Rose, is very ordinary, but all that's beside the point. I'm very glad we have decided to write to each other.

The spelling is very good. It's even punctuated correctly. This is considerably better than our Divisional Chief can do, although he claims to have gone to some university or other. Let's see further on:

I believe that sharing feelings and impressions with another is one of the main blessings in life. . . .

Hm! The thought is stolen from a work translated from the German. The author's name escapes me now.

I speak from experience although I've never been much further than the gates of our house. But then, isn't my life full of blessings? My young mistress, whom her papa calls Sophie, is crazy about me.

Ouch! Never mind, never mind. Silence!

Papa often pets me too. I drink tea and coffee with cream. I must tell you, my dear, that I am not in the least tempted by the half-gnawed bones which our Fido chews on in the kitchen. I only like the bones of game and, even then, only if the marrow hasn't been sucked out by someone else. A mixture of sauces is nice as long as they contain no capers or vegetables. What I hate is people who give dogs the little pellets they knead out of bread. Some person sitting at the table, who has previously touched all sorts of filthy things, begins to knead a piece of bread with those same hands, then calls you and thrusts the pellet into your mouth. It is awkward somehow to refuse and, disgusted, you eat it up. . . .

What's that all about? What rubbish! As though there weren't more interesting things to write about. Let's see the next page. There may be something less stupid.

Now, I'll tell you with pleasure what goes on in this household. I have mentioned the main character, whom Sophie calls Papa. He's a very strange man. . . .

At last! I knew they had very shrewd judgment, whatever the subject. Let's see what Papa's like.

. . . a very strange man. He's usually silent. He speaks very little, but a week ago he never stopped saying to himself: Will I get it or not? Once he even asked me: What do you say, Madgie, will I get it or won't I? I could make no sense out of it so I smelled his shoe and left the room. Then, a week later, Papa came home overjoyed. All that morning formally dressed people came and congratulated him. At dinner Papa was gayer than I'd ever seen him before, and after dinner, he picked me up and held me level with his chest, saying: Look, Madgie, what's this? I saw some sort of a ribbon. I sniffed at it but it had no fragrance whatever. Finally, discreetly, I gave it a lick: slightly salty.

Hm. The mutt really goes too far . . . she needs a good whipping . . . So he is that vain is he? I must take it into account.

Good-bye, my dear, I must run along . . . blah-blah-blah-blah . . . will finish this letter tomorrow. Hello, I am back with you. Today my mistress, Sophie . . .

Aha! Let's see what she says about Sophie. I really *am* a rogue! But never mind, never mind. Let's go on.

. . . my mistress, Sophie, was in a terrific to-do. She was getting ready for a ball and I intended to take advantage of her absence and write to you. Sophie is always very happy when she's about to leave for a ball but is always very irritable while she's getting dressed for it. You know, my dear, I personally can see no pleasure in going to a ball. Sophie usually returns home at 6 A.M., and I can tell by her pale and emaciated features that the poor thing hasn't been given a bite to eat. I confess I could never lead such a life. If I had to go without game in sauce or chicken-wing stews, I don't know what would become of me. A sauce is not at all bad with porridge. But nothing can make carrots, turnips, and artichokes palatable. . . .

The style is very jerky. You can see that it's not written by a man. She starts off all right and then lapses into dogginess. Let's see another letter. Looks rather long . . . hm . . . no date . . .

Oh, my dear, how strongly I feel the approach of spring. My heart beats as though it were waiting for something. In my ears, there's a constant buzz. Very often I listen so intently behind doors that I raise my front paw. And, confidentially, I have plenty of suitors. I often sit by the window and watch them. If only you could see some of them, they're so ugly. There is a horrible mongrel with stupidity written all over him, who swaggers along the street and imagines he is a person of breeding and that everyone is bound to admire him. I paid no attention to him, as though I hadn't even noticed him. Then you should have seen the terrifying Great Dane that stopped in front of my window! If that one stood up on his hind legs, which, incidentally, the clod is incapable of doing, he would be a head taller than Sophie's Papa, who's quite tall himself and fat besides. Moreover, the lump seems to be very arrogant. I growled at him but it didn't put him off in the least. He just hung his tongue out, drooped his huge ears, and kept staring at my window, the oaf! But, my dear, you don't really imagine, do you, that my heart is indifferent to all the hopefuls? . . . You should have seen the dashing young lover that came jumping over the fence into our courtyard. His name is Treasure and he has such a nice face. . . .

Ah, damn it all! What rubbish! How much of her letters is she going to fill with such stupid stuff? I'm after *people*, not dogs! I need spiritual food and I am served these inanities. . . . Let's skip a page, perhaps we'll find something more interesting. . . .

. . . Sophie was sitting at the table sewing something. I was looking out of the window; I like to watch people in the street. Suddenly the manservant came in and announced someone. "Show him in!" Sophie said. She hugged me hard and murmured, "Oh Madgie, darling, if you only knew who that is. He's a Guards officer, his hair is black and his eyes are so dark and so light at the same time . . . like fire." And Sophie rushed out. A minute later a young officer with black side whiskers appeared. He went to the mirror and smoothed his hair; then he looked around the room. I growled a little and settled down by my window. Soon Sophie came back, greeted him gaily, while I pretended to be busy looking out of the window. In fact, however, I turned my head sideways a little, so that I could catch what they said. You cannot imagine, Fidele dear, the silliness of that conversation. They spoke about some lady who, during a dance, kept doing a certain step instead of the one she was expected to do, then about somebody called Bobov, who looked like a stork and almost fell over, then about one Lidina, who thought she had blue eyes when they were really green, and so on and on. Oh no, I said to myself, this officer doesn't compare to Treasure. Heavens, what a difference! To start with, the officer has a wide face, quite bald except for his side whiskers which, in fact, look like a black kerchief tied around it, whereas Treasure's face is narrow and fine and he has a sweet white patch on his brow. Treasure's waist is incomparably slenderer than the officer's, and his eyes, his gestures, and his ways are vastly superior. Really, a tremendous difference! I wonder what she finds in her officer. What on earth can she admire in him? . . .

Yes, here I tend to agree. Something seems wrong. It is quite unbelievable that this officer should have swept her off her feet. Let's see:

If she likes the officer, I think she'll soon be liking the civil-service clerk who sits in Papa's study. That one, my dear, is a real scarecrow. He looks a bit like a turtle caught in a bag. . . .

Which clerk can that be? . . .

He has a funny name and he's always sitting sharpening quills. The hair on his head is like straw. Papa sends him on errands like a servant. . . .

The filthy cur seems to be trying to get its own back! Why is my hair like straw?

Sophie can hardly control her laughter when she sees him.

You wretched, lying dog! What a filthy, poisonous tongue! As if I didn't know it's all your jealousy. I know whose tricks these are. I recognize the hand of the Divisional Chief here. For some reason, that man has sworn undying hatred for me and he is trying to harm me, to harm me every minute of the day and night. Still, let's see one more letter. It may make it clear.

My dear Fidele, forgive me for not writing to you all this time. I've been going around in absolute ecstasy. I agree, without reservation, with the philosopher who said that love is a second life. Moreover, a lot of things are changing in our household. The officer comes every day now. Sophie is madly in love with him. Papa is very gay. I even heard our Gregory, who always talks to himself while sweeping the floors, say that the wedding is close at hand, because Papa always wanted to see Sophie married to a high official or to an army officer with a brilliant career ahead of him. . . .

Hell! . . . I can't go on. . . . High officials, senior officers, they get all the best things in this world. You discover a crumb of happiness, you reach out for it and then along comes a high official or an officer and snatches it away. Goddammit! I would like so much to become a high official myself and not just to obtain her hand in marriage either. No, I'd like to be a high official just so that I could watch them jump around for my benefit; I'd listen for a while to their courtly jokes and innuendoes and then tell them what they could do with themselves. It hurts, though. Oh hell! . . . I tore the stupid little dog's letter to shreds.

DECEMBER 3

Impossible! Lies! There can't be a wedding. So what if he has a commission in the Guards? That's nothing but position, you can't touch it with your hand. A Guards officer does not have a third eye in the middle of his forehead, his nose is not made of gold but the same stuff as mine or anyone else's and he uses it to sniff not to eat, for sneezing not for coughing. I've often tried to discover where all these differences lie. Why am I a clerk? Why should I be a clerk? Perhaps I'm really a general or a count and only seem to be a clerk? Maybe I don't really know who I am? There are plenty of instances in history when somebody quite ordinary, not necessarily an aristocrat, some middle-class person or even a peasant, suddenly turns out to be a public figure and perhaps even the ruler of a country. If a peasant can turn into someone so important, where are the limits to the possibilities for a man of breeding? Imagine, for instance, me, entering a room in a general's uniform. There's an epaulet on my right shoulder, an epaulet on my left, a blue ribbon across my chest. How would that be? What tune would my beauty sing then? And Papa himself, our Director, what would he say? Ow, he's so vain! He's a Mason, no mistake about it, although he may pretend to be this or that; I noticed from the start that when he shakes hands, he sticks out two fingers only. But I can't be promoted to general or governor or anything like that overnight. What I'd like to know is, why am I a clerk? Why precisely a clerk?

DECEMBER 5

I read the newspapers all morning. Strange things are happening in Spain. I can't even make them out properly. They write that the throne has been vacated and that the ranking grandees are having difficulty in selecting an heir. It seems there's discontent. Sounds very strange to me. How can a throne be vacant? They say that some donna may accede. A donna cannot accede to a throne. It's absolutely impossible. A king should sit on a throne. But they say there is no king. It's impossible that there should be no king. There must be a king but he's hidden away somewhere in anonymity. It's even possible that he's around but is being forced to remain in hiding for family reasons or for fear of some neighboring country such as France. Or there may be other reasons.

DECEMBER 8

I was on the point of going to the office but various considerations held me back. I couldn't get those Spanish affairs out of my head. How can a donna possibly become ruler? They won't allow it. In the first place, England won't stand for it. Then we must keep in mind the political setup of the rest of Europe: the Austrian Emperor, our Tsar. . . . I confess I was so perturbed and hurt by these events that I could do nothing all day. Marva remarked that I was very absent-minded during dinner. . . . In fact, I believe I absent-mindedly threw a couple of plates on the floor, where they broke at once. After dinner, I walked the streets, uphill and downhill. Came across nothing of interest. Then, mostly lay on my bed and thought about the Spanish question.

YEAR 2000, APRIL 43

This is a day of great jubilation. Spain has a king. They've found him. *I* am the King. I discovered it today. It all came to me in a flash. It's incredible to me now that I could have imagined that I was a civil-service clerk. How could such a crazy idea ever have entered my head? Thank God no one thought of slapping me into a lunatic asylum. Now I see everything clearly, as clearly as if it lay in the palm of my hand. But what was happening to me before? Then things loomed at me out of a fog. Now, I believe that all troubles stem from the misconception that human brains are located in the head. They are not: human brains are blown in by the winds from somewhere around the Caspian Sea.

Marva was the first to whom I revealed my identity. When she heard that she was facing the King of Spain, she flung up her hands in awe. She almost died of terror. The silly woman had never seen a King of Spain before. However, I tried to calm her and, speaking graciously, did my best to assure her of my royal favor. I was not going to hold against her all the times she had failed to shine my boots properly. The masses are so ignorant. One can't talk to them on lofty subjects. Probably she was so frightened because she thought that all kings of Spain are like Philip II. But I carefully pointed out that I wasn't like Philip II at all. I didn't go to the office. The hell with it. No, my friends, you won't entice me there now; never again shall I copy your dreadful documents.

MARTOBER 86. BETWEEN DAY AND NIGHT

Today, our Divisional Chief sent someone to make me go to the office. I hadn't been there for over three weeks. I went, just for a lark. The Divisional Chief expected me to come apologizing to him but I just looked at him indifferently, with not too much ire, nor too much benevolence either; then I sat down in my usual place as though unaware of the people around me. I looked around at all that scribbling rabble and thought: If only you had an inkling of who's sitting here among you, oh Lord, what a fuss you'd make. There'd be a terrific to-do and the Divisional Chief himself would bow deeply to me, as he does to the Director. They put some papers in front of me which I was supposed to abstract or something. I didn't even stir. A few minutes later, there was a general commotion. They said the Director was on his way. Several clerks jumped up, hoping he'd notice them. But I didn't budge. When word came that the Director was about to pass through our Division, they all buttoned up their coats. I did nothing of the sort. What kind of a Director does he think he is? Who says I should get up for him? Never! He's an old cork, not a Director. Yes, just an ordinary cork, the kind used for stoppering a bottle. That's all he is. But the funniest thing of all was when they gave me a paper to sign. They expected I'd sign it in the corner: head clerk such and such. Well, let them think again. I wrote in the main space, the one reserved for the Director's signature: Ferdinand VIII. You should have witnessed the awed silence that followed; but I merely waved my hand graciously and said: "Dispense with the manifestation of allegiance!" and walked out of the room. From there, I went straight to the Director's house. He was not at home. The footman tried to stop me from going in but what I said made his arms drop limp at his sides. I went straight to her boudoir. She was sitting in front of her mirror. She jumped up and stepped back, away from me. Still I did not tell her that I was the

King of Spain. I simply told her that she couldn't even imagine the happiness awaiting her and that despite all our enemies' intrigues, we would be together. I did not want to say more and left. Oh, women are such perfidious things! Only now did I understand what a woman is like. So far, no one has found out whom Woman is in love with. I was the first to discover it: Woman is in love with the Devil. And I'm not joking either. Physicists write a lot of drivel about her being this, that and the other. She loves only the Devil. Look, do you see over there, in the front tier of the boxes? She raises her lorgnette. You think she's looking at that fat man with the star over there? Nothing of the sort. She's staring at the Devil, the Devil hiding behind the fat man's back. See, now he has hidden himself in the star and he's beckoning to her with his finger! And she'll marry him too. She will for sure. As for all the rest of them, all those who lick boots and proclaim their patriotism, all they really want is annuities and more annuities. Some patriots! They'd sell their mother, their father, and their God for money, the strutting betrayers of Christ! And all this crazy ambition and vanity come from the little bubble under the tongue which has a tiny worm about the size of a pinhead in it, and it's all the work of a barber on Pea Street. I can't recall his name but the moving force behind it all is the Sultan of Turkey who pays the barber to spread Mohammedanism all over the world. They say that in France, already, the majority of the people have embraced the Mohammedan faith.

NO DATE. A DAY WITHOUT DATE

Went along Nevsky Avenue incognito. Saw the Tsar riding past. Everybody was doffing his hat, and so did I. I gave no sign that I was the King of Spain. I thought it would be undignified to reveal my identity there, in front of all those people, that it would be more proper to be presented at Court first. What has prevented me so far is the fact that I haven't got Spanish royal attire. If only I could get hold of a royal mantle of some sort. I thought of having one made but tailors are so stupid. Besides, they don't seem to be interested in their trade nowadays and go in for speculation, so that most of them end up mending roads. I decided to make a mantle out of my best coat, which I had only worn twice. But I didn't want those good-for-nothings to mess it all up—I preferred to do it myself. I locked my door so as not to be seen. I had to cut my coat to ribbons with the scissors since a mantle has a completely different style.

CAN'T REMEMBER THE DAY.
NOR WAS THERE A MONTH.
DAMNED IF I KNOW WHAT'S BEEN GOING ON

The mantle is ready. Marva really let out a yell when I put it on. Even so, I still don't feel ready to be presented at Court. My retinue hasn't as yet arrived from Spain. The absence of a retinue would be incompatible with my dignity. I'm expecting them at any time.

1st DATE

I'm puzzled by the unaccountable delay in the arrival of my retinue. What can be holding them up? I went to the post office and inquired whether the Spanish delegates had arrived. But the post-master is an utter fool and knows nothing: No, he says, there are no Spanish delegates around here but if you wish to mail a letter, we'll accept it. What the hell is he talking about? What letter? Letter my foot! Let druggists write letters. . . .

MADRID, FEBRUARIUS THE THIRTIETH

So I'm in Spain. It all happened so quickly that I hardly had time to realize it. This morning the Spanish delegation finally arrived for me and we all got into a carriage. I was somewhat bewildered by the extraordinary speed at which we traveled. We went so fast that in half an hour we reached the Spanish border. But then, nowadays there are railroads all over Europe and the ships go so fast too. Spain is a strange country. When we entered the first room, I saw a multitude of people with shaven heads. I soon realized, though, that these must be Dominican or Capuchin monks because they always shave their heads. I also thought that the manners of the King's Chancellor, who was leading me by the hand, were rather strange. He pushed me into a small room and said: "You sit quiet and don't you call yourself King Ferdinand again or I'll beat the nonsense out of your head." But I knew that I was just being tested and refused to submit. For this, the Chancellor hit me across the back with a stick, twice, so painfully that I almost let out a cry. But I contained myself, remembering that this is customary procedure among knights on initiation into an exalted order. To this day, they adhere to the chivalric code in Spain.

Left to myself, I decided to devote some time to affairs of state. I have discovered that China and Spain are the same thing and it's only ignorance that makes people take them for two separate countries. I advise anybody who doubts it to take a piece of paper and write the word "Spain" and they'll see for themselves that it comes out "China." I also gave much thought to a sad event that must occur tomorrow at seven o'clock. As foreseen by the famous English chemist Wellington, the Earth will mount the Moon. I confess I was deeply worried when I thought of the Moon's extraordinary sensitivity and fragility. The Moon, of course, is made in Hamburg, and I must say they do a very poor job. I wonder why England doesn't do something about it. It's a lame cooper that makes the Moon, and it's quite obvious that the fool has no conception of what the Moon should be. He uses tarred rope and olive oil and that's why the stench is so awful all over the Earth and we are forced to plug our noses. And that's why the Moon itself is such a delicate ball that men cannot live there—only noses. And that's why we can't see our own noses: they are all on the Moon. And when I thought what a heavy thing the Earth is and that, sitting down on the Moon, it would crush our noses into a powder, I became so worried that I put on my socks and shoes and rushed into the State Council Room to order my police force to stand by to prevent the Earth from mounting the Moon. The Capuchin monks I found in the State Council Room were very clever people and when I said, "Gentlemen, let's save the Moon, the Earth is preparing to mount it," they all rushed at once to execute my royal wish and many tried to climb the wall to reach the Moon. But at that moment, the Grand Chancellor came in. As soon as they saw him, they scattered. Being the King, I remained there alone. But to my surprise, the Chancellor hit me with his stick and chased me into my room. Such is the power of popular tradition in Spain!

JANUARY OF THE SAME YEAR WHICH HAPPENED
AFTER FEBRUARIUS

I still can't make out what sort of a place Spain is. The customs and the etiquette at the Court are quite incredible. I don't see, I don't grasp it, I don't understand at all! Today, they shaved my head, although I shouted with all my might that I did not want to become a monk. But then they began to drip cold water on my head and everything went blank. Never have I been through such hell. I just can't understand the point of this peculiar custom, so stupid, so senseless. And the irresponsibility of the kings who never got around to outlawing this custom is quite beyond me.

Some indications make me wonder whether I haven't fallen into the hands of the Inquisition. Maybe the man I took for the Chancellor is really the Grand Inquisitor himself? But then, I can't see how the King can be subjected to the Inquisition. True, this could be the work of France, especially Polignac. That Polignac is an absolute beast. He has sworn to drive me to my death. And so he maneuvers on and on. But I know, my fine fellow, that you in turn are being led by the English. The English are great politicians. They sow the seeds of dissension everywhere. The whole world knows that when England takes snuff, France sneezes.

25th DATE

Today, the Grand Inquisitor entered my room. I heard his steps approaching while he was still far off and hid under a chair. He looked around and, not seeing me, he began to call out. First he shouted my name and civil-service rank. I remained silent. Then, Ferdinand VIII, King of Spain! I was about to stick my head out but thought to myself: No, they won't get me that way! They may want to pour cold water on my head again. But he saw me and chased me out from under the chair with his stick. His damn stick hurts dreadfully. But my very latest discovery made me feel better: I had found that every rooster has his own Spain and he has it under his feathers. The Grand Inquisitor left very angry, threatening me with some punishment or other. Of course, I completely ignored his helpless fury. I knew he was a puppet. A tool of England.

DA 34 TE MNTH. YR. YRAURBEF 349

No, I have no strength left. I can't stand any more. My God! What they're doing to me! They pour cold water on my head. They don't listen to me, they don't hear me, they don't see me. What have I done to them? Why do they torture me so? What do they want from me? What can I give them? I haven't anything to give. I have no strength, I cannot bear this suffering, my head is on fire, and everything goes around me in circles. Save me! Take me away from here! Give me a carriage with horses swift as wind! Drive on, coachman, let the harness bells ring! Soar upward, my horses, carry me away from this world! Further, further, where I will see nothing, nothing. There is the sky smoking before me. A star twinkles far away, the forest rushes past with its dark trees and the crescent moon. The violet fog is a carpet underfoot. I hear the twanging of a guitar string through the fog; on one side, the sea, and on the other, Italy. Then Russian huts come into sight. Perhaps that's my house over there, looking blue in the distance. And isn't that my mother sitting by the window? Mother, save your wretched son! Let your tears fall on his sick head! See how they torture him! Hold me, a poor waif, in your arms. There's no room for him in this world. They are chasing him. Mother, take pity on your sick child. . . .

And, by the way, have you heard that the Dey of Algiers has a wart right under his nose?

Childhood Schizophrenia

The relationship of childhood schizophrenia to the adult forms of this disorder is still unclear. We do know that small children suffer conditions marked by severe defects in perception, cognition, and interpersonal relationships, analogous but not identical to those displayed by the adult psychotic. Many special syndromes have been described, the primary ones being infantile autism and the symbiotic psychoses. Autism is a grave psychological disturbance appearing as early as the first two years of life and characterized by an almost total inability to tolerate human contact, to accept anything novel and new, or to exhibit any of the plastic mastery responses of early childhood. The autistic child is sealed off and alone, living in a world of stereotyped activity revolving either around his own body or some mechanical object which plays the role of a magic companion.

The selections below portray two types of schizophrenic children. The brief excerpt from Rubin's *Jordi* is a startlingly real portrait of an autistic child, demonstrating his subjective, distorted experience of reality and his attempt to find solace in his magic toy, a "jiggler." Aiken's classic, "Silent Snow, Secret Snow," concerns itself with an older schizophrenic child, who, finding reality and parental pressure unbearable, begins to withdraw farther and farther into a world of fantasy which promises nepenthean respite, at the cost of his severing relationships with life around him.

Theodore Isaac Rubin

JORDI

He woke up suddenly, looked around the room, and jumped out of bed. People were talking in the kitchen. The woman's voice was high-pitched, tremulous, and sounded very angry. The man's voice said, "Yes—OK, already, OK," and then the door slammed and it was quiet again. He felt like eating but was afraid to go into the kitchen. The garbage pail under the sink, with its greasy, gaping, smelly hole frightened him awfully.

Shaking miserably, he finally opened the door and walked into the room backward. The woman shook her head and said, "Why can't you walk like all of us, Jordi?" He couldn't answer—the pail might hear him. The big hole was like an ear, and it could hear everything—sometimes even his thoughts. If he kept quiet and thought nothing, maybe he could shut it out and make himself safe.

He gulped down his orange juice and ran out of the house. He made it—he was safe again—but he had to be careful of the garbage pails on the street.

And then he remembered that he forgot his jiggler. He had to have his jiggler if he wanted to get by the garbage cans safely. He knew that he had to face the woman again. She just couldn't understand why he wouldn't talk. Sometimes she hugged and kissed him. Sometimes she gave up and shook him.

He marveled at her fearlessness. She talked in front of the can,

Theodore Isaac Rubin, from Jordi. *New York: MacMillan, 1960*

even picked it up and shook it. But her voice—when that voice got loud and angry, the whole room shook. It felt like he would be crushed by it. It went through him and made him shake and scream inside—stop, stop, stop, stop, stop, but her voice would go on. Sometimes, though, the man's voice, which was kind of deep and smooth, would say, "Stop," and her voice stopped.

He tiptoed into the house, but she saw him and said, "God, Jordi, walk like the rest of us." He took the doorknob attached to a long string and ran past her out of the house. He had his jiggler and was now truly safe.

He let the jiggler hang down in front of him and waited. Soon it would tell his feet where to go. Funny, how his feet followed the jiggler without his even thinking about them. He walked and walked and felt that he was all alone even though there were people here and there.

His feet finally came to the jiggler's destination. There it was—a water tower, very high—sitting up there in the clouds, alone and quiet. He looked at the tower, and it made him feel good inside. He stared at it for a long time, and then the jiggler reminded him that he had to go home again.

All the way home he thought of water towers, flagpoles, high buildings, trees, and many things much taller than he was. Before he knew it, he and his jiggler were in the kitchen eating lunch. Her voice asked if he had a nice walk, and he nodded yes. She kissed the top of his head lovingly, and he said, "It was high—so high, so beautiful."

"What was high? What, Jordi?"

But he was quiet and didn't feel like talking again. . . .

Conrad Aiken

SILENT SNOW,
SECRET SNOW

I

Just why it should have happened, or why it should have happened just when it did, he could not, of course, possibly have said; nor perhaps would it even have occurred to him to ask. The thing was above all a secret, something to be preciously concealed from Mother and Father; and to that very fact it owed an enormous part of its deliciousness. It was like a peculiarly beautiful trinket to be carried unmentioned in one's trouser-pocket—a rare stamp, an old coin, a few tiny gold links found trodden out of shape on the path in the park, a pebble of carnelian, a seashell distinguishable from all others by an unusual spot or stripe—and, as if it were any one of these, he carried around with him everywhere a warm and persistent and increasingly beautiful sense of possession. Nor was it only a sense of possession—it was also a sense of protection. It was as if, in some delightful way, his secret gave him a fortress, a wall behind which he could retreat into heavenly seclusion. This was almost the first thing he had noticed about it—apart from the oddness of the thing itself—and it was this that now again, for the fiftieth time, occurred to him, as he sat in the little schoolroom. It was the half-hour for geography. Miss Buell was revolving with one finger, slowly, a huge terrestrial globe which had been placed on her

Conrad Aiken, "*Silent Snow, Secret Snow*," *in* The Collected Short Stories of Conrad Aiken. *New York: World, 1960.*

desk. The green and yellow continents passed and repassed, questions were asked and answered, and now the little girl in front of him, Deirdre, who had a funny little constellation of freckles on the back of her neck, exactly like the Big Dipper, was standing up and telling Miss Buell that the equator was the line that ran round the middle.

Miss Buell's face, which was old and grayish and kindly, with gray stiff curls beside the cheeks, and eyes that swam very brightly, like little minnows, behind thick glasses, wrinkled itself into a complication of amusements.

"Ah! I see. The earth is wearing a belt, or a sash. Or some one drew a line round it!"

"Oh no—not that—I mean—"

In the general laughter, he did not share, or only a very little. He was thinking about the Arctic and Antarctic regions, which of course, on the globe, were white. Miss Buell was now telling them about the tropics, the jungles, the steamy heat of equatorial swamps, where the birds and butterflies, and even the snakes, were like living jewels. As he listened to these things, he was already, with a pleasant sense of half-effort, putting his secret between himself and the words. Was it really an effort at all? For effort implied something voluntary, and perhaps even something one did not especially want; whereas this was distinctly pleasant, and came almost of its own accord. All he needed to do was to think of that morning, the first one, and then all the others—

But it was all so absurdly simple! It had amounted to so little. It was nothing, just an idea—and just why it should have become so wonderful, so permanent, was a mystery—a very pleasant one, to be sure, but also, in an amusing way, foolish. However, without ceasing to listen to Miss Buell, who had now moved up to the north temperate zones, he deliberately invited his memory of the first morning. It was only a moment or two after he had waked up—or perhaps the moment itself. But was there, to be exact, an exact moment? Was one awake all at once? or was it gradual? Anyway, it was after he had stretched a lazy hand up toward the headrail, and yawned, and then relaxed again among his warm covers, all the more grateful on a December morning, that the thing had happened. Suddenly, for no reason, he had thought of the postman, he remembered the postman. Perhaps there was nothing so odd in that. After all, he heard the postman almost every morning in his life—his heavy boots could be heard clumping round the corner at the top of the little cobbled hill-street, and then, progressively nearer, progressively louder, the double knock at each door, the crossings and re-crossings of the street, till finally the clumsy steps came stumbling across to the very door, and the tremendous knock came which shook the house itself.

(Miss Buell was saying "Vast wheat-growing areas in North America and Siberia."

Deirdre had for the moment placed her left hand across the back of her neck.)

But on this particular morning, the first morning, as he lay there with his eyes closed, he had for some reason *waited* for the postman. He wanted to hear him come round the corner. And that was precisely the joke—he never did. He never came. He never had come—*round the corner*—again. For when at last the steps *were* heard, they had already, he was quite sure, come a little down the hill, to the first house; and even so, the steps were curiously different—they were softer, they had a new secrecy about them, they were muffled and indistinct; and while the rhythm of them was the same, it now said a new thing—it said peace, it said remoteness, it said cold, it said sleep. And he had understood the situation at once—nothing could have seemed simpler—there had been snow in the night, such as all winter he had been longing for; and it was this which had rendered the postman's first footsteps inaudible, and the later ones faint. Of course! How lovely! And even now it must be snowing—it was going to be a snowy day—the long white ragged lines were drifting and sifting across the street, across the faces of the old houses, whispering and hushing, making little triangles of white in the corners between cobblestones, seething a little when the wind blew them over the ground to a drifted corner; and so it would be all day, getting deeper and deeper and silenter and silenter.

(Miss Buell was saying "Land of perpetual snow.")

All this time, of course (while he lay in bed), he had kept his eyes closed, listening to the nearer progress of the postman, the muffled footsteps thumping and slipping on the snow-sheathed cobbles; and all the other sounds—the double knocks, a frosty far-off voice or two, a bell ringing thinly and softly as if under a sheet of ice—had the same slightly abstracted quality, as if removed by one degree from actuality—as if everything in the world had been insulated by snow. But when at last, pleased, he opened his eyes, and turned them toward the window, to see for himself this long-desired and now so clearly imagined miracle—what he saw instead was brilliant sunlight on a roof; and when, astonished, he jumped out of bed and stared down into the street, expecting to see the cobbles obliterated by the snow, he saw nothing but the bare bright cobbles themselves.

Queer, the effect this extraordinary surprise had had upon him—all the following morning he had kept with him a sense as of snow falling about him, a secret screen of new snow between himself and the world. If he had not dreamed such a thing—and how could he have dreamed it while awake?—how else could one explain it? In any case, the delusion had been so vivid as to affect his entire behavior. He could not now remember whether it was on the first or the second morning—or was it even the third?—that his mother had drawn attention to some oddness in his manner.

"But my darling—" she had said at the breakfast table—"what has come over you? You don't seem to be listening. . . ."

And how often that very thing had happened since!

(Miss Buell was now asking if any one knew the difference between the North Pole and the Magnetic Pole. Deirdre was holding up her flickering brown hand, and he could see the four white dimples that marked the knuckles.)

Perhaps it hadn't been either the second or third morning—or even the fourth or fifth. How could he be sure? How could he be sure just when the delicious *progress* had become clear? Just when it had really *begun?* The intervals weren't very precise. . . . All he now knew was, that at some point or other—perhaps the second day, perhaps the sixth—he had noticed that the presence of the snow was a little more insistent, the sound of it clearer; and, conversely, the sound of the postman's footsteps more indistinct. Not only could he not hear the steps come round the corner, he could not even hear them at the first house. It was below the first house that he heard them; and then, a few days later, it was below the second house that he heard them; and a few days later again, below the third. Gradually, gradually, the snow was becoming heavier, the sound of its seething louder, the cobblestones more and more muffled. When he found, each morning, on going to the window, after the ritual of listening, that the roofs and cobbles were as bare as ever, it made no difference. This was, after all, only what he had expected. It was even what pleased him, what rewarded him: the thing was his own, belonged to no one else. No one else knew about it, not even his mother and father. There, outside, were the bare cobbles; and here, inside, was the snow. Snow growing heavier each day, muffling the world, hiding the ugly, and deadening increasingly—above all—the steps of the postman.

"But my darling—" she had said at the luncheon table—"what has come over you? You don't seem to listen when people speak to you. That's the third time I've asked you to pass your plate. . . ."

How was one to explain this to Mother? or to Father? There was, of course, nothing to be done about it: nothing. All one could do was to laugh embarrassedly, pretend to be a little ashamed, apologize, and take a sudden and somewhat disingenuous interest in what was being done or said. The cat had stayed out all night. He had a curious swelling on his left cheek—perhaps somebody had kicked him, or a stone had struck him. Mrs. Kempton was or was not coming to tea. The house was going to be housecleaned, or "turned out," on Wednesday instead of Friday. A new lamp was provided for his evening work—perhaps it was eyestrain which accounted for this new and so peculiar vagueness of his—Mother was looking at him with amusement as she said this, but with something else as well. A new lamp? A new lamp. Yes, Mother, No, Mother, Yes, Mother. School is going very well. The geometry is very easy. The history is very dull. The geography is very interesting—particularly when it takes one to the North Pole. Why the North Pole? Oh, well, it would be fun to be an explorer. Another Peary or Scott or Shackleton. And then abruptly he found his interest in the talk at an end, stared at the pudding on his plate, listened, waited, and began once more—ah, how heavenly, too, the first beginnings—to hear or feel—for could he actually hear it?—the silent snow, the secret snow.

(Miss Buell was telling them about the search for the Northwest Passage, about Hendrik Hudson, the *Half Moon*.)

This had been, indeed, the only distressing feature of the new experience; the fact that it so increasingly had brought him into a kind of mute misunderstanding, or even conflict, with his father and mother. It was as if he were trying to lead a double life. On the one hand, he had to be Paul Hasleman, and keep up the appearance of being that person—dress, wash, and answer intelligently when spoken to—; on the other, he had to explore this new world which had been opened to him. Nor could there be the slightest doubt—not the slightest—that the new world was the profounder and more wonderful of the two. It was irresistible. It was miraculous. Its beauty was simply beyond anything—beyond speech as beyond thought— utterly incommunicable. But how then, between the two worlds, of which he was thus constantly aware, was he to keep a balance? One must get up, one must go to breakfast, one must talk with Mother, go to school, do one's lessons—and, in all this, try not to appear too much of a fool. But if all the while one was also trying to extract the full deliciousness of another and quite separate existence, one which could not easily (if at all) be spoken of—how was one to manage? How was one to explain? Would it be safe to explain? Would it be absurd? Would it merely mean that he would get into some obscure kind of trouble?

These thoughts came and went, came and went, as softly and secretly as the snow; they were not precisely a disturbance, perhaps they were even a pleasure; he liked to have them; their presence was something almost palpable, something he could stroke with his hand, without closing his eyes, and without ceasing to see Miss Buell and the schoolroom and the globe and the freckles on Deirdre's neck; nevertheless he did in a sense cease to see, or to see the obvious external world, and substituted for this vision the vision of snow, the sound of snow, and the slow, almost soundless, approach of the postman. Yesterday, it had been only at the sixth house that the postman had become audible; the snow was much deeper now, it was falling more swiftly and heavily, the sound of its seething was more distinct, more soothing, more persistent. And this morning, it had been—as nearly as he could figure—just above the seventh house—perhaps only a step or two above: at most, he had heard two or three footsteps before the knock had sounded. . . . And with each such narrowing of the sphere, each nearer approach of the limit at which the postman was first audible, it was odd how sharply was increased the amount of illusion which had to be carried into the ordinary business of daily life. Each day, it was harder to get out of bed, to go to the window, to look out at the—as always—perfectly empty and snowless street.

Each day it was more difficult to go through the perfunctory motions of greeting Mother and Father at breakfast, to reply to their questions, to put his books together and go to school. And at school, how extraordinarily hard to conduct with success simultaneously the public life and the life that was secret! There were times when he longed—positively ached—to tell every one about it—to burst out with it—only to be checked almost at once by a far-off feeling as of some faint absurdity which was inherent in it—but *was* it absurd?— and more importantly by a sense of mysterious power in his very secrecy. Yes: it must be kept secret. That, more and more, became clear. At whatever cost to himself, whatever pain to others—

(Miss Buell looked straight at him, smiling, and said, "Perhaps we'll ask Paul. I'm sure Paul will come out of his daydream long enough to be able to tell us. Won't you, Paul." He rose slowly from his chair, resting one hand on the brightly varnished desk, and deliberately stared through the snow toward the blackboard. It was an effort, but it was amusing to make it. "Yes," he said slowly, "it was what we now call the Hudson River. This he thought to be the Northwest Passage. He was disappointed." He sat down again, and as he did so Deirdre half turned in her chair and gave him a shy smile, of approval and admiration.)

At whatever pain to others.

This part of it was very puzzling, very puzzling. Mother was very nice, and so was Father. Yes, that was all true enough. He wanted to be nice to them, to tell them everything—and yet, was it really wrong of him to want to have a secret place of his own?

At bed-time, the night before, Mother had said, "If this goes on, my lad, we'll have to see a doctor, we will! We can't have our boy—" But what was it she had said? "Live in another world"? "Live so far away"? The word "far" had been in it, he was sure, and then Mother had taken up a magazine again and laughed a little, but with an expression which wasn't mirthful. He had felt sorry for her. . . .

The bell rang for dismissal. The sound came to him through long curved parallels of falling snow. He saw Deirdre rise, and had himself risen almost as soon—but not quite as soon—as she.

II

On the walk homeward, which was timeless, it pleased him to see through the accompaniment, or counterpoint, of snow, the items of mere externality on his way. There were many kinds of brick in the sidewalks, and laid in many kinds of pattern. The garden walls too were various, some of wooden palings, some of plaster, some of stone. Twigs of bushes leaned over the walls: the little hard green winter-buds of lilac, on gray stems, sheathed and fat; other branches very thin and fine and black and dessicated. Dirty sparrows huddled in the bushes, as dull in color as dead fruit left in leafless trees. A single starling creaked on a weather vane. In the gutter, beside a drain, was a scrap of torn and dirty newspaper, caught in a little delta of filth: the word ECZEMA appeared in large capitals, and below it was a letter from Mrs. Amelia D. Cravath, 2100 Pine Street, Fort Worth, Texas, to the effect that after being a sufferer for years she had been cured by Caley's Ointment. In the little delta, beside the fan-shaped and deeply runnelled continent of brown mud, were lost twigs, descended from their parent trees, dead matches, a rusty horse-chestnut burr, a small concentration of eggshell, a streak of yellow sawdust which had been wet and now was dry and congealed, a brown pebble, and a broken feather. Farther on was a cement side-walk, ruled into geometrical parallelograms, with a brass inlay at one end commemorating the contractors who had laid it, and, half-way across, an irregular and random series of dog-tracks, immortal-ized in synthetic stone. He knew these well, and always stepped on them; to cover the little hollows with his own foot had always been a queer pleasure; to-day he did it once more, but perfunctorily and detachedly, all the while thinking of something else. That was a dog, a long time ago, who had made a mistake and walked on the cement while it was still wet. He had probably wagged his tail, but that hadn't been recorded. Now, Paul Hasleman, aged twelve, on his way home from school, crossed the same river, which in the meantime had frozen into rock. Homeward through the snow, the snow falling in bright sunshine. Homeward?

Then came the gateway with the two posts surmounted by egg-shaped stones which had been cunningly balanced on their ends, as if by Columbus, and mortared in the very act of balance: a source of perpetual wonder. On the brick wall just beyond, the letter H had been stenciled, presumably for some purpose. H? H.

The green hydrant, with a little green-painted chain attached to the brass screw-cap.

The elm tree, with the great gray wound in the bark, kidney-shaped, into which he always put his hand—to feel the cold but living wood. The injury, he had been sure, was due to the gnawings of a tethered horse. But now it deserved only a passing palm, a merely tolerant eye. There were more important things. Miracles. Beyond the thoughts of trees, mere elms. Beyond the thoughts of sidewalks, mere stone, mere brick, mere cement. Beyond the thoughts even of his own shoes, which trod these sidewalks obediently, bearing a burden—far above—of elaborate mystery. He watched them. They were not very well polished; he had neglected them, for a very good reason: they were one of the many parts of the increasing difficulty of the daily return to daily life, the morning struggle. To get up, having at last opened one's eyes, to go to the window, and discover no snow, to wash, to dress, to descend the curving stairs to breakfast—

At whatever pain to others, nevertheless, one must persevere in severance, since the incommunicability of the experience demanded it. It was desirable of course to be kind to Mother and Father, especially as they seemed to be worried, but it was also desirable to be resolute. If they should decide—as appeared likely—to consult the doctor, Doctor Howells, and have Paul inspected, his heart listened to through a kind of dictaphone, his lungs, his stomach—well, that was all right. He would go through with it. He would give them answer for question, too—perhaps such answers as they hadn't expected? No. That would never do. For the secret world must, at all costs, be preserved.

The bird-house in the apple tree was empty—it was the wrong time of year for wrens. The little round black door had lost its pleasure. The wrens were enjoying other houses, other nests, remoter trees. But this too was a notion which he only vaguely and grazingly entertained—as if, for the moment, he merely touched an edge of it; there was something further on, which was already assuming a sharper importance; something which already teased at the corners of his eyes, teasing also at the corner of his mind. It was funny to

think that he so wanted this, so awaited it—and yet found himself
enjoying this momentary dalliance with the bird-house, as if for a
quite deliberate postponement and enhancement of the approaching
pleasure. He was aware of his delay, of his smiling and detached and
now almost uncomprehending gaze at the little bird-house; he knew
what he was going to look at next: it was his own little cobbled hill-
street, his own house, the little river at the bottom of the hill, the
grocer's shop with the cardboard man in the window—and now,
thinking of all this, he turned his head, still smiling, and looking
quickly right and left through the snow-laden sunlight.

And the mist of snow, as he had foreseen, was still on it—a ghost
of snow falling in the bright sunlight, softly and steadily floating and
turning and pausing, soundlessly meeting the snow that covered, as
with a transparent mirage, the bare bright cobbles. He loved it—he
stood still and loved it. Its beauty was paralyzing—beyond all words,
all experience, all dream. No fairy-story he had ever read could be
compared with it—none had ever given him this extraordinary com-
bination of ethereal loveliness with a something else, unnameable,
which was just faintly and deliciously terrifying. What was this
thing? As he thought of it, he looked upward toward his own bedroom window, which was open—and it was as if he looked straight
into the room and saw himself lying half awake in his bed. There he
was—at this very instant he was still perhaps actually there—more
truly there than standing here at the edge of the cobbled hill-
street, with one hand lifted to shade his eyes against the snow-sun.
Had he indeed ever left his room, in all this time? since that
very first morning? Was the whole progress still being enacted
there, was it still the same morning, and himself not yet wholly
awake? And even now, had the postman not yet come round the
corner? . . .

This idea amused him, and automatically, as he thought of it, he
turned his head and looked toward the top of the hill. There was, of
course, nothing there—nothing and no one. The street was empty
and quiet. And all the more because of its emptiness it occurred to
him to count the houses—a thing which, oddly enough, he hadn't
before thought of doing. Of course, he had known there weren't many
—many, that is, on his own side of the street, which were the ones
that figured in the postman's progress—but nevertheless it came as

something of a shock to find that there were precisely *six*, above his own house—his own house was the seventh.

Six!

Astonished, he looked at his own house—looked at the door, on which was the number thirteen—and then realized that the whole thing was exactly and logically and absurdly what he ought to have known. Just the same, the realization gave him abruptly, and even a little frighteningly, a sense of hurry. He was being hurried—he was being rushed. For—he knit his brows—he couldn't be mistaken—it was just above the *seventh* house, his *own* house, that the postman had first been audible this very morning. But in that case—in that case— did it mean that to-morrow he would hear nothing? The knock he had heard must have been the knock of their own door. Did it mean —and this was an idea which gave him a really extraordinary feeling of surprise—that he would never hear the postman again?—that to-morrow morning the postman would already have passed the house, in a snow so deep as to render his footsteps completely in- audible? That he would have made his approach down the snow- filled street so soundlessly, so secretly, that he, Paul Hasleman, there lying in bed, would not have waked in time, or waking, would have heard nothing?

But how could that be? Unless even the knocker should be muffled in the snow—frozen tight perhaps? . . . But in that case—

A vague feeling of disappointment came over him; a vague sadness as if he felt himself deprived of something which he had long looked forward to, something much prized. After all this, all this beautiful progress, the slow delicious advance of the postman through the silent and secret snow, the knock creeping closer each day, and the footsteps nearer, the audible compass of the world thus daily narrowed, narrowed, narrowed, as the snow soothingly and beautifully encroached and deepened, after all this, was he to be defrauded of the one thing he had so wanted—to be able to count, as it were, the last two or three solemn footsteps, as they finally approached his own door? Was it all going to happen, at the end, so suddenly? or indeed, had it already happened? with no slow and subtle gradations of menace, in which he could luxuriate?

He gazed upward again, toward his own window which flashed in the sun: and this time almost with a feeling that it would be better if he *were* still in bed, in that room; for in that case this must still be the first morning, and there would be six more mornings to come—or, for that matter, seven or eight or nine—how could he be sure?—or even more.

III

After supper, the inquisition began. He stood before the doctor, under the lamp, and submitted silently to the usual thumpings and tappings.

"Now will you please say 'Ah!'?"

"Ah!"

"Now again please, if you don't mind."

"Ah."

"Say it slowly, and hold it if you can—"

"Ah-h-h-h-h-h—"

"Good."

How silly all this was. As if it had anything to do with his throat! Or his heart or lungs!

Relaxing his mouth, of which the corners, after all this absurd stretching, felt uncomfortable, he avoided the doctor's eyes, and stared toward the fireplace, past his mother's feet (in gray slippers) which projected from the green chair, and his father's feet (in brown slippers) which stood neatly side by side on the hearth rug.

"Hm. There is certainly nothing wrong there . . . ?"

He felt the doctor's eyes fixed upon him, and, as if merely to be polite, returned the look, but with a feeling of justifiable evasiveness.

"Now, young man, tell me—do you feel all right?"

"Yes, sir, quite all right."

"No headaches? no dizziness?"

"No, I don't think so."

"Let me see. Let's get a book, if you don't mind—yes, thank you, that will do splendidly—and now, Paul, if you'll just read it, holding it as you would normally hold it—"

He took the book and read:

"And another praise have I to tell for this the city our mother, the gift of a great god, a glory of the land most high; the might of horses, the might of young horses, the might of the sea. . . . For thou, son of

Cronus, our lord Poseidon, hath throned herein this pride, since in these roads first thou didst show forth the curb that cures the rage of steeds. And the shapely oar, apt to men's hands, hath a wondrous speed on the brine, following the hundred-footed Nereids. . . . O land that art praised above all lands, now is it for thee to make those bright praises seen in deeds."

He stopped, tentatively, and lowered the heavy book.

"No—as I thought—there is certainly no superficial sign of eyestrain."

Silence thronged the room, and he was aware of the focussed scrutiny of the three people who confronted him. . . .

"We could have his eyes examined—but I believe it is something else."

"What could it be?" That was his father's voice.

"It's only this curious absent-mindedness—" This was his mother's voice.

In the presence of the doctor, they both seemed irritatingly apologetic.

"I believe it is something else. Now Paul—I would like very much to ask you a question or two. You will answer them, won't you— you know I'm an old, old friend of yours, eh? That's right! . . ."

His back was thumped twice by the doctor's fat fist—then the doctor was grinning at him with false amiability, while with one fingernail he was scratching the top button of his waistcoat. Beyond the doctor's shoulder was the fire, the fingers of flame making light prestidigitation against the sooty fireback, the soft sound of their random flutter the only sound.

"I would like to know—is there anything that worries you?"

The doctor was again smiling, his eyelids low against the little black pupils, in each of which was a tiny white bead of light. Why answer him? why answer him at all? "At whatever pain to others"— but it was all a nuisance, this necessity for resistance, this necessity for attention: it was as if one had been stood up on a brilliantly lighted stage, under a great round blaze of spotlight; as if one were merely a trained seal, or a performing dog, or a fish, dipped out of an aquarium and held up by the tail. It would serve them right if he were merely to bark or growl. And meanwhile, to miss these last few precious hours, these hours of which each minute was more

beautiful than the last, more menacing—! He still looked, as if from
a great distance, at the beads of light in the doctor's eyes, at the fixed
false smile, and then, beyond, once more at his mother's slippers, his
father's slippers, the soft flutter of the fire. Even here, even amongst
these hostile presences, and in this arranged light, he could see the
snow, he could hear it—it was in the corners of the room, where the
shadow was deepest, under the sofa, behind the half-opened door
which led to the dining room. It was gentler here, softer, its seethe
the quietest of whispers, as if, in deference to a drawing-room, it had
quite deliberately put on its "manners"; it kept itself out of sight, obliterated itself, but distinctly with an air of saying, "Ah, but just
wait! Wait till we are alone together! Then I will begin to tell you
something new! Something white! something cold! something
sleepy! something of cease, and peace, and the long bright curve of
space! Tell them to go away. Banish them. Refuse to speak. Leave
them, go upstairs to your room, turn out the light and get into bed—
I will go with you, I will be waiting for you, I will tell you a better
story than Little Kay of the Skates, or The Snow Ghost—I will
surround your bed, I will close the windows, pile a deep drift against
the door, so that none will ever again be able to enter. Speak to
them! . . ." It seemed as if the little hissing voice came from a slow
white spiral of falling flakes in the corner by the front window—but
he could not be sure. He felt himself smiling, then, and said to the
doctor, but without looking at him, looking beyond him still—

"Oh no, I think not—"

"But are you sure, my boy?"

His father's voice came softly and coldly then—the familiar voice
of silken warning.

"You needn't answer at once, Paul—remember we're trying to
help you—think it over and be quite sure, won't you?"

He felt himself smiling again, at the notion of being quite sure.
What a joke! As if he weren't so sure that reassurance was no longer
necessary, and all this cross-examination a ridiculous farce, a grotesque parody! What could they know about it? these gross intelli-
gences, these humdrum minds so bound to the usual, the ordinary?
Impossible to tell them about it! Why, even now, even now, with the
proof so abundant, so formidable, so imminent, so appallingly
present here in this very room, could they believe it?—could even

his mother believe it? No—it was only too plain that if anything were said about it, the merest hint given, they would be incredulous —they would laugh—they would say "Absurd!"—think things about him which weren't true. . . .

"Why no, I'm not worried—why should I be?"

He looked then straight at the doctor's low-lidded eyes, looked from one of them to the other, from one bead of light to the other, and gave a little laugh.

The doctor seemed to be disconcerted by this. He drew back in his chair, resting a fat white hand on either knee. The smile faded slowly from his face.

"Well, Paul!" he said, and paused gravely, "I'm afraid you don't take this quite seriously enough. I think you perhaps don't quite realize—don't quite realize—" He took a deep quick breath, and turned, as if helplessly, at a loss for words, to the others. But Mother and Father were both silent—no help was forthcoming.

"You must surely know, be aware, that you have not been quite yourself, of late? don't you know that? . . ."

It was amusing to watch the doctor's renewed attempt at a smile, a queer disorganized look, as of confidential embarrassment.

"I feel all right, sir," he said, and again gave the little laugh.

"And we're trying to help you." The doctor's tone sharpened.

"Yes sir, I know. But why? I'm all right. I'm just *thinking*, that's all."

His mother made a quick movement forward, resting a hand on the back of the doctor's chair.

"Thinking?" she said. "But my dear, about what?"

This was a direct challenge—and would have to be directly met. But before he met it, he looked again into the corner by the door, as if for reassurance. He smiled again at what he saw, at what he heard. The little spiral was still there, still softly whirling, like the ghost of a white kitten chasing the ghost of a white tail, and making as it did so the faintest of whispers. It was all right! If only he could remain firm, everything was going to be all right.

"Oh, about anything, about nothing—*you* know the way you do!"

"You mean—daydreaming?"

"Oh, no—thinking!"

"But thinking about *what?*"

"Anything."

He laughed a third time—but this time, happening to glance upward toward his mother's face, he was appalled at the effect his laughter seemed to have upon her. Her mouth had opened in an expression of horror. . . . This was too bad! Unfortunate! He had known it would cause pain, of course—but he hadn't expected it to be quite so bad as this. Perhaps—perhaps if he just gave them a tiny gleaming hint—?

"About the snow," he said.

"What on earth!" This was his father's voice. The brown slippers came a step nearer on the hearth-rug.

"But my dear, what do you mean?" This was his mother's voice. The doctor merely stared.

"Just *snow*, that's all. I like to think about it."

"Tell us about it, my boy."

"But that's all it is. There's nothing to tell. *You* know what snow is?"

This he said almost angrily, for he felt that they were trying to corner him. He turned sideways so as no longer to face the doctor, and the better to see the inch of blackness between the window-sill and the lowered curtain—the cold inch of beckoning and delicious night. At once he felt better, more assured.

"Mother—can I go to bed, now, please? I've got a headache."

"But I thought you said—"

"It's just come. It's all these questions—! Can I, mother?"

"You can go as soon as the doctor has finished."

"Don't you think this thing ought to be gone into thoroughly, and *now?*" This was Father's voice. The brown slippers again came a step nearer, the voice was the well-known "punishment" voice, resonant and cruel.

"Oh, what's the use, Norman—"

Quite suddenly, every one was silent. And without precisely facing them, nevertheless he was aware that all three of them were watching him with an extraordinary intensity—staring hard at him —as if he had done something monstrous, or was himself some kind of monster. He could hear the soft irregular flutter of the flames; the cluck-click-cluck-click of the clock; far and faint, two sudden spurts of laughter from the kitchen, as quickly cut off as begun; a murmur of water in the pipes; and then, the silence seemed to deepen, to spread out, to become world-long and world-wide, to become timeless and shapeless, and to center inevitably and rightly, with a slow and sleepy but enormous concentration of all power, on the beginning of a new sound. What this new sound was going to be, he knew perfectly well. It might begin with a hiss, but it would end with a roar—there was no time to lose—he must escape. It mustn't happen here—

Without another word, he turned and ran up the stairs.

IV

Not a moment too soon. The darkness was coming in long white waves. A prolonged sibilance filled the night—a great seamless seethe of wild influence went abruptly across it—a cold low humming shook the windows. He shut the door and flung off his clothes in the dark. The bare black floor was like a little raft tossed in waves of snow, almost overwhelmed, washed under whitely, up again, smothered in curled billows of feather. The snow was laughing: it spoke from all sides at once: it pressed closer to him as he ran and jumped exulting into his bed.

"Listen to us!" it said. "Listen! We have come to tell you the story we told you about. You remember? Lie down. Shut your eyes, now—you will no longer see much—in this white darkness who could see, or want to see? We will take the place of everything. . . . Listen—"

A beautiful varying dance of snow began at the front of the room, came forward and then retreated, flattened out toward the floor, then rose fountain-like to the ceiling, swayed, recruited itself from a new stream of flakes which poured laughing in through the humming window, advanced again, lifted long white arms. It said peace, it said remoteness, it said cold—it said—

But then a gash of horrible light fell brutally across the room from the opening door—the snow drew back hissing—something alien had come into the room—something hostile. This thing rushed at him, clutched at him, shook him—and he was not merely horrified, he was filled with such a loathing as he had never known. What was this? this cruel disturbance? this act of anger and hate? It was as if

he had to reach up a hand toward another world for any understanding of it—an effort of which he was only barely capable. But of
that other world he still remembered just enough to know the
exorcising words. They tore themselves from his other life suddenly—
    "Mother! Mother! Go away! I hate you!"
    And with that effort, everything was solved, everything became all
right: the seamless hiss advanced once more, the long white waver-
ing lines rose and fell like enormous whispering sea-waves, the whisper becoming louder, the laughter more numerous.
    "Listen!" it said. "We'll tell you the last, the most beautiful and
secret story—shut your eyes—it is a very small story—a story that
gets smaller and smaller—it comes inward instead of opening like a
flower—it is a flower becoming a seed—a little cold seed—do you
hear? we are leaning closer to you—"
    The hiss was now becoming a roar—the whole world was a vast
moving screen of snow—but even now it said peace, it said remoteness, it said cold, it said sleep.

Paranoid Reactions

The subject of the paranoid conditions can best be introduced by quoting the words of Harry Stack Sullivan:

> Now, at the beginning of this transformation [of personality], the only impression one has is of a person in the grip of horror, of uncanny devastation which makes everyone threatening beyond belief. But if the person is not utterly crushed by the process, he can begin rather rapidly to elaborate personifications of evil creatures . . . the beginning phase of the paranoid state has a curious relationship with what I call moments of "Illumination" . . .The beginning of this process comes literally as a sudden insight into some suspicion and it comes with a blaze of horror.[1]

As Sullivan describes him, the paranoid psychotic, who usually shows a reasonable ability for acceptable intellectual and emotional responsiveness, lives in the tense grip of apprehension and uncertainty until he suddenly comes to a realization about the "true" meaning of the events taking place around him, a realization which "explains" the prodromal sensations of agitation and distress. The delusions of these individuals are often highly elaborated and organized and are, almost invariably, of a persecutory nature—*they* have it in for him.

Hindele, in Singer's "The Black Wedding," distressed and unhappy about her arranged marriage suddenly "understands" her state of fear and trembling when she comes to "see" her husband as a demon and the wedding as a "satanic hoax." Ivan, the tense and

[1] H. S. Sullivan. *The Interpersonal Theory of Psychiatry*. New York: Norton, 1953, pp. 361-362.

gloomy hero of Chekhov's "Ward No. 6," passes through a cycle from a vague feeling of suspiciousness and unrest to an "illumination" and on to a powerful experience of paranoid anxiety—" . . . and it seemed to him that the scattered violences of the whole world had united and were chasing him through the town."

Isaac Bashevis Singer

THE BLACK WEDDING

From the time that the marriage negotiations started until the wedding, Hindele did not stop crying. She cried at the celebration of the writing of the marriage contract, she cried when the tailors fitted her trousseau, she cried when she was led to the ritual bath. There she was ashamed to undress for the immersion before the attendants and the other women, and they had to tear off her stays and her underpants. She would not let them remove from her neck the little bag which contained an amber charm and the tooth of a wolf. She was afraid to immerse herself in the water. The two attendants who led her into the bath, held her tightly by her wrists and she trembled like the sacrificial chicken the day before Yom Kippur. When Reb Simon lifted the veil from Hindele's face after the wedding, she saw him for the first time. He was a tall man with a broad fur hat, a pitch-black disheveled beard, wild eyes, a broad nose, thick lips, and a long moustache. He gazed at her like an animal. He breathed noisily and smelled of perspiration. Clusters of hair grew out of his nostrils and ears. His hands, too, had a growth of hair as thick as fur. The moment Hindele saw him she knew what she had suspected long before—that her bridegroom was a demon and that the wedding was nothing but black magic, a satanic hoax. She wanted to call out "Hear, O Israel" but she remembered her

Isaac Bashevis Singer, from "The Black Wedding," in The Spinoza of Market Street, *tr. by Martha Glicklich. New York: Noonday Press, 1960. This selection is a single paragraph from a longer story.*

father's deathbed admonition to keep silent. How strange that the moment Hindele understood that her husband was an evil spirit, she could immediately discern what was true and what was false. Although she saw herself sitting in her mother's living room, she knew she was really in a forest. It appeared to be light, but she knew it was dark. She was surrounded by Chassidim with fur hats and satin gabardines, as well as by women who wore silk bonnets and velvet capes, but she knew it was all imaginary and that the fancy garments hid heads grown with elf-locks, goose-feet, unhuman navels, long snouts. The sashes of the young men were snakes in reality, their sable hats were actually hedgehogs, their beards clusters of worms. The men spoke Yiddish and sang familiar songs, but the noise they made was really the bellowing of oxen, the hissing of vipers, the howling of wolves. The musicians had tails, and horns grew from their heads. The maids who attended Hindele had canine paws, hoofs of calves, snouts of pigs. The wedding jester was all beard and tongue. The so-called relatives on the groom's side were lions, bears, boars. It was raining in the forest and a wind was blowing. It thundered and flashed lightning. Alas, this was not a human wedding, but a Black Wedding. Hindele knew, from reading holy books, that demons sometimes married human virgins whom they later carried away behind the black mountains to cohabit with them and sire their children. There was only one thing to do in such a case— not to comply with them, never willingly submit to them, to let them get everything by force as one kind word spoken to Satan is equivalent to sacrificing to the idols. Hindele remembered the story of Joseph De La Rinah and the misfortune that befell him when he felt sorry for the evil one and gave him a pinch of tobacco.

Anton Chekhov

WARD NO. 6

I

At the side of the hospital yard stands a large wing, nearly sur-rounded by a forest of burdocks, nettles, and wild hemp. The roof is red, the chimney is on the point of tumbling, the steps are rotten and overgrown with grass, and of the plaster only traces remain. The front gazes at the hospital, the back looks into the fields, from which it is separated only by a grey, spiked fence. The spikes with their sharp points sticking upwards, the fence, the wing itself, have that melancholy, God-forsaken air which is seen only in hospitals and prisons.

If you are not afraid of being stung by nettles, come along the narrow path, and see what is going on inside. Open the hall-door and enter the hall. Here, against the walls nad around the stove, are heaped whole mountains of rubbish. Mattresses, old tattered dress-ing-gowns, trousers, blue-striped shirts, worn-out footgear, all good-for-nothing, lie in tangled and crushed heaps, rot, and exhale a suffocating smell.

On the top of this rubbish heap, pipe eternally in mouth, lies the watchman Nikita, an old soldier. His face is coarse and drink-sodden, his hanging eye-brows give him the appearance of a sheep-dog, he is

Anton Chekhov, "Ward No. 6," in The Black Monk and Other Stories, *tr. by R. E. C. Long. London: Duckworth, 1903.*

small and sinewy, but his carriage is impressive and his fists are strong. He belongs to that class of simple, expeditious, positive, and dull persons, who above all things in the world worship order, and find in this a justification of their existence. He beats his charges in the face, in the chest, in the back, in short, wherever his fists chance to strike; and he is convinced that without this beating there would be no order in the universe.

After you pass through Nikita's hall, you enter the large, roomy dormitory which takes up the rest of the wing. In this room the walls are painted a dirty blue, the ceiling is black with soot like the ceiling of a chimneyless hut; it is plain that in winter the stove smokes, and the air is suffocating. The windows are disfigured with iron bars, the floor is damp and splintered, there is a smell of sour cabbage, a smell of unsnuffed wicks, a smell of bugs and ammonia. And at the moment of entry all these smells produce upon you the impression that you have entered a cage of wild beasts.

Around the room stand beds, screwed to the floor. Sitting or lying on them, dressed in blue dressing-gowns, and wearing nightcaps after the manner of our forefathers, are men. It is the lunatic asylum, and these are the lunatics.

There are only five patients. One is of noble birth, the others are men of lower origin. The nearest to the door, a tall, thin man of the petty trading class, looks fixedly at one point. He has a red moustache and tear-stained eyes, and supports his head on one hand. In the books of the asylum his complaint is described as hypochondria; in reality, he is suffering from progressive paralysis. Day and night he mourns, shakes his head, sighs, and smiles bitterly. In conversation he seldom joins, and usually refuses to answer questions. He eats and drinks mechanically. Judged by his emaciation, his flushed cheeks, and his painful, hacking cough, he is wasting away from consumption.

Beside him is a little, active old man with a pointed beard, and the black, fuzzy hair of a negro. He spends all day in walking from window to window, or sitting on his bed, with legs doubled underneath him as if he were a Turk. He is as tireless as a bullfinch, and all day chirrups, titters, and sings in a low voice. His childish gaiety and lively character are shown also at night, when he rises to "pray to God," that is, to beat his breast with his clenched fists, and pick at the doors. This is Moséika, a Jew and an idiot. He went out of his mind twenty years ago when his cap factory was destroyed by fire. Of all the captives in Ward No. 6, he alone has permission to leave the asylum, and he is even allowed to wander about the yard and the streets. This privilege, which he has enjoyed for many years, was probably accorded to him as the oldest inmate of the asylum, and as a quiet, harmless fool, the jester of the town, who may be seen in the streets surrounded by dogs and little boys. Wrapped in his old dressing-gown, with a ridiculous nightcap and slippers, sometimes barefooted, and generally without his trousers, he walks the streets, stopping at doorways and entering small shops to beg for kopecks. Sometimes he is given *kvas*, sometimes bread, sometimes a kopeck, so that he returns to the ward wealthy and sated. But all that he brings home is taken by Nikita for his own particular benefit. The old soldier does this roughly and angrily, turning out the Jew's pockets, calling God to witness that he will never allow him outside the asylum again, and swearing that to him disorder is the most detestable thing in the world.

Moséika loves to make himself useful to others. He fetches water for his companions, tucks them in when they go to bed, promises to bring each a kopeck when he next returns from the town, and to make them new caps. He feeds with a spoon his paralytic neighbour on the left; and all this he does, not out of sympathy for others or for considerations of humanity, but from a love of imitation, and in a sort of involuntary subjection to his neighbour on the right, Iván Gromof.

Iván Dmítritch Gromof is a man of thirty-three years of age. He is a noble by birth, and has been an usher in the law courts, and a government secretary; but now he suffers from the mania of persecution. He lies upon his bed twisted into a lump resembling a roll of bread, or marches from corner to corner for the sake of motion. He is always in a state of excitement and agitation; and seems strained by some dull, indefinable expectation. It needs but the slightest rustle in the hall, the slightest noise in the yard, to make him raise his head and listen intently. Is it for him they are coming? Are they searching for him? And his face immediately takes on an expression of restlessness and repulsion.

There is something attractive about his broad, high cheek-boned face, which reflects, as a mirror, the tortured wrestlings and eternal terror of his mind. His grimaces are strange and sickly; but the delicate lines engraven on his face by sincere suffering express reason and intelligence, and his eyes burn with a healthy and passionate glow. There is something attractive also in his character, in his politeness, his attentiveness, and in the singular delicacy of his bearing towards everyone except Nikita. If his neighbour drops a spoon or a button he jumps immediately out of bed and picks it up. When he wakes he invariably says, "Good morning!" to his companions; and every evening on going to bed wishes them "good night!"

But madness shows itself in other things besides his grimaces and continual mental tension. In the evening he wraps himself in his dressing-gown, and, trembling all over, and chattering his teeth, he walks from corner to corner, and in between the beds. He seems to be in a state of fever. From his sudden stoppages and strange looks at his fellow-prisoners it is plain that he has something very serious to say; but, no doubt, remembering that they will neither listen nor understand, he says nothing, shakes his head impatiently, and continues his walk. But at last the desire to speak conquers all other considerations, and he gives way, and speaks passionately. His words are incoherent, gusty, and delirious; he cannot always be understood; but the sound of his voice expresses some exceptional goodness. In every word you hear the madman and the man. He speaks of human baseness, of violence trampling over truth, of the beautiful life on earth that is to come, and of the barred windows which remind him every moment of the folly and cruelty of the strong. And he hums medleys of old but forgotten songs.

II

Fifteen years before, in his own house, in the best street in the town, lived an official named Gromof—a solid and prosperous man. Gromof had two sons, Sergéi and Iván. Sergéi, when a student in the fourth class, was seized with consumption and died; and his death was the first of a series of misfortunes which overtook the Gromofs. A week after Sergéi's death his old father was tried for forgery and misappropriation of public moneys, and soon afterwards died of typhus in the prison infirmary. His house and all his belongings were sold by auction, and Iván Dmítritch and his mother remained without a penny.

When his father was alive, Iván Dmítritch studied at St. Petersburg University, received an allowance of sixty or seventy roubles a month, and had no idea of the meaning of poverty. Now he had to change his whole life. From early morning till late at night he gave cheap lessons to students and copied documents, yet starved, for all his earnings went to support his mother. The life was impossible, and Iván Dmítritch ruined his health and spirits, threw up his university studies, and returned home. Through interest he obtained an appointment as usher in the district school; but he was disliked by his colleagues, failed to get on with the pupils, and gave up the post. His mother died. For six months he lived without resources, eating black bread and drinking water, until at last he obtained an appointment as Usher of the Court. This duty he fulfilled until he was discharged owing to illness.

Never, even in his student days, had he had the appearance of a strong man. He was pale, thin, and sensitive to cold; he ate little and slept badly. A single glass of wine made him giddy and sent him into hysterics. His disposition impelled him to seek companionship, but thanks to his irritable and suspicious character he never became intimate with anyone, and had no friends. Of his fellow-citizens he always spoke with contempt, condemning as disgusting and repulsive their gross ignorance and torpid, animal life. He spoke in a tenor voice, loudly and passionately, and always seemed to be in a sincere state of indignation, excitement, or rapture. However he began a conversation, it ended always in one way—in a lament that the town was stifling and tiresome, that its people had no high interests, but led a dull, unmeaning life, varied only by violence, coarse debauchery and hypocrisy; that scoundrels were fed and clothed while honest men ate crusts; that the town was crying out for schools, honest newspapers, a theatre, public lectures, a union of intellectual forces; and that the time had come for the townspeople to awaken to, and be shocked at, the state of affairs. In his judgments of men he laid on his colours thickly, using only white and black, and recognising no gradations; for him humanity was divided into two sections, honest men and rogues—there was nothing between. Of woman and woman's love he spoke passionately and with rapture. But he had never been in love.

In the town, notwithstanding his nervous character and censorious temper, he was loved, and called caressingly "Vanya." His innate delicacy, his attentiveness, his neatness, his moral purity, his worn coat, his sickly appearance, the misfortunes of his family, inspired in all feelings of warmth and compassion. Besides, he was educated and well-read; in the opinion of the townsmen he knew everything; and occupied among them the place of a walking reference-book. He read much. He would sit for hours at the club, pluck nervously at his beard, and turn over the pages of books and magazines—by his face it might be seen that he was not reading but devouring. Yet reading was apparently merely one of his nervous habits, for with equal avidity he read everything that fell into his hands, even old newspapers and calendars. At home he always read, lying down.

III

One autumn morning, Iván Dmítritch, with the collar of his coat turned up, trudged through the mud to the house of a certain tradesman to receive money due on a writ of execution. As always in the morning, he was in a gloomy mood. Passing through a lane, he met two convicts in chains and with them four warders armed with rifles. Iván Dmítritch had often met convicts before, and they had awakened in him a feeling of sympathy and confusion. But this meeting produced upon him an unusual impression. It suddenly occurred to him that he too might be shackled and driven through the mud to prison. Having finished his work, he was returning home when he met a police-inspector, an acquaintance, who greeted him and walked with him a few yards down the street. This seemed to him for some reason suspicious. At home visions of convicts and of soldiers armed with rifles haunted him all day, and an inexplicable spiritual dread prevented him from reading or concentrating his mind. In the evening he sat without a fire, and lay awake all night thinking how he also might be arrested, manacled, and flung into prison. He knew that he had committed no crime, and was quite confident that he would never commit murder, arson, or robbery; but then, he remembered, how easy it was to commit a crime by accident or involuntarily, and how common were convictions on false evidence and owing to judicial errors! And in the present state of human affairs how probable, how little to be wondered at, were judicial errors! Men who witness the sufferings of others only from a professional standpoint; for instance, judges, policemen, doctors, became hardened to such a degree that even if they wished otherwise they could not resist the habit of treating accused persons formally; they got to resemble those peasants who kill sheep and calves in their back-yards without even noticing the blood. In view of the soulless relationship to human personality which everywhere obtains, all that a judge thinks of is the observance of certain formalities, and then all is over, and an innocent man perhaps deprived of his civil rights or sent to the galleys. Who indeed would expect justice or intercession in this dirty, sleepy little town, two hundred versts from the nearest railway? And indeed was it not ridiculous to expect justice when society regards every form of violence as rational, expedient, and necessary; and when an act of common mercy such as the acquittal of an accused man calls forth an explosion of unsatisfied vindictiveness!

Next morning Iván Dmítritch awoke in terror with drops of cold sweat on his forehead. He felt convinced that he might be arrested at any moment. That the evening's gloomy thoughts had haunted him so persistently, he concluded, must mean that there was some ground for his apprehensions. Could such thoughts come into his head without cause?

A policeman walked slowly past the window; that must mean something. Two men in plain clothes stopped outside the gate, and stood without saying a word. Why were they silent?

For a time, Iván Dmítritch spent his days and nights in torture. Every man who passed the window or entered the yard was a spy or detective. Every day at twelve o'clock the Chief Constable drove through the street on his way from his suburban house to the Department of Police, and every day it seemed to Iván Dmítritch that the Constable was driving with unaccustomed haste, and that there was a peculiar expression on his face; he was going, in short, to announce that a great criminal had appeared in the town. Iván Dmítritch shuddered at every sound, trembled at every knock at the yard-gate, and was in torment when any strange man visited his landlady. When he met a gendarme in the street, he smiled, whistled, and tried to assume an indifferent air. For whole nights, expecting arrest, he never closed his eyes, but snored carefully so that his landlady might think he was asleep; for if a man did not sleep at night it meant that he was tormented by the gnawings of conscience, and that might be taken as a clue. Reality and healthy reasoning convinced him that his fears were absurd and psychopathic, and that, regarded from a broad standpoint, there was nothing very terrible in arrest and imprisonment for a man whose conscience was clean. But the more consistently and logically he reasoned the stronger grew his spiritual torture; his efforts reminded him of the efforts of a pioneer to hack a path through virgin forest, the harder he worked with the hatchet the thicker and stronger became the undergrowth. So in the end, seeing that his efforts were useless, he ceased to struggle, and gave himself up to terror and despair.

He avoided others and became more and more solitary in his habits. His duties had always been detestable, now they became intolerable. He imagined that someone would hide money in his pockets and then denounce him for taking bribes, that he would make mistakes in official documents which were equivalent to forgery, or that he would lose the money entrusted to him. Never was his mind so supple and ingenious as when he was engaged in inventing various reasons for fearing for his freedom and honour. On the other hand, his interest in the outside world decreased correspondingly, he lost his passion for books, and his memory daily betrayed him.

Next spring when the snow had melted, the semidecomposed corpses of an old woman and a boy, marked with indications of violence, were found in a ravine beside the graveyard. The townspeople talked of nothing but the discovery and the problem: who were the unknown murderers? In order to avert suspicion, Iván Dmítritch walked about the streets and smiled; and when he met his acquaintances, first grew pale and then blushed, and declared vehemently that there was no more detestable crime than the killing of the weak and defenceless. But this pretence soon exhausted him, and after consideration he decided that the best thing he could do was to hide in his landlady's cellar. In the cellar therefore, chilled to the bone, he remained all day, all next night, and yet another day, after which, waiting until it was dark, he crept secretly back to his room. Till daylight he stood motionless in the middle of the room, and listened. At sunrise a number of artisans rang at the gate. Iván Dmítritch knew very well that they had come to put up a new stove in the kitchen; but his terror suggested that they were constables in disguise. He crept quietly out of his room, and overcome by panic, without cap or coat, fled down the street. Behind him ran barking dogs, a woman called after him, in his ears the wind whistled, and it seemed to him that the scattered violences of the whole world had united and were chasing him through the town.

He was captured and brought home. His landlady sent for a doctor. Doctor Andréi Yéfimitch Rágin, of whom we shall hear again, prescribed cold compresses for his head, ordered him to take drops of bay rum, and went away saying that he would come no more, as it was not right to prevent people going out of their minds. So, as there were no means of treating him at home, Iván Dmítritch was sent to hospital, and put into the ward for sick men. He did not sleep at night, was unruly, and disturbed his neighbours, so that soon, by arrangement with Doctor Andréi Yéfimitch, he was transferred to Ward No. 6.

Before a year had passed, the townspeople had quite forgotten Iván Dmítritch; and his books, piled up in a sledge by his landlady and covered with a curtain, were torn to pieces by children.

Affective Reactions

Affective psychotic disorders include the various forms of severe depressive reactions as well as the conditions called mania or acute excitement. All of these are severe disturbances of mood, grotesque exaggerations of the normal feeling states of sorrow and elation, whose symptom pictures had already been delineated in ancient times. If there are periodic attacks of extreme depression and elation, the disorder is called manic-depressive psychosis.

The chief characteristic of these disturbances, marking them off from the neurotic depressions, is their extremity. In the psychotic depressive syndrome, exemplified by Amalia in Svevo's *As a Man Grows Older*, the individual retreats into delusional thinking marked by themes of sin and guilt, often with a sexual coloring. Throughout the novel, Amalia has suffered an unspoken and unrequited love for Stefano Balli, her brother Emilio's friend. The final realization that all hopes for such a relationship have been shattered intensifies her grief beyond endurance, and she lapses into a delirious psychotic state. Her syndrome matches very well the triad of symptoms of this type of disorder outlined by Arieti[1]; (1) a pervasive feeling of melancholia, (2) disordered thought processes marked by retardation in thinking and unusual content, and (3) psychomotor retardation, a severe slowing down in activity with developing listless indifference.

---

[1] S. Arieti. Manic-depressive psychosis. In S. Arieti (ed.), *American Handbook of Psychiatry*. New York: Basic Books, 1959, 2 vols., pp. 419-454.

AS A MAN GROWS OLDER

He had just shut the door of his flat behind him and was standing hat in hand in the dining-room, uncertain what to do next, and wondering whether he could after all face an hour of boredom in his sister's mute society. Suddenly there came from Amalia's room the sound of two or three unintelligible words, and finally a whole phrase: "Get away, you ugly brute!" He shuddered. Her voice was so changed by fatigue or emotion that it resembled his sister's only as an inarticulate shout proceeding from the throat can resemble the modulated speaking voice. Was she asleep at this hour and dreaming by day?

He opened the door noiselessly, and a sight presented itself to his eyes which till his dying day he could never forget. For ever afterwards one or other of the details of that scene had only to strike his senses for him to recall the whole of it immediately and to feel again the appalling horror of it. Some peasants were passing in a road near by, and for ever afterwards the monotonous air they were singing at that moment brought tears to Emilio's eyes. All the sounds which reached him were monotonous, without warmth or sense. In a neighbouring flat someone who could not play at all was strumming a vulgar waltz. Played like that the waltz sounded to him like a funeral march—how often it recurred to him afterwards! Even the

Italo Svevo [pseud], from As a Man Grows Older, tr. by *Beryl de Zoete. New York: New Directions, 1949 [?].*

cheerful day outside became sad for him. It was not long after midday and a dazzling sunlight was reflected from the windows of the
opposite house into the lonely room. Yet his memory of that moment
was always associated with a sensation of darkness and of frightful
cold.

Amalia's clothes lay scattered all over the floor and a skirt prevented him from opening the door completely; there were a few garments under the bed, her bodice was shut between the window-
panes, and her boots had been arranged with evident care in the
middle of the table.

Amalia was sitting on the edge of the bed, clothed only in a short
chemise. She had not noticed her brother's entry, and continued
gently to pass her hands up and down her legs, which were as thin as
spindles. Emilio was surprised and shocked to see that her naked
body resembled that of an ill-nourished child.

He did not realise at first that she was delirious. He did not see that
she was physically worn out; he attributed her noisy breathing and
the difficulty she had in drawing each breath to the tiring position
she was sitting in. His first feeling was of anger; he had hardly
escaped from Angiolina before he found this other woman ready to
annoy him and cause him fresh anxiety. "Amalia! What are you
doing?" he said reprovingly.

She did not hear him, though she seemed to be conscious of the
sounds of the waltz, for she marked its rhythm with her hands as she
continued to pass them up and down her legs.

"Amalia!" he repeated in a faint voice, overwhelmed by this
obvious proof that she was delirious. He put his hand on her shoulder. Then she turned. She looked first at the hand whose touch she
had felt, then she looked him in the face; but there was no recognition in her eyes, only a feverish glitter and the effort to see. Her
cheeks were flaming, and her lips purple and dry and shapeless like
an old wound which refuses to heal. Her eye passed to the window
flooded in sunlight but, hurt perhaps by the glare, returned at once
to her naked legs which she continued to gaze at with curious in-
tentness.

"Oh Amalia!" he cried, letting all his horror find vent in that one
cry which he hoped might recall her to herself. A weak man dreads
delirium and insanity as if they were contagious diseases; Emilio's

loathing was such that he had to put great restraint upon himself in order not to fly from the room. Overcoming with an effort his violent repulsion, he again touched his sister's shoulder and cried: "Amalia! Amalia!" It was a call for help.

It was a slight relief to him to notice that she had heard him. She looked at him again, thoughtfully, as if she were trying to understand the meaning of those cries and of the repeated pressure on her shoulder. She touched her chest as if she had suddenly become conscious of the weight upon it which tormented her. Then, forgetting Emilio and her own exhaustion, she shouted again: "Oh, still those horrible creatures!" and there was a break in her voice as if she were going to burst out crying. She rubbed her legs vigorously with both her hands; then bent down with a swift movement as if she were about to surprise an animal in the act of escaping. She seized one of her toes in her right hand and covered it over with her left, then carefully raised both her closed hands as if she were holding something in them. When she saw they were empty she examined them several times, then returned to her foot, ready to stoop down again and renew her strange chase.

A shivering attack reminded Emilio that he ought to induce her to get into bed. He approached her, horrified at the thought of having perhaps to resort to force. His task was however quite easy, for she obeyed the first firm pressure of his hand; she lifted one leg after the other on to the bed, without any shame, and allowed him to pull the bedclothes over her. But she showed an inexplicable reluctance to lie down altogether, and remained leaning on one elbow. Very soon, however, she could no longer hold out in that position, and abandoned herself on the pillow, uttering for the first time an intelligible sound of grief. "Oh, my God! my God!"

"But what has happened to you?" asked Emilio who, at the sound of that one sensible cry, thought that he could talk to her like a reasonable person. She made no reply, for she was intent on discovering what it was that still went on tormenting her, even under the bedclothes. She hunched herself all up together, sought out her legs with her hands, and in the deep plot she was evidently meditating against the things or creatures which tormented her, she even contrived to make her breathing less noisy. Then she drew up her hands again and gazed at them in incredulous surprise when she found them empty. She lay for a while beneath the sheets in a state of such distress that she seemed even to forget her terrible bodily fatigue.

"Are you better?" Emilio asked, in a tone of entreaty. He wanted to console himself by the sound of his own voice, which he modulated softly in an effort to forget his recent dread that he might have to restrain her by violecne. He bent over her, so that she might hear him better.

She lay looking at him for a long time, while her quick, feeble breath rose towards him. She recognised him; the warmth of the bed seemed to have revived her senses. However far she wandered afterwards in her delirium, he never forgot that she had recognised him. She was evidently getting better. "Now let us leave this house," she said, pronouncing each syllable with care. She stretched out a leg as if she were meditating getting out of bed, but when he restrained her, with perhaps unnecessary force, she at once resigned herself and forgot what it was which had prompted her to the act.

She repeated it again soon afterwards, but without the same energy; she seemed to remember that she had been ordered to lie down, and not to get out of bed. Now she was speaking again. She thought they had changed houses and that there was a great deal to do, that she would have to work desperately to put it all in order. "My God! how dirty it all is here. I knew it was, but you would come to it. And now? Aren't we going away?"

He tried to calm her by playing up to her fancy. He caressed her gently, saying that it didn't look to him so dirty, and that now they were in the house they would do better to stay there.

Amalia listened to all he had to say, but she seemed also to be listening inwardly to other words beside his; then she said: "If you want it I must do it. We will stay here then, but . . . so much dirt . . ." Two tears flowed down her cheeks which had been dry till that moment; they rolled like two pearls down her flaming cheeks.

Soon after she forgot that grievance, but her delirium soon produced another source of distress. She had been out fishing, and could not catch any fish: "I can't understand! What is the good of going out fishing if there are not any fish? One has to go such a long, long way, and it is so cold." The others had taken all the fish and there were none left for them. All her grief and fatigue now seemed to be due to that fact. Her fevered words, to which her exhaustion gave a kind of tired rhythm, were continually interrupted by some sound of distress.

He had ceased to pay any attention to her; he must find some way out of the situation, he must devise some means of fetching a doctor. Every idea which his despair suggested to him was examined in turn, as if it would have been possible to act on them. He looked round to see if he could find a cord to bind the sick woman to the bed and leave her alone; he took a step towards the window, to call for help from there, and at last, forgetting that it was impossible to make himself intelligible to Amalia, he began talking to her, trying to get her to promise to stay quiet during his absence. Patting the bed-clothes gently down on her shoulders to show her that she was to stay in bed, he said: "Will you stay like that, Amalia? Promise me you will!"

But now she was talking about clothes. They had enough to last a year, so they would not have to spend anything on them for a whole year. "We are not rich, but we have everything we need—everything." Signora Birlini might look down on them, because she was better off than they were. But Amalia was glad she was better off, for she was fond of her. She went on babbling in this childish, contented way, and it wrung his heart to hear her say how happy she was amid so much suffering.

He must decide something, and at once. Amalia had shown no sign of violence in her delirium, either in speech or gesture, and when Emilio had recovered from the bewilderment into which he had fallen from the moment he had come in and found her in that state, he left the room and rushed to the front-door. He thought of calling the porter, or that he would run and fetch the doctor himself, or that he would go and ask Balli's advice. He had not made up his mind yet what he should do, but he must make haste and get some help for his unfortunate sister. He could not bear to remember her pitiful state of nakedness.

[All of his attempts to soothe Amalia having proved futile, Emilio sends for the doctor and Balli.]

. . . It was some time since the patient had said a single comprehensible word; she murmured indistinctly, as if she were trying to give herself practise in pronouncing difficult words. Emilio rested his head on his hand and sat listening to that weary flow of dizzy sound. He had been listening to it since the morning till it seemed to have become a quality of his own ear, a sound from which he would never again be able to free himself. He remembered getting up one evening in his nightshirt, in spite of the cold, to wait on his sister who was suffering in the room next to his; and how he had offered to take her to the theatre the next evening. The gratitude in Amalia's voice on that occasion had been very consoling to him. Then he had forgotten the incident and had never tried to revive it. Oh, if only he had known that his life contained such a precious mission as to guard and cherish this life which was entrusted solely to him, he would never have felt the need of approaching Angiolina again. Now, when it was perhaps too late, he was cured of his unhappy love. Sitting there in the shadow he wept silently, bitterly.

"Stefano," called the patient, in a low voice. Emilio started and looked at Balli, who was sitting in a part of the room on which the light from the window still faintly shone. Stefano apparently had not heard, for he made no movement.

"If you want to, I do too," said Amalia. They were the identical words, and with them the same dreams sprang to life again, stifled though they had been by Balli's sudden desertion. The patient had opened her eyes now and was staring at the wall opposite her. "I am ready," she said. "Do it, but quickly." A fit of coughing made her face contract with pain, but immediately afterwards she said: "Oh, what a perfect day! I have waited for it so long." And she shut her eyes again.

Emilio thought he ought to send Balli out of the room, but he had not the courage to do so. He had done so much harm the only other time when he had interfered between Balli and Amalia.

Amalia again started to babble incomprehensibly, but just as Emilio was beginning to be reassured, she said aloud and clearly, after a fresh fit of coughing: "Oh Stefano, I feel so ill."

"Is she calling me?" asked Balli, getting up and coming to the bedside.

"I couldn't hear," said Emilio, uncomfortably.

"I don't understand, doctor," said Amalia, with her face turned towards Balli: "I am lying quite still, I am looking after myself, but I still seem to be ill."

Surprised that she had not recognised him after calling for him, Balli spoke to her as if he had been the doctor; he advised her to go on being good, and said that she would soon be quite well again.

She went on talking: "What do I need all this for—this—this—this?" She touched her chest and her side. Her exhaustion became more apparent when she was silent, but she paused in search of a word, and not for lack of breath.

"This pain," suggested Balli, supplying the word which she had been seeking for in vain.

"This pain," she repeated gratefully. But soon after her doubt returned as to whether she had expressed herself badly, and she made a painful effort to continue. "What did I need this . . . for, to-day? What shall we do with this . . . this . . . on such a day?"

Only Emilio understood her. She was dreaming of her wedding.

But Amalia never gave expression to such a thought. She repeated that she did not need it, that nobody needed it, especially now . . . especially now. But the adverb was never defined more clearly than that, and Balli could not understand what she meant. When she was lying back on her pillow and looking straight in front of her, or keeping her eyes shut, she was at once completely at home with the object of her dreams; when she opened them again she did not see that the person himself was there in flesh and bone beside her bed. The only one who could understand the dream was Emilio, for he alone knew all the real facts as well as all the dreams that had led up to this delirium. He felt that his presence by the bed was more than ever useless. Amalia did not belong to him in her delirium; she was still less his than when she was in possession of her senses. . . .

PART THREE

CHARACTER AND PERSONALITY DISORDERS

There is no area of psychiatric diagnosis which is as cloudy and confused as that relating to the group of conditions known variously as personality disorders, character disorders, and conduct disorders. The American Psychiatric Association manual characterizes these individuals as suffering from "developmental defects or pathological trends in the personality structure, with minimal subjective anxiety, and little or no sense of distress,"[1] and includes under this rubric everything from stuttering and enuresis to transvestism and drug addiction, making it a sort of psychiatric wastebasket.

The selections illustrate a sample of the many forms of character disturbance—the homosexual, the psychopath, the addict, and the schizoid personality. In standard nomenclature, the first three types are labeled as sociopathic personality disturbances. These are individuals with poor conscience development and a lack of impulse control, who can't (or won't) conform to society's social expectations nor accept responsibility for their actions. The schizoid personality represents what is known as a personality pattern disturbance, a form of deep-rooted character distortion, with few resources for coping with stress.

---

[1] American Psychiatric Association. *Diagnostic and Statistical Manual: Mental Disorders*. Washington, D.C., 1952, p. 34.

Two other broad categories of this form of psychological maldevelopment are commonly recognized: the personality trait disturbances which include certain types of immature, dependent characters, and the special symptom reactions, involving any kind of symptom from sleepwalking to facial tics.

Perhaps the simplest way of portraying the psychological difficulties of these individuals is in terms of what Alfred Adler called the "life style," the sum total of characteristic ways a person develops to cope with his environment. A character distortion is an early-developed and well-maintained constellation of behaviors designed to minimize the inevitable anxiety which is intrinsic to psychosocial development. These distortions are the antithesis of flexibility, so that each life crisis is met in a rigid, automatic way, precluding any kind of "learning from experience." As Norman Cameron notes:

> The end-result may be an adult who seems always inhibited in certain areas of function, or who shows exaggerations of certain personality characteristics, or who stands chronically apart from the affairs of the marketplace, or rushes impetuously into every quickening stream that passes near him. If such an adult and those who are close to him accept his peculiarities as simply his nature he is not likely to find them disturbing or seek to change them. He may be proud of them and consider them, not incorrectly, as signs of his individuality.[2]

---

[2] Norman Cameron. *Personality Development and Psychopathology.* Boston: Houghton Mifflin Co., 1963, p. 639.

Sexual Deviancy
(Homosexuality)

The most common form of sexual deviation in our culture is homosexuality. Its etiology, despite many years of research and speculation, still remains something of a mystery and this enigma is compounded by societal misunderstanding of homosexuality as a psychological phenomenon, a situation which has led to the creation of legal sanctions against the homosexual. Fear and suspicion mark the usual cultural response to this disorder, creating an atmosphere hardly conducive to scientific investigation.

Homosexuality can be simply defined as adult preference for sexual relations with his or her own sex where potential partners of the opposite sex are available. Until the development of psychoanalytic thinking, homosexuality was considered to be a biological abnormality, the result of anatomical, physiological, or genetic aberrations. Psychological hypotheses are more concerned with examining the vicissitudes of early parent-child relations and have discovered evidence pointing to several possible sources for this deviant personality development. Inadequate same-sex identification figures, seductive parental responses, a too-frightening opposite-sexed parent—these are some of the potential etiological agents for the development and maintenance of homosexual behavior.

Proust's masterful description of the world of the homosexual, the many types of such men, their behavior and response pattern, their place in society and the isolation they experience, is unsurpassed and demonstrates that the feeling of being a cultural pariah has long been the lot of the homosexual.

Marcel Proust

CITIES OF THE PLAIN

From the beginning of this scene a revolution, in my unsealed eyes, had occurred in M. de Charlus, as complete, as immediate as if he had been touched by a magician's wand. Until then, because I had not understood, I had not seen. The vice (we use the word for convenience only), the vice of each of us accompanies him through life after the manner of the familiar genius who was invisible to men so long as they were unaware of his presence. Our goodness, our meanness, our name, our social relations do not disclose themselves to the eye, we carry them hidden within us. Even Ulysses did not at once recognise Athena. But the gods are immediately perceptible to one another, as quickly like to like, and so too had M. de Charlus been to Jupien. Until that moment I had been, in the presence of M. de Charlus, in the position of an absent-minded man who, standing before a pregnant woman whose distended outline he has failed to remark, persists, while she smilingly reiterates: "Yes, I am a little tired just now," in asking her indiscreetly: "Why, what is the matter with you?" But let some one say to him: "She is expecting a child," suddenly he catches sight of her abdomen and ceases to see anything else. It is the explanation that opens our eyes; the dispelling of an error gives us an additional sense.

Those of my readers who do not care to refer, for examples of this

Marcel Proust, from Cities of the Plain, *in* Remembrance of Things Past, *tr. by* C. K. Scott Moncrieff. New York: Random House, 1955.

law, to the Messieurs de Charlus of their acquaintance, whom for long years they had never suspected, until the day when, upon the smooth surface of the individual just like everyone else, there suddenly appeared, traced in an ink hitherto invisible, the characters that compose the word dear to the ancient Greeks, have only, in order to convince themselves that the world which surrounds them appears to them at first naked, bare of a thousand ornaments which it offers to the eyes of others better informed, to remind themselves how many times in the course of their lives they have found themselves on the point of making a blunder. Nothing upon the blank, undocumented face of this man or that could have led them to suppose that he was precisely the brother, or the intended husband, or the lover of a woman of whom they were just going to remark: "What a cow!" But then, fortunately, a word whispered to them by some one standing near arrests the fatal expression on their lips. At once there appear, like a *Mene, Tekel, Upharsin*, the words: "He is engaged to," or, "he is the brother of," or "he is the lover of the woman whom we ought not to describe, in his hearing, as a cow." And this one new conception will bring about an entire regrouping, thrusting some back, others forward, of the fractional conceptions, henceforward a complete whole, which we possessed of the rest of the family. In M. de Charlus another creature might indeed have coupled itself with him which made him as different from other men as the horse makes the centaur, this creature might indeed have incorporated itself in the Baron, I had never caught a glimpse of it. Now the abstraction had become materialised, the creature at last discerned had lost its power of remaining invisible, and the transformation of M. de Charlus into a new person was so complete that not only the contrasts of his face, of his voice, but, in retrospect, the very ups and downs of his relations with myself, everything that hitherto had seemed to my mind incoherent, became intelligible, brought itself into evidence, just as a sentence which presents no meaning so long as it remains broken up in letters scattered at random upon a table, expresses, if these letters be rearranged in the proper order, a thought which one can never afterwards forget.

I now understood, moreover, how, earlier in the day, when I had seen him coming away from Mme. de Villeparisis's, I had managed to arrive at the conclusion that M. de Charlus looked like a woman:

he was one! He belonged to that race of beings, less paradoxical than they appear, whose ideal is manly simply because their temperament is feminine and who in their life resemble in appearance only the rest of men; there where each of us carries, inscribed in those eyes through which he beholds everything in the universe, a human outline engraved on the surface of the pupil, for them it is that not of a nymph but of a youth. Race upon which a curse weighs and which must live amid falsehood and perjury, because it knows the world to regard as a punishable and a scandalous, as an inadmissible thing, its desire, that which constitutes for every human creature the greatest happiness in life; which must deny its God, since even Christians, when at the bar of justice they appear and are arraigned, must before Christ and in His Name defend themselves, as from a calumny, from the charge of what to them is life itself; sons without a mother, to whom they are obliged to lie all her life long and even in the hour when they close her dying eyes; friends without friendships, despite all those which their charm, frequently recognised, inspires and their hearts, often generous, would gladly feel; but can we describe as friendship those relations which flourish only by virtue of a lie and from which the first outburst of confidence and sincerity in which they might be tempted to indulge would make them be expelled with disgust, unless they are dealing with an impartial, that is to say a sympathetic mind, which however in that case, misled with regard to them by a conventional psychology, will suppose to spring from the vice confessed the very affection that is most alien to it, just as certain judges assume and are more inclined to pardon murder in inverts and treason in Jews for reasons derived from original sin and racial predestination. And lastly—according at least to the first theory which I sketched in outline at the time and which we shall see subjected to some modification in the sequel, a theory by which this would have angered them above all things, had not the paradox been hidden from their eyes by the very illusion that made them see and live—lovers from whom is always precluded the possibility of that love the hope of which gives them the strength to endure so many risks and so much loneliness, since they fall in love with precisely that type of man who has nothing feminine about him, who is not an invert and consequently cannot love them in return; with the result that their desire would be for ever insatiable did not their money procure for them real men, and their imagination end by making them take for real men the inverts to whom they had prostituted themselves. Their honour precarious, their liberty provisional, lasting only until the discovery of their crime; their position unstable, like that of the poet who one day was feasted at every table, applauded in every theatre in London, and on the next was driven from every lodging, unable to find a pillow upon which to lay his head, turning the mill like Samson and saying like him: "The two sexes shall die, each in a place apart!"; excluded even, save on the days of general disaster when the majority rally round the victim as the Jews rallied round Dreyfus, from the sympathy—at times from the society—of their fellows, in whom they inspire only disgust at seeing themselves as they are, portrayed in a mirror which, ceasing to flatter them, accentuates every blemish that they have refused to observe in themselves, and makes them understand that what they have been calling their love (a thing to which, playing upon the word, they have by association annexed all that poetry, painting, music, chivalry, asceticism have contrived to add to love) springs not from an ideal of beauty which they have chosen but from an incurable malady; like the Jews again (save some who will associate only with others of their race and have always on their lips ritual words and consecrated pleasantries), shunning one another, seeking out those who are most directly their opposite, who do not desire their company, pardoning their rebuffs, moved to ecstasy by their condescension; but also brought into the company of their own kind by the ostracism that strikes them, the opprobrium under which they have fallen, having finally been invested, by a persecution similar to that of Israel, with the physical and moral characteristics of a race, sometimes beautiful, often hideous, finding (in spite of all the mockery with which he who, more closely blended with, better assimilated to the opposing race, is relatively, in appearance, the least inverted, heaps upon him who has remained more so) a relief in frequenting the society of their kind, and even some corroboration of their own life, so much so that, while steadfastly denying that they are a race (the name of which is the vilest of insults), those who succeed in concealing the fact that they belong to it they readily unmask, with a view less to injuring them, though they have no scruple about that, than to excusing themselves; and, going in search (as a doctor seeks cases of appendicitis) of cases of inversion in history, taking pleasure in recalling that Socrates was one of themselves, as the Israelites claim that Jesus was one of them, without reflecting that there were no abnormals when homosexuality was the norm, no anti-Christians before Christ, that the disgrace alone makes the crime because it has allowed to survive only those who remained obdurate to every warning, to every example, to every punishment, by virtue of an innate disposition so peculiar that it is more repugnant to other men (even though it may be accompanied by exalted moral qualities) than certain other vices which exclude those qualities, such as theft, cruelty, breach of faith, vices better understood and so more readily excused by the generality of men; forming a freemasonry far more extensive, more powerful and less suspected than that of the Lodges, for it rests upon an identity of tastes, needs, habits, dangers, apprenticeship, knowledge, traffic, glossary, and one in which the members themselves, who intend not to know one another, recognise one another immediately by natural or conventional, involuntary or deliberate signs which indicate one of his congeners to the beggar in the street, in the great nobleman whose carriage door he is shutting, to the father in the suitor for his daughter's hand, to him who has sought healing, absolution, defence, in the doctor, the priest, the barrister to whom he has had recourse; all of them obliged to protect their own secret but having their part in a secret shared with the others, which the rest of humanity does not suspect and which means that to them the most wildly improbable tales of adventure seem true, for in this romantic, anachronistic life the ambassador is a bosom friend of the felon, the prince, with a certain independence of action with which his aristocratic breeding has furnished him, and which the trembling little cit would lack, on leaving the duchess's party goes off to confer in private with the hooligan; a reprobate part of the human whole, but an important part, suspected where it does not exist, flaunting itself, insolent and unpunished, where its existence is never guessed; numbering its adherents everywhere, among the people, in the army, in the church, in the prison, on the throne; living, in short, at least to a great extent, in a playful and perilous intimacy with the men of the other race, provoking them, playing with them by speaking of its vice as of something alien to it; a game that is rendered easy by the blindness or duplicity of the others, a game that may be kept up for years until the day of the scandal, on which these lion-tamers are devoured; until then, obliged to make a secret of their lives, to turn away their eyes from the things on which they would naturally fasten them, to fasten them upon those from which they would naturally turn away, to change the gender of many of the words in their vocabulary, a social constraint, slight in comparison with the inward constraint which their vice, or what is improperly so called, imposes upon them with regard not so much now to others as to themselves, and in such a way that to themselves it does not appear a vice. But certain among them, more practical, busier men who have not the time to go and drive their own bargains, or to dispense with the simplification of life and that saving of time which may result from cooperation, have formed two societies of which the second is composed exclusively of persons similar to themselves.

This is noticeable in those who are poor and have come up from the country, without friends, with nothing but their ambition to be some day a celebrated doctor or barrister, with a mind still barren of opinions, a person unadorned with manners, which they intend, as soon as possible, to decorate, just as they would buy furniture for their little attic in the Latin quarter, copying whatever they had observed in those who had already 'arrived' in the useful and serious profession in which they also intend to establish themselves and to become famous; in these their special taste, unconsciously inherited like a weakness for drawing, for music, a weakness of vision, is perhaps the only living and despotic originality—which on certain evenings compels them to miss some meeting, advantageous to their career, with people whose ways, in other respect, of speaking, thinking, dressing, parting their hair, they have adopted. In their quarter, where otherwise they mix only with their brother students, their teachers or some fellow-provincial who has succeeded and can help them on, they have speedily discovered other young men whom the same peculiar taste attracts to them, as in a small town one sees an intimacy grow up between the assistant master and the lawyer, who are both interested in chamber music or mediaeval ivories; applying to the object of their distraction the same utilitarian instinct, the same professional spirit which guides them in their career, they meet these young men at gatherings to which no profane outsider is admitted any more than to those that bring together collectors of old snuff-boxes, Japanese prints or rare flowers, and at which, what with the pleasure of gaining information, the practical value of making exchanges and the fear of competition, there prevail simultaneously, as in a saleroom of postage stamps, the close cooperation of the specialists and the fierce rivalries of the collectors. No one moreover in the café where they have their table knows what the gathering is, whether it is that of an angling club, of an editorial staff, or the of 'Sons of the Indre,' so correct is their attire, so cold and reserved their manner, so modestly do they refrain from anything more than the most covert glances at the young men of fashion, the young 'lions' who, a few feet away, are making a great clamour about their mistresses, and among whom those who are admiring them without venturing to raise their eyes will learn only twenty years later, when they themselves are on the eve of admission to the Academy, and the others are middle-aged gentlemen in club windows, that the most seductive among them, now a stout and grizzled Charlus, was in reality akin to themselves, but differently, in another world, beneath other external symbols, with foreign labels, the strangeness of which led them into error. But these groups are at varying stages of advancement; and, just as the 'Union of the Left' differs from the 'Socialist Federation' or some Mendelssohnian musical club from the Schola Cantorum, on certain evenings, at another table, there are extremists who allow a bracelet to slip down from beneath a cuff, sometimes a necklace to gleam in the gap of a collar, who by their persistent stares, their cooings, their laughter, their mutual caresses, oblige a band of students to depart in hot haste, and are served with a civility beneath which indignation boils by a waiter who, as on the evenings when he has to serve Dreyfusards, would find pleasure in summoning the police did he not find profit in pocketing their gratuities.

It is with these professional organisations that the mind contrasts the taste of the solitaries, and in one respect without straining the points of difference, since it is doing no more than copy the solitaries themselves who imagine that nothing differs more widely from organised vice than what appears to them to be a misunderstood love, but with some strain nevertheless, for these different classes correspond, no less than to diverse physiological types, to succes-

sive stages in a pathological or merely social evolution. And it
is, in fact, very rarely that, one day or another, it is not in some such
organisation that the solitaries come to merge themselves, sometimes from simple weariness, or for convenience (just as the people
who have been most strongly opposed to such innovations end by
having the telephone installed, inviting the Iénas to their parties, or
dealing with Potin). They meet there, for that matter, with none
too friendly a reception as a rule, for, in their relatively pure lives,
their want of experience, the saturation in dreams to which they
have been reduced, have branded more strongly upon them those
special marks of effeminacy which the professionals have sought to
efface. And it must be admitted that, among certain of these new-
comers, the woman is not only inwardly united to the man but
hideously visible, agitated as one sees them by a hysterical spasm,
by a shrill laugh which convulses their knees and hands, looking no
more like the common run of men than those monkeys with melancholy, shadowed eyes and prehensile feet who dress up in dinner-
jackets and black bow ties; so that these new recruits are judged by
others, less chaste for all that themselves, to be compromising
associates, and their admission is hedged with difficulties; they are
accepted, nevertheless, and they benefit then by those facilities by
which commerce, great undertakings have transformed the lives of
individuals, and have brought within their reach commodities hitherto too costly to acquire and indeed hard to find, which now sub-
merge them beneath the plethora of what by themselves they had
never succeeded in discovering amid the densest crowds. But, even
with these innumerable outlets, the burden of social constraint is still
too heavy for some, recruited principally among those who have not
made a practice of self-control, and who still take to be rarer than
it actually is their way of love. Let us leave out of consideration for
the moment those who, the exceptional character of their inclinations
making them regard themselves as superior to the other sex, look
down upon women, make homosexuality the privilege of great genius
and of glorious epochs of history, and, when they seek to communicate their taste to others, approach not so much those who seem to
them to be predisposed towards it (as the morphinomaniac does
with his morphia) as those who seem to them to be worthy of it, from
apostolic zeal, just as others preach Zionism, conscientious objection

to military service, Saint-Simonism, vegetarianism or anarchy. Here is one who, should we intrude upon him in the morning, still in bed, will present to our gaze an admirable female head, so general is its expression and typical of the sex as a whole; his very hair affirms this, so feminine is its ripple; unbrushed, it falls so naturally in long curls over the cheek that one marvels how the young woman, the girl, the Galatea barely awakened to life, in the unconscious mass of this male body in which she is imprisoned, has contrived so ingeniously by herself, without instruction from anyone, to make use of the narrowest apertures in her prison wall to find what was necessary to her existence. No doubt the young man who sports this delicious head does not say: "I am a woman." Even—if for any of the countless possible reasons—he lives with a woman, he can deny to her that he is himself one, can swear to her that he has never had intercourse with men. But let her look at him as we have just revealed him, lying back in bed, in pyjamas, his arms bare, his throat and neck bare also beneath the darkness of his hair. The pyjama jacket becomes a woman's shift, the head that of a pretty Spanish girl. The mistress is astounded by these confidences offered to her gaze, truer than any spoken confidence could be, or indeed any action, which his actions, indeed, if they have not already done so, cannot fail later on to confirm, for every creature follows the line of his own pleasure, and if this creature is not too vicious he will seek it in a sex complementary to his own. And for the invert vice begins, not when he forms relations (for there are all sorts of reasons that may enjoin these), but when he takes his pleasure with women. The young man whom we have been attempting to portray was so evidently a woman that the women who looked upon him with longing were doomed (failing a special taste on their part) to the same disappointment as those who in Shakespeare's comedies are taken in by a girl in disguise who passes as a youth. The deception is mutual, the invert is himself aware of it, he guesses the disillusionment which, once the mask is removed, the woman will experience, and feels to what an extent this mistake as to sex is a source of poetical imaginings. Besides, even from his exacting mistress, in vain does he keep back the admission (if she, that is to say, be not herself a denizen of Gomorrah): "I am a woman!" when all the time with what stratagems, what agility, what obstinacy as of a climbing plant the unconscious but visible woman in him seeks the masculine organ. We have only to look at that head of curling hair on the white pillow to understand that if, in the evening, this young man slips through his guardians' fingers, in spite of anything that they, or he himself can do to restrain him, it will not be to go in pursuit of women. His mistress may chastise him, may lock him up; next day, the man-woman will have found some way of attaching himself to a man, as the convolvulus throws out its tendrils wherever it finds a convenient post or rake. Why, when we admire in the face of this person a delicacy that touches our hearts, a gracefulness, a spontaneous affability such as men do not possess, should we be dismayed to learn that this young man runs after boxers? They are different aspects of an identical reality. And indeed, what repels us is the most touching thing of all, more touching than any refinement of delicacy, for it represents an admirable though unconscious effort on the part of nature: the recognition of his sex by itself, in spite of the sexual deception, becomes apparent, the unconfessed attempt to escape from itself towards what an initial error on the part of society has segregated from it. Some, those no doubt who have been most timid in childhood, are scarcely concerned with the material kind of the pleasure they receive, provided that they can associate it with a masculine face. Whereas others, whose sensuality is doubtless more violent, imperiously restrict their material pleasure within certain definite limitations. These live perhaps less exclusively beneath the sway of Saturn's outrider, since for them women are not entirely barred, as for the former sort, in whose eyes women would have no existence apart from conversation, flirtation, loves not of the heart but of the head. But the second sort seek out those women who love other women; who can procure for them a young man, enhance the pleasure which they feel on finding themselves in his company; better still, they can, in the same fashion, enjoy with such women the same pleasure as with a man. Whence it arises that jealousy is kindled in those who love the first sort only by the pleasure which they may be enjoying with a man, which alone seems to their lovers a betrayal, since these do not participate in the love of women, have practised it only as a habit, and, so as to reserve for themselves the possibility of eventual marriage, representing to themselves so little the pleasure that it is capable of giving that they cannot be distressed by the thought that he whom they love is enjoying that pleasure; whereas the other sort often inspire jealousy by their love-affairs with women. For, in the relations which they have with her, they play, for the woman who loves her own sex, the part of another woman, and she offers them at the same time more or less what they find in other men, so that the jealous friend suffers from the feeling that he whom he loves is riveted to her who is to him almost a man, and at the same time feels his beloved almost escape him because, to these women, he is something which the lover himself cannot conceive, a sort of woman. We need not pause here to consider those young fools who by a sort of arrested development, to tease their friends or to shock their families, proceed with a kind of frenzy to choose clothes that resemble women's dress, to redden their lips and blacken their eyelashes; we may leave them out of account, for they are those whom we shall find later on, when they have suffered the all too cruel penalty of their affectation, spending what remains of their lifetime in vain attempts to repair by a sternly protestant demeanour the wrong that they did to themselves when they were carried away by the same demon that urges young women of the Faubourg Saint-Germain to live in a scandalous fashion, to set every convention at defiance, to scoff at the entreaties of their relatives, until the day when they set themselves with perseverance but without success to reascend the slope down which it had seemed to them that it would be so amusing to glide, down which they had found it so amusing, or rather had not been able to stop themselves from gliding. Finally, let us leave to a later volume the men who have sealed a pact with Gomorrah. We shall deal with them when M. de Charlus comes to know them. Let us leave out for the present all those, of one sort or another, who will appear each in his turn, and, to conclude this first sketch of the subject, let us say a word only of those whom we began to mention just now, the solitary class. Supposing their vice to be more exceptional than it is, they have retired into solitude from the day on which they discovered it, after having carried it within themselves for a long time without knowing it, for a longer time only than certain other men. For no one can tell at first that he is an invert or a poet or a snob or a scoundrel. The boy who has been reading erotic poetry or looking at indecent pictures, if he then presses his body against a schoolfellow's, imagines himself only to be communing with him in an identical desire for a woman. How should he suppose that he is not like everybody else when he recognises the substance of what he feels on reading Mme. de Lafayette, Racine, Baudelaire, Walter Scott, at a time when he is still too little capable of observing himself to take into account what he has added from his own store to the picture, and that if the sentiment be the same the object differs, that what he desires is Rob Roy, and not Diana Vernon? With many, by a defensive prudence on the part of the instinct that precedes the clearer vision of the intellect, the mirror and walls of their bedroom vanish beneath a cloud of coloured prints of actresses; they compose poetry such as:

> I love but Chloe in the world,
>   For Chloe is divine;
> Her golden hair is sweetly curled,
>   For her my heart doth pine.

Must we on that account attribute to the opening phase of such lives a taste which we shall never find in them later on, like those flaxen ringlets on the heads of children which are destined to change to the darkest brown? Who can tell whether the photographs of women are not a first sign of hypocrisy, a first sign also of horror at other inverts? But the solitary kind are precisely those to whom hypocrisy is painful. Possibly even the example of the Jews, of a different type of colony, is not strong enough to account for the frail hold that their upbringing has upon them, or for the artfulness with which they find their way back (perhaps not to anything so sheerly terrible as the suicide to which maniacs, whatever precautions one may take with them, return, and, pulled out of the river into which they have flung themselves, take poison, procure revolvers, and so forth; but) to a life of which the men of the other race not only do not understand, cannot imagine, abominate the essential pleasures but would be filled with horror by the thought of its frequent danger and everlasting shame. Perhaps, to form a picture of these, we ought to think, if not of the wild animals that never become domesticated, of the lion-cubs said to be tame but lions still at heart, then at least of the Negroes whom the comfortable existence of the white man renders desperately unhappy and who prefer the risks of a life of savagery and its incomprehensible joys. When the day has dawned on which they have discovered themselves to be incapable at once of lying to others and of lying to themselves, they go away to live in the country, shunning the society of their own kind (whom they believe to be few in number) from horror of the monstrosity or fear of the temptation, and that of the rest of humanity from shame. Never having arrived at true maturity, plunged in a constant melancholy, now and again, some Sunday evening when there is no moon, they go for a solitary walk as far as a crossroads where, although not a word has been said, there has come to meet them one of their boyhoods friends who is living in a house in the neighbourhood. And they begin again the pastimes of long ago, on the grass, in the night, neither uttering a word. During the week, they meet in their respective houses, talk of no matter what, without any allusion to what has occurred between them, exactly as though they had done nothing and were not to do anything again, save, in their relations, a trace of coldness, of irony, of irritability and rancour, at times of hatred. Then the neighbour sets out on a strenuous expedition on horseback, and, on a mule, climbs mountain peaks, sleeps in the snow; his friend, who identifies his own vice with a weakness of temperament, the cabined and timid life, realises that vice can no longer exist in his friend now emancipated, so many thousands of feet above sea-level. And, sure enough, the other takes a wife. And yet the abandoned one is not cured (in spite of the cases in which, as we shall see, inversion is curable). He insists upon going down himself every morning to the kitchen to receive the milk from the hands of the dairyman's boy, and on the evenings when desire is too strong for him will go out of his way to set a drunkard on the right road or to "adjust the dress" of a blind man. No doubt the life of certain inverts appears at times to change, their vice (as it is called) is no longer apparent in their habits; but nothing is ever lost; a missing jewel turns up again; when the quantity of a sick man's urine decreases, it is because he is perspiring more freely, but the excretion must invariably occur. One day this homosexual hears of the death of a young cousin, and from his inconsolable grief we learned that it was to this love, chaste possibly and aimed rather at retaining esteem than at obtaining possession, that his desires have passed by a sort of virescence, as, in budget, without any alteration in the total, certain expenditure is carried under another head. As is the case with invalids in whom a sudden attack of urticaria makes their chronic ailments temporarily disappear, this pure love for a young relative seems, in the invert, to have momentarily replaced, by metastasis, habits that will, one day or another, return to fill the place of the vicarious, cured malady.

Meanwhile the married neighbour of our recluse has returned; before the beauty of the young bride and the demonstrative affection of her husband, on the day when their friend is obliged to invite them to dinner, he feels ashamed of the past. Already in an interesting condition, she must return home early, leaving her husband behind; he, when the time has come for him to go home also, asks his host to accompany him for part of the way; at first, no suspicion enters his mind, but at the crossroads he finds himself thrown down on the grass, with not a word said, by the mountaineer who is shortly to become a father. And their meetings begin again, and continue until the day when there comes to live not far off a cousin of the young woman, with whom her husband is now constantly to be seen. And he, if the twice-abandoned friend calls in the evening and endeavours to approach him, is furious, and repulses him with indignation that the other has not had the tact to foresee the disgust which he must henceforward inspire. Once, however, there appears a stranger, sent to him by his faithless friend; but being busy at the time, the abandoned one cannot see him, and only afterwards learns with what object his visitor came.

Then the solitary languishes alone. He has no other diversion than to go to the neighbouring watering-place to ask for some information or other from a certain railwayman there. But the latter has obtained promotion, has been transferred to the other end of the country; the solitary will no longer be able to go and ask him the times of the trains or the price of a first class ticket, and, before retiring to dream, Griselda-like, in his tower, loiters upon the beach, a strange Andromeda whom no Argonaut will come to free, a sterile Medusa that must perish upon the sand, or else he stands idly, until his train starts, upon the platform, casting over the crowd of passengers a gaze that will seem indifferent, contemptuous or distracted to those of another race, but, like the luminous glow with which certain insects bedeck themselves in order to attract others of their species, or like the nectar which certain flowers offer to attract the insects that will fertilise them, would not deceive the almost undiscoverable sharer of a pleasure too singular, too hard to place, which is offered him, the colleague with whom our specialist could converse in the half-forgotten tongue; in which last, at the most, some seedy loafer upon the platform will put up a show of interest, but for pecuniary gain alone, like those people who, at the Collège de France, in the room in which the Professor of Sanskrit lectures without an audience, attend his course but only because the room itself is heated. . . .

Antisocial Reactions
(The Psychopath)

The psychopath or antisocial individual is an enigmatic case. He displays none of the anxiety or symptomatology of the neurotic or psychotic; he may not commit any overt acts of criminality; he can make a good impression, charm those around him, and display a lively intelligence. At first blush he may appear a model citizen. Yet closer examination of these individuals shows an insidious side to their personalities. That is, they are typically without morals or a sense of guilt. They are constantly self-defeating and irresponsible, living on the surface of life and unable to create a meaningful world of relationships.

The swindler, the con-man, the pathological liar are examples of antisocial personalities. And, in his individual way, so is Gogol's Nozdryov. He is irresponsible; unable to distinguish the truth from his pious falsehoods, rationalizations, and patent lies; and unable to accept blame. He is a shallow, loveless man, who "minds the main chance" and never learns from his experience. Without conscience or anxiety, he acts and reacts like an impulsive child, unable to postpone gratification and unmindful of all those around him.

Nikolai Gogol

DEAD SOULS

The personality of Nozdryov is certainly to some extent familiar to the reader already. Every one must have met more than a few like him. They are called dashing fellows and are known even in childhood and at school as good companions, though they are apt to get a good many hard knocks for all that. There is always something open, direct, and reckless in their faces. They are quick to make friends, and you can hardly look round before they have begun addressing you as though they had known you all their lives. One would think they were friends for life; but it almost always happens that their new friend quarrels with them the very evening when they are celebrating their friendship. They are always great talkers, rakes, and dare-devils, and are always to the fore in everything. At thirty-five, Nozdryov was exactly the same as he had been at eighteen and twenty: given up to the pursuit of pleasure. His marriage did not change him in the least, especially as his wife departed to a better world soon after it, leaving him two small children who were not at all what he wanted. The children, however, were looked after by an engaging little nurse. He could never stay at home for more than a day at a time. He never failed to get wind of any fairs, assemblies, or balls for miles around; in a twinkling of an eye he was there, squabbling and getting up a row at the green table, for like all men of his kind, he had a great passion for cards.

Nikolai Gogol, from Dead Souls, *tr. by Constance Garnett. New York: Knopf, 1923.*

As we have seen in the first chapter, his play was not quite above suspicion, he was up to all sorts of tricks and dodges, and so the game often ended in sport of a different kind: either he got a good drubbing or had his fine thick whiskers pulled out, so that he often returned home with only one whisker and that somewhat attenuated. But his full healthy cheeks were so happily constituted and capable of such luxuriant growth, that his whiskers soon sprouted and were finer than ever. And what is strangest of all and only possible in Russia, within a short time he would meet again the very friends who had given him such a dressing, and meet them as though nothing had happened: he, as the saying is, did not turn a hair and they did not turn a hair.

Nozdryov was in a certain sense an *historical* character. No gathering at which he was present went off without some "history." Some sort of scandal invariably occurred: either he was conducted out of the ballroom by the police, or his friends were forced to eject him themselves. If that did not occur, something would be sure to happen that never would happen to any one else: either he would get so drunk at the refreshment bar that he did nothing but laugh, or he would tell such fantastic lies that at last he felt ashamed of himself. And he would lie without any provocation: he would suddenly assert that he had a horse whose coat was a light blue or pink colour, and nonsense of that sort, so that at last his listeners would walk away from him, saying: "Well, my lad, it seems you are drawing the long-bow." There are people who have a passion for playing nasty tricks on their neighbours, sometimes without the slightest provocation. Even a man of good position and gentlemanly appearance, with a decoration on his breast will, for instance, shake hands, and converse with you on intellectual subjects that call for deep reflection, and in another minute before your very eyes he is playing you a nasty trick like the humblest little copying clerk and not at all like a man with a decoration on his breast conversing on subjects that call for deep reflection, so that you simply stand amazed and can do nothing but shrug your shoulders. Nozdryov had this strange passion too. The more intimate any one was with him, the readier he was to do him a bad turn; he would spread the most incredible tales which would have been hard to beat for silliness, upset a wedding or a business transaction, and all the while would be far from regarding himself as your enemy; on the contrary, if chance threw you with him again, he would behave in the most friendly way again and would even say: "You are a wretch, you never come to see me." In a certain sense Nozdryov was a many-sided man, that is, a man who could turn his hand to anything. In the same breath he would offer to go with you to the furthest ends of the earth, to undertake any enterprise you might choose, to swop anything in the world for anything you like. Guns, dogs, horses, anything would do for a swop, not with the slightest idea of gain; it all sprang from an irresistible impetuosity and recklessness of character. If he had the luck to hit upon a simpleton at a fair and rook him, he bought masses of things because they caught his eye in the shops: horse collars, fumigating candles, kerchiefs for the nurse, a stallion, raisins, a silver washing-basin, holland linen, fine wheaten flour, tobacco, pistols, herrings, pictures, a lathe, pots, boots, china— as long as his money lasted. However, it rarely happened that all this wealth was carried home; almost the same day it would pass into the hands of some luckier gambler, sometimes even with the addition of a peculiar pipe with a tobacco pouch and a mouth-piece, and another time with all his four horses, carriage, and coachman, so that their former owner has to set to work in a short jacket or a jerkin to look out for a friend to give him a lift in his carriage. Such was Nozdryov! Perhaps he will be called a hackneyed character, and it will be said that there are no Nozdryovs now. Alas! those who say so are wrong. It will be many long years before the Nozdryovs are extinct. They are everywhere among us, and the only difference perhaps is that they are wearing a different cut of coat; but people are carelessly unobservant and a man in a different coat seems to them a different man. . . .

Drug Addiction

Many drugs are involved in the problem of drug addiction, ranging from the powerful opiates such as morphine and heroin to the barbiturates ("sedatives") and most recently the amphetamines ("energizers"). Like an alcoholic, the drug addict often begins his career as part of an anxiety-driven search for relief from inner tension. Once he is "hooked" the addict's life becomes a nightmare of anxiety about obtaining his "fix" and once again experiencing the euphoria and high feeling the drug brings.

No single personality constellation is represented among the approximately 45,000 addicts in the United States. They are generally considered passive individuals, however, who need to find in drugs an escape from the tense competitiveness of life.

In this frightening scene from Nelson Algren's *The Man with the Golden Arm* the symptoms of the addict, as well as the cruel and vicious world he inhabits, are powerfully portrayed.

Nelson Algren

THE MAN WITH THE
GOLDEN ARM

The clock in the room above the Safari told only Junkie Time. For every hour here was Old Junkie's Hour and the walls were the color of all old junkie's dreams: the hue of diluted morphine in the moment before the needle draws the suffering blood.

Walls that went up and up like walls in a troubled dream. Walls like water where no legend could be written and no hand grasp metal or wood. For Nifty Louie paid the rent and Frankie knew too well who the landlord was. He had met him before, that certain down-at-heel vet growing stooped from carrying a thirty-five-pound monkey on his back. Frankie remembered that face, ravaged by love of its own suffering as by some endless all-night orgy. A face forged out of his own wound fever in a windy ward tent on the narrow Meuse. He had met Private McGantic before: both had served their country well.

This was the fellow who looked somehow a little like everyone else in the world and was more real to a junkie than any real man could ever be. The projected image of one's own pain when that pain has become too great to be borne. The image of one hooked so hopelessly on morphine that there would be no getting the monkey off without another's help. There are so few ways to help old sad frayed and weary West Side junkies.

Frankie felt no pity for himself, yet felt compassion for this

Nelson Algren, from The Man with the Golden Arm. *New York: Doubleday, 1949.*

McGantic. He worried, as the sickness rose in himself, about what in God's name McGantic would do tomorrow when the money and the morphine both gave out. Where then, in that terrible hour, would Private M. find the strength to carry the monkey through one more endless day?

By the time Frankie got inside the room he was so weak Louie had to help him onto the army cot beside the oil stove. He lay on his back with one arm flung across his eyes as if in shame; and his lips were blue with cold. The pain had hit him with an icy fist in the groin's very pit, momentarily tapering off to a single probing finger touching the genitals to get the maximum of pain. He tried twisting to get away from the finger: the finger was worse than the fist. His throat was so dry that, though he spoke, the lips moved and made no sound. But Fomorowski read such lips well.

"Fix me. Make it stop. Fix me."

"I'll fix you, Dealer," Louie assured him softly.

Louie had his own bedside manner. He perched on the red leather and chrome bar stool borrowed from the Safari, with the amber toes of his two-tone shoes catching the light and the polo ponies galloping down his shirt. This was Nifty Louie's Hour. The time when he did the dealing and the dealer had to take what Louie chose to toss him in Louie's own good time.

He lit a match with his fingertip and held it away from the bottom of the tiny glass tube containing the fuzzy white cap of morphine, holding it just far enough away to keep the cap from being melted by the flame. There was time and time and lots of time for that. Let the dealer do a bit of melting first; the longer it took the higher the price. "You can pay me off when Zero pays you," he assured Frankie. There was no hurry. "You're good with me any time, Dealer."

Frankie moaned like an animal that cannot understand its own pain. His shirt had soaked through and the pain had frozen so deep in his bones nothing could make him warm again.

"Hit me, Fixer. Hit me."

A sievelike smile drained through Louie's teeth. This was his hour and this hour didn't come every day. He snuffed out the match's flame as it touched his fingers and snapped the head of another match into flame with his nail, letting its glow flicker one moment over that sievelike smile; then brought the tube down cautiously and watched it dissolve at the flame's fierce touch. When the stuff had melted he held both needle and tube in one hand, took the dealer's loose-hanging arm firmly with the other and pumped it in a long, loose arc. Frankie let him swing it as if it were attached to someone else. The cold was coming *up from* within now: a colorless cold spreading through stomach and liver and breathing across the heart like an odorless gas. To make the very brain tighten and congeal under its icy touch.

"Warm. Make me warm."

And still there was no rush, no hurry at all. Louie pressed the hypo down to the cotton; the stuff came too high these days to lose the fraction of a drop. "Don't vomit, student," he taunted Frankie to remind him of the first fix he'd had after his discharge—but it was too cold to answer. He was falling between glacial walls, he didn't know how anyone could fall so far away from everyone else in the world. So far to fall, so cold all the way, so steep and dark between those morphine-colored walls of Private McGantic's terrible pit.

He couldn't feel Louie probing into the dark red knot above his elbow at all. Nor see the way the first blood sprayed faintly up into the delicate hypo to tinge the melted morphine with blood as warm as the needle's heated point.

When Louie sensed the vein he pressed it down with the certainty of a good doctor's touch, let it linger a moment in the vein to give the heart what it needed and withdrew gently, daubed the blood with a piece of cotton, tenderly, and waited.

Louie waited. Waited to see it hit.

Louie liked to see the stuff hit. It meant a lot to Louie, seeing it hit.

"Sure I like to watch," he was ready to acknowledge any time. "Man, their *eyes* when that big drive hits 'n goes tinglin' down to the toes. They retch, they sweat, they itch—then the big drive hits 'n here they come out of it cryin' like a baby 'r laughin' like a loon. *Sure* I like to watch. *Sure* I like to see it hit. Heroin got the drive awright —but there's not a tingle to a ton—you got to get M to get that tingle-tingle."

It hit all right. It hit the heart like a runaway locomotive, it hit like a falling wall. Frankie's whole body lifted with that smashing surge, the very heart seemed to lift up-up-up—then rolled over and he slipped into a long warm bath with one long orgasmic sigh of relief. Frankie opened his eyes.

He was in a room. Somebody's dust-colored wavy-walled room and he wasn't quite dead after all. He had died, had felt himself fall away and die but now he wasn't dead any more. Just sick. But not too sick. He wasn't going to be really sick, he wasn't a student any more. Maybe he wasn't going to be sick at all, he was beginning to feel just right.

Then it went over him like a dream where everything is love and he wasn't even sweating. All he had to do the rest of his life was to lie right here feeling better and better with every beat of his heart till he'd never felt so good in all his life.

"Wow," he grinned gratefully at Louie, "that was one good *whan*."

"I seen it," Louie boasted smugly. "I seen it was one good *whan*" —and lapsed into the sort of impromptu jargon which pleases junkies for no reason they can say—"vraza-s'vraza-s'vraza—it was one good *whan-whan-whan*." He dabbed a silk handkerchief at a blob of blood oozing where the needle had entered Frankie's arm.

"There's a silver buck and a buck 'n a half in change in my jacket pocket," Frankie told him lazily. "I'm feelin' too good to get up 'n get it myself."

Louie reached in the pocket with the handkerchief bound about his palm and plucked the silver out. Two-fifty for a quarter grain wasn't too high. He gave Frankie the grin that drained through the teeth for a receipt. The dealer was coming along nicely these days, thank you.

The dealer didn't know that yet, of course. That first fix had only cost him a dollar, it had quieted the everlasting dull ache in his stomach and sent him coasting one whole week end. So what was the use of spending forty dollars in the bars when you could do better at home on one? That was how Frankie had it figured *that* week end. To Louie, listening close, he'd already talked like a twenty-dollar-a-day man.

Given a bit of time.

And wondered idly now where in the world the dealer would get that kind of money when the day came that he'd need half a C just to taper off. He'd get it all right. They always got it. He'd seen them coming in the rain, the unkjays with their peculiarly rigid, panicky walk, wearing some policeman's castoff rubbers, no socks at all, a pair of Salvation Army pants a size too small or a size too large and a pajama top for a shirt—but with twenty dollars clutched in the sweating palm for that big twenty-dollar fix.

"Nothing can take the place of junk—just junk"—the dealer would learn. As Louie himself had learned long ago.

Louie was the best fixer of them all because he knew what it was to need to get well. Louie had had a big habit—he was one man who could tell you you lied if you said no junkie could kick the habit once he was hooked. For Louie was the one junkie in ten thousand who'd kicked it and kicked it for keeps.

He'd taken the sweat cure in a little Milwaukee Avenue hotel room cutting himself down, as he put it, "from monkey to zero." From three full grains a day to one, then a half of that and a half of that straight down to zero, though he'd been half out of his mind with the pain two nights running and was so weak, for days after, that he could hardly tie his own shoelaces.

Back on the street at last, he'd gotten the chuck horrors: for two full days he'd eaten candy bars, sweet rolls and strawberry malteds. It had seemed that there would be no end to his hunger for sweets.

Louie never had the sweet-roll horrors any more. Yet sometimes himself sensed that something had twisted in his brain in those nights when he'd gotten the monkey off his back on Milwaukee Avenue.

"*Habit? Man,*" he liked to remember, "I had a great *big* habit. One time I knocked out one of my own teet' to get the gold for a fix. You call that bein' hooked or not? *Hooked?* Man, I wasn't hooked, I was *crucified.* The monkey got so big he was carryin' *me.* 'Cause the way it starts is like this, students: you let the habit feed you first 'n one mornin' you wake up 'n you're feedin' the habit.

"But don't tell *me* you can't kick it if you *want* to. When I hear a junkie tell me he wants to kick the habit but he just can't I know he lies even if *he* don't know he does. He *wants* to carry the monkey, he's punishin' hisself for somethin' 'n don't even know it. It's what I was doin' for six years, punishin' myself for things I'd done 'n thought I'd forgot. So I told myself how I wasn't to blame for what I done in the first place, I was only tryin' to live like everyone else 'n doin' them things was the only way I had of livin'. Then I got forty grains 'n went up to the room 'n went from monkey to nothin' in twenny-eight days 'n that's nine-ten years ago 'n the monkey's dead."

"The monkey's never dead, Fixer," Frankie told him knowingly.

Louie glanced at Frankie slyly. "You know that awready, Dealer? You know how he don't die? It's what they say awright, the monkey never dies. When you kick him off he just hops onto somebody else's back." Behind the film of glaze that always veiled Louie's eyes Frankie saw the twisted look. "*You* got my monkey, Dealer? You take my nice old monkey away from me? Is that my monkey ridin' your back these days, Dealer?" . . .

Schizoid Personality

"Many schizoid individuals," the German psychiatrist Ernst Kretschmer once wrote, "are like bare Roman houses, villas which have closed their blinds from the glaring sun; in the dampened interiors, however, feasts and celebrations are carried on."[1]

The "feasts and celebrations" of those personalities like Paul are hollow substitutes, however, for the basic interpersonal isolation they forever experience. For if there is any difficulty in living which characterizes the schizoid person, it is his inability to make meaningful contact with others. He may, like Paul, tell tall tales to his peers to receive some momentary adulation, he may even find an outlet for the flux of his inner feelings in some artistic endeavor, but his "oddness," strange sensitivities, and detached quality inevitably keep him apart from the world around him.

The life-long sense of dread which Paul describes, his disgust at being touched, and his inability to express directly his angry feelings to others all exemplify the schizoid disorder.

---

[1] Quoted in E. Bohm. *A Textbook in Rorschach Test Diagnosis.* New York: Grune & Stratton, 1958, p. 241.

Willa Cather

PAUL'S CASE

It was Paul's afternoon to appear before the faculty of the Pittsburgh High School to account for his various misdemeanours. He had been suspended a week ago, and his father had called at the Principal's office and confessed his perplexity about his son. Paul entered the faculty room suave and smiling. His clothes were a trifle outgrown, and the tan velvet on the collar of his open overcoat was frayed and worn; but for all that there was something of the dandy about him, and he wore an opal pin in his neatly knotted black four-in-hand, and a red carnation in his button-hole. This latter adornment the faculty somehow felt was not properly significant of the contrite spirit befitting a boy under the ban of suspension.

Paul was tall for his age and very thin, with high, cramped shoulders and a narrow chest. His eyes were remarkable for a certain hysterical brilliancy, and he continually used them in a conscious, theatrical sort of way, peculiarly offensive in a boy. The pupils were abnormally large, as though he were addicted to bella-donna, but there was a glassy glitter about them which that drug does not produce.

When questioned by the Principal as to why he was there, Paul stated, politely enough, that he wanted to come back to school. This was a lie, but Paul was quite accustomed to lying; found it, indeed,

Willa Cather, "Paul's Case," in Youth and the Bright Medusa. *New York: Knopf.* 1933.

indispensable for overcoming friction. His teachers were asked to state their respective charges against him, which they did with such a rancour and aggrievedness as evinced that this was not a usual case. Disorder and impertinence were among the offences named, yet each of his instructors felt that it was scarcely possible to put into words the real cause of the trouble, which lay in a sort of hysterically defiant manner of the boy's; in the contempt which they all knew he felt for them, and which he seemingly made not the least effort to conceal. Once, when he had been making a synopsis of a paragraph at the blackboard, his English teacher had stepped to his side and attempted to guide his hand. Paul had started back with a shudder and thrust his hands violently behind him. The astonished woman could scarcely have been more hurt and embarrassed had he struck at her. The insult was so involuntary and definitely personal as to be unforgettable. In one way and another, he had made all his teachers, men and women alike, conscious of the same feeling of physical aversion. In one class he habitually sat with his hand shading his eyes; in another he always looked out of the window during the recitation; in another he made a running commentary on the lecture, with humorous intent.

His teachers felt this afternoon that his whole attitude was symbolized by his shrug and his flippantly red carnation flower, and they fell upon him without mercy, his English teacher leading the pack. He stood through it smiling, his pale lips parted over his white teeth. (His lips were continually twitching, and he had a habit of raising his eyebrows that was contemptuous and irritating to the last degree.) Older boys than Paul had broken down and shed tears under that ordeal, but his set smile did not once desert him, and his only sign of discomfort was the nervous trembling of the fingers that toyed with the buttons of his overcoat, and an occasional jerking of the other hand which held his hat. Paul was always smiling, always glancing about him, seeming to feel that people might be watching him and trying to detect something. This conscious expression, since it was as far as possible from boyish mirthfulness, was usually attributed to insolence or "smartness."

As the inquisition proceeded, one of his instructors repeated an impertinent remark of the boy's, and the Principal asked him whether he thought that a courteous speech to make to a woman. Paul shrugged his shoulders slightly and his eyebrows twitched.

"I don't know," he replied. "I didn't mean to be polite or impolite, either. I guess it's a sort of way I have, of saying things regardless."

The Principal asked him whether he didn't think that a way it would be well to get rid of. Paul grinned and said he guessed so. When he was told that he could go, he bowed gracefully and went out. His bow was like a repetition of the scandalous red carnation.

His teachers were in despair, and his drawing master voiced the feeling of them all when he declared there was something about the boy which none of them understood. He added: "I don't really believe that smile of his comes altogether from insolence; there's something sort of haunted about it. The boy is not strong, for one thing. There is something wrong about the fellow."

The drawing master had come to realize that, in looking at Paul, one saw only his white teeth and the forced animation of his eyes. One warm afternoon the boy had gone to sleep at his drawing-board, and his master had noted with amazement what a white, blue-veined face it was; drawn and wrinkled like an old man's about the eyes, the lips twitching even in his sleep.

His teachers left the building dissatisfied and unhappy; humiliated to have felt so vindictive toward a mere boy, to have uttered this feeling in cutting terms, and to have set each other on, as it were, in the grewsome game of intemperate reproach. One of them remembered having seen a miserable street cat set at bay by a ring of tormentors.

As for Paul, he ran down the hill whistling the Soldiers' Chorus from *Faust*, looking behind him now and then to see whether some of his teachers were not there to witness his light-heartedness. As it was now late in the afternoon and Paul was on duty that evening as usher at Carnegie Hall, he decided that he would not go home to supper.

When he reached the concert hall, the doors were not yet open. It was chilly outside, and he decided to go up into the picture gallery —always deserted at this hour—where there were some of Raffelli's gay studies of Paris streets and an airy blue Venetian scene or two that always exhilarated him. He was delighted to find no one in the gallery but the old guard, who sat in the corner, a newspaper on his knee, a black patch over one eye and the other closed. Paul possessed himself of the place and walked confidently up and down, whistling under his breath. After a while he sat down before a blue Rico and lost himself. When he bethought him to look at his watch, it was after seven o'clock, and he rose with a start and ran downstairs, making a face at Augustus Caesar, peering out from the cast-room, and an evil gesture at the Venus of Milo as he passed her on the stairway.

When Paul reached the ushers' dressing-room, half-a-dozen boys were there already, and he began excitedly to tumble into his uniform. It was one of the few that at all approached fitting, and Paul thought it very becoming—though he knew the tight, straight coat accentuated his narrow chest, about which he was exceedingly sensitive. He was always excited while he dressed, twanging all over to the tuning of the strings and the preliminary flourishes of the horns in the music-room; but tonight he seemed quite beside himself, and he teased and plagued the boys until, telling him that he was crazy, they put him down on the floor and sat on him.

Somewhat calmed by his suppression, Paul dashed out to the front of the house to seat the early comers. He was a model usher. Gracious and smiling he ran up and down the aisles. Nothing was too much trouble for him; he carried messages and brought programmes as though it were his greatest pleasure in life, and all the people in his section thought him a charming boy, feeling that he remembered and admired them. As the house filled, he grew more and more vivacious and animated, and the colour came to his cheeks and lips. It was very much as though this were a great reception and Paul were the host. Just as the musicians came out to take their places, his English teacher arrived with cheques for the seats which a prominent manufacturer had taken for the season. She betrayed some embarrassment when she handed Paul the tickets, and a *hauteur* which subsequently made her feel very foolish. Paul was startled for a moment, and had the feeling of wanting to put her out; what business had she here among all these fine people and gay colours? He looked her over and decided that she was not appropriately dressed and must be a fool to sit downstairs in such togs. The tickets had probably been sent her out of kindness, he reflected, as he put down a seat for her, and she had about as much right to sit there as he had.

When the symphony began, Paul sank into one of the rear seats with a long sigh of relief, and lost himself as he had done before the Rico. It was not that symphonies, as such, meant anything in particular to Paul, but the first sigh of the instruments seemed to free some hilarious spirit within him; something that struggled there like the Genius in the bottle found by the Arab fisherman. He felt a sudden zest of life; the lights danced before his eyes and the concert hall blazed into unimaginable splendour. When the soprano soloist came on, Paul forgot even the nastiness of his teacher's being there, and gave himself up to the peculiar intoxication such personages always had for him. The soloist chanced to be a German woman, by no means in her first youth, and the mother of many children; but she wore a satin gown and a tiara, and she had that indefinable air of achievement, that world-shine upon her, which always blinded Paul to possible defects.

After a concert was over, Paul was often irritable and wretched until he got to sleep—and tonight he was even more than usually restless. He had the feeling of not being able to let down; of its being impossible to give up this delicious excitement which was the only thing that could be called living at all. During the last number he withdrew and, after hastily changing his clothes in the dressing-room, slipped out to the side door where the singer's carriage stood. Here he began pacing rapidly up and down the walk, waiting to see her come out.

Over yonder the Schenley, in its vacant stretch, loomed big and square through the fine rain, the windows of its twelve stories glowing like those of a lighted cardboard house under a Christmas tree. All the actors and singers of any importance stayed there when they were in Pittsburgh, and a number of the big manufacturers of the place lived there in the winter. Paul had often hung about the hotel, watching the people go in and out, longing to enter and leave school-masters and dull care behind him forever.

At last the singer came out, accompanied by the conductor, who helped her into her carriage and closed the door with a cordial *auf wiedersehen*—which set Paul to wondering whether she were not an old sweetheart of his. Paul followed the carriage over to the hotel, walking so rapidly as not to be far from the entrance when the singer alighted and disappeared behind the swinging glass doors which were opened by a negro in a tall hat and a long coat. In the moment that the door was ajar, it seemed to Paul that he, too, entered. He seemed to feel himself go after her up the steps, into the warm, lighted building, into an exotic, a tropical world of shiny, glistening surfaces and basking ease. He reflected upon the mysterious dishes that were brought into the dining-room, the green bottles in buckets of ice, as he had seen them in the supper party pictures of the Sunday supplement. A quick gust of wind brought the rain down with sudden vehemence, and Paul was startled to find that he was still outside in the slush of the gravel driveway; that his boots were letting in the water and his scanty overcoat was clinging wet about him; that the lights in front of the concert hall were out, and that the rain was driving in sheets between him and the orange glow of the windows above him. There it was, what he wanted—tangibly before him, like the fairy world of a Christmas pantomime; as the rain beat in his face, Paul wondered whether he were destined always to shiver in the black night outside, looking up at it.

He turned and walked reluctantly toward the car tracks. The end had to come sometime; his father in his night-clothes at the top of the stairs, explanations that did not explain, hastily improvised fictions that were forever tripping him up, his upstairs room and its horrible yellow wallpaper, the creaking bureau with the greasy plush collar-box, and over his painted wooden bed the pictures of George Washington and John Calvin, and the framed motto, "Feed my Lambs," which had been worked in red worsted by his mother, whom Paul could not remember.

Half an hour later, Paul alighted from the Negley Avenue car and went slowly down one of the side streets off the main thoroughfare. It was a highly respectable street, where all the houses were exactly alike, and where business men of moderate means begot and reared large families of children, all of whom went to Sabbath-school and learned the shorter catechism, and were interested in arithmetic; all of whom were as exactly alike as their homes, and of a piece with the monotony in which they lived. Paul never went up Cordelia Street without a shudder of loathing. His home was next the house of the Cumberland minister. He approached it tonight with the nerveless sense of defeat, the hopeless feeling of sinking back forever into ugliness and commonness that he had always had when he came home. The moment he turned into Cordelia Street he felt the waters close above his head. After each of these orgies of living, he experienced all the physical depression which follows a debauch; the loathing of respectable beds, of common food, of a house permeated by kitchen odours; a shuddering repulsion for the flavourless, colourless mass of every-day existence; a morbid desire for cool things and soft lights and fresh flowers.

The nearer he approached the house, the more absolutely unequal Paul felt to the sight of it all: his ugly sleeping chamber; the cold bath-room with the grimy zinc tub, the cracked mirror, the dripping spigots; his father, at the top of the stairs, his hairy legs sticking out from his nightshirt, his feet thrust into carpet slippers. He was so much later than usual that there would certainly be enquiries and reproaches. Paul stopped short before the door. He felt that he could not be accosted by his father tonight; that he could not toss again on that miserable bed. He would not go in. He would tell his father that he had no car fare, and it was raining so hard he had gone home with one of the boys and stayed all night.

Meanwhile, he was wet and cold. He went around to the back of the house and tried one of the basement windows, found it open, raised it cautiously, and scrambled down the cellar wall to the floor. There he stood, holding his breath, terrified by the noise he had made; but the floor above him was silent, and there was no creak on the stairs. He found a soap-box, and carried it over to the soft ring of light that streamed from the furnace door, and sat down. He was horribly afraid of rats, so he did not try to sleep, but sat looking distrustfully at the dark, still terrified lest he might have awakened his father.

In such reactions, after one of the experiences which made days and nights out of the dreary blanks of the calendar, when his senses were deadened, Paul's head was always singularly clear. Suppose his father had heard him getting in at the window and had come down and shot him for a burglar? Then, again, suppose his father had come down, pistol in hand, and he had cried out in time to save himself, and his father had been horrified to think how nearly he had killed him? Then, again, suppose a day should come when his father would remember that night, and wish there had been no warning cry to stay his hand? With this last supposition Paul entertained himself until daybreak.

The following Sunday was fine; the sodden November chill was broken by the last flash of autumnal summer. In the morning Paul had to go to church and Sabbath-school, as always. On seasonable Sunday afternoons the burghers of Cordelia Street usually sat out on their front "stoops," and talked to their neighbours on the next stoop, or called to those across the street in neighbourly fashion. The men sat placidly on gay cushions placed upon the steps that led down to the sidewalk, while the women, in their Sunday "waists," sat in rockers on the cramped porches, pretending to be greatly at their ease. The children played in the streets; there were so many of them that the place resembled the recreation grounds of a kinder-garten. The men on the steps, all in their shirt sleeves, their vests unbuttoned, sat with their legs well apart, their stomachs comfor-tably protruding, and talked of the prices of things, or told anec-dotes of the sagacity of their various chiefs and overlords. They occasionally looked over the multitude of squabbling children, listened affectionately to their high-pitched, nasal voices, smiling to see their own proclivities reproduced in their offspring, and inter-spersed their legends of the iron kings with remarks about their sons' progress at school, their grades in arithmetic, and the amounts they had saved in their toy banks.

On this last Sunday of November, Paul sat all the afternoon on the lowest step of his "stoop," staring into the street, while his sisters, in their rockers, were talking to the minister's daughters next door about how many shirt-waists they had made in the last week, and how many waffles someone had eaten at the last church supper. When the weather was warm, and his father was in a particularly jovial frame of mind, the girls made lemonade, which was always brought out in a red-glass pitcher, ornamented with forget-me-nots in blue enamel. This the girls thought very fine, and the neighbours joked about the suspicious colour of the pitcher.

Today Paul's father, on the top step, was talking to a young man who shifted a restless baby from knee to knee. He happened to be the young man who was daily held up to Paul as a model, and after whom it was his father's dearest hope that he would pattern. This young man was of a ruddy complexion, with a compressed, red mouth, and faded, near-sighted eyes, over which he wore thick spectacles, with gold bows that curved about his ears. He was clerk to one of the magnates of a great steel corporation, and was looked upon in Cordelia Street as a young man with a future. There was a story that, some five years ago—he was now barely twenty-six— he had been a trifle "dissipated," but in order to curb his appetites and save the loss of time and strength that a sowing of wild oats might have entailed, he had taken his chief's advice, oft reiterated to his employés, and at twenty-one had married the first woman whom he could persuade to share his fortunes. She happened to be an angular school-mistress, much older than he, who also wore thick glasses, and who had now borne him four children, all near-sighted like herself.

The young man was relating how his chief, now cruising in the Mediterranean, kept in touch with all the details of the business, arranging his office hours on his yacht just as though he were at home, and "knocking off work enough to keep two stenographers busy." His father told, in turn, the plan his corporation was considering, of putting in an electric railway plant at Cairo. Paul snapped his teeth; he had an awful apprehension that they might spoil it all before he got there. Yet he rather liked to hear these legends of the iron kings, that were told and retold on Sundays and holidays; these stories of palaces in Venice, yachts on the Mediterranean, and high play at Monte Carlo appealed to his fancy, and he was interested in the triumphs of cash boys who had become famous, though he had no mind for the cash boy stage.

After supper was over, and he had helped to dry the dishes, Paul nervously asked his father whether he could go to George's to get some help in his geometry, and still more nervously asked for car-fare. This latter request he had to repeat, as his father, on principle, did not like to hear requests for money, whether much or little. He asked Paul whether he could not go to some boy who lived nearer, and told him that he ought not to leave his school work until Sunday; but he gave him the dime. He was not a poor man, but he had a worthy ambition to come up in the world. His only reason for allowing Paul to usher was that he thought a boy ought to be earning a little.

Paul bounded upstairs, scrubbed the greasy odour of the dishwater from his hands with the ill-smelling soap he hated, and then shook over his fingers a few drops of violet water from the bottle he kept hidden in his drawer. He left the house with his geometry conspicuously under his arm, and the moment he got out of Cordelia Street and boarded a downtown car, he shook off the lethargy of two deadening days, and began to live again.

The leading juvenile of the permanent stock company which played at one of the downtown theatres was an acquaintance of Paul's, and the boy had been invited to drop in at the Sunday-night rehearsals whenever he could. For more than a year Paul had spent every available moment loitering about Charley Edwards's dressing-room. He had won a place among Edwards's following not only because the young actor, who could not afford to employ a dresser, often found him useful, but because he recognized in Paul something akin to what churchmen term "vocation."

It was at the theatre and at Carnegie Hall that Paul really lived; the rest was but a sleep and a forgetting. This was Paul's fairy tale, and it had for him all the allurement of a secret love. The moment he inhaled the gassy, painty, dusty odour behind the scenes, he breathed like a prisoner set free, and felt within him the possibility of doing or saying splendid, brilliant things. The moment the cracked orchestra beat out the overture from *Martha*, or jerked at the serenade from *Rigoletto*, all stupid and ugly things slid from him, and his senses were deliciously, yet delicately fired.

Perhaps it was because, in Paul's world, the natural nearly always wore the guise of ugliness, that a certain element of artificiality seemed to him necessery in beauty. Perhaps it was because his experience of life elsewhere was so full of Sabbath-school picnics, petty economies, wholesome advice as to how to succeed in life, and the unescapable odours of cooking, that he found this existence so alluring, these smartly-clad men and women so attractive, that he was so moved by these starry apple orchards that bloomed perennially under the lime-light. It would be difficult to put it strongly enough how convincingly the stage entrance of that theatre was for Paul the actual portal of Romance. Certainly none of the company ever suspected it, least of all Charley Edwards. It was very like the old stories that used to float about London of fabulously rich Jews, who had subterranean halls, with palms, and fountains, and soft lamps and richly apparelled women who never saw the disenchanting light of London day. So, in the midst of that smoke-palled city, enamoured of figures and grimy toil, Paul had his secret temple, his wishing-carpet, his bit of blue-and-white Mediterranean shore bathed in perpetual sunshine.

Several of Paul's teachers had a theory that his imagination had been perverted by garish fiction; but the truth was, he scarcely ever read at all. The books at home were not such as would either tempt or corrupt a youthful mind, and as for reading the novels that some of his friends urged upon him—well, he got what he wanted much more quickly from music; any sort of music, from an orchestra to a barrel organ. He needed only the spark, the indescribable thrill that made his imagination master of his senses, and he could make plots and pictures enough of his own. It was equally true that he was not stage-struck—not, at any rate, in the usual acceptation of that expression. He had no desire to become an actor, any more than he had to become a musician. He felt no necessity to do any of these things; what he wanted was to see, to be in the atmospere, float on the wave of it, to be carried out, blue league after league, away from everything.

After a night behind the scenes, Paul found the schoolroom more than ever repulsive; the bare floors and naked walls; the prosy men who never wore frock coats, or violets in their buttonholes; the women with their dull gowns, shrill voices, and pitiful seriousness about prepositions that govern the dative. He could not bear to have the other pupils think, for a moment, that he took these people seriously; he must convey to them that he considered it all trivial, and was there only by way of a joke, anyway. He had autographed pictures of all the members of the stock company which he showed his classmates, telling them the most incredible stories of his familiarity with these people, of his acquaintance with the soloists who came to Carnegie Hall, his suppers with them and the flowers he sent them. When these stories lost their effect, and his audience grew listless, he would bid all the boys good-bye, announcing that he was going to travel for a while; going to Naples, to California, to Egypt. Then, next Monday, he would slip back, conscious and nervously smiling; his sister was ill, and he would have to defer his voyage until spring.

Matters went steadily worse with Paul at school. In the itch to let his instructors know how heartily he despised them, and how thoroughly he was appreciated elsewhere, he mentioned once or twice that he had no time to fool with theorems; adding—with a twitch of the eyebrows and a touch of that nervous bravado which so perplexed them—that he was helping the people down at the stock company; they were old friends of his.

The upshot of the matter was that the Principal went to Paul's father, and Paul was taken out of school and put to work. The manager at Carnegie Hall was told to get another usher in his stead; the doorkeeper at the theatre was warned not to admit him to the house; and Charley Edwards remorsefully promised the boy's father not to see him again.

The members of the stock company were vastly amused when some of Paul's stories reached them—especially the women. They were hard-working women, most of them supporting indolent husbands or brothers, and they laughed rather bitterly at having stirred the boy to such fervid and florid inventions. They agreed with the faculty and with his father, that Paul's was a bad case.

The east-bound train was ploughing through a January snow-storm; the dull dawn was beginning to show grey when the engine whistled a mile out of Newark. Paul started up from the seat where he had lain curled in uneasy slumber, rubbed the breath-misted window glass with his hand, and peered out. The snow was whirling in curling eddies above the white bottom lands, and the drifts lay already deep in the fields and along the fences, while here and there the tall dead grass and dried weed stalks protruded black above it. Lights shone from the scattered houses, and a gang of labourers who stood beside the track waved their lanterns.

Paul had slept very little, and he felt grimy and uncomfortable. He had made the all-night journey in a day coach because he was afraid if he took a Pullman he might be seen by some Pittsburgh business man who had noticed him in Denny & Carson's office. When the whistle woke him, he clutched quickly at his breast pocket, glancing about him with an uncertain smile. But the little, clay-bespattered Italians were still sleeping, the slatternly women across the aisle were in open-mouthed oblivion, and even the crumby, crying babies were for the nonce stilled. Paul settled back to struggle with his impatience as best he could.

When he arrived at the Jersey City station, he hurried through his breakfast, manifestly ill at ease and keeping a sharp eye about him. After he reached the Twenty-third Street station, he consulted a cabman, and had himself driven to a men's furnishing establishment which was just opening for the day. He spent upward of two hours there, buying with endless reconsidering and great care. His new street suit he put on in the fitting-room; the frock coat and dress clothes he had bundled into the cab with his new shirts. Then he drove to a hatter's and a shoe house. His next errand was at Tiffany's, where he selected silver mounted brushes and a scarf-pin. He would not wait to have his silver marked, he said. Lastly, he stopped at a trunk shop on Broadway, and had his purchases packed into various travelling bags.

It was a little after one o'clock when he drove up to the Waldorf, and, after settling with the cabman, went into the office. He registered from Washington; said his mother and father had been abroad, and that he had come down to await the arrival of their steamer. He told his story plausibly and had no trouble, since he offered to pay for them in advance, in engaging his rooms; a sleeping-room, sitting-room and bath.

Not once, but a hundred times Paul had planned this entry into New York. He had gone over every detail of it with Charley Edwards, and in his scrap book at home there were pages of description about New York hotels, cut from the Sunday papers.

When he was shown to his sitting-room on the eighth floor, he saw at a glance that everything was as it should be; there was but one detail in his mental picture that the place did not realize, so he rang for the bell boy and sent him down for flowers. He moved about nervously until the boy returned, putting away his new linen and fingering it delightedly as he did so. When the flowers came, he put them hastily into water, and then tumbled into a hot bath. Presently he came out of his white bathroom, resplendent in his new silk underwear, and playing with the tassels of his red robe. The snow was whirling so fiercely outside his windows that he could scarcely see across the street; but within, the air was deliciously soft and fragrant. He put the violets and jonquils on the tabouret beside the couch, and threw himself down with a long sigh, covering himself with a Roman blanket. He was thoroughly tired; he had been in such haste, he had stood up to such a strain, covered so much ground in the last twenty-four hours, that he wanted to think how it had all come about. Lulled by the sound of the wind, the warm air, and the cool fragrance of the flowers, he sank into deep, drowsy retrospection.

It had been wonderfully simple; when they had shut him out of the theatre and concert hall, when they had taken away his bone, the whole thing was virtually determined. The rest was a mere matter of opportunity. The only thing that at all surprised him was his own courage—for he realized well enough that he had always been tormented by fear, a sort of apprehensive dread which, of late years, as the meshes of the lies he had told closed about him, had been pulling the muscles of his body tighter and tighter. Until now, he could not remember a time when he had not been dreading something. Even when he was a little boy, it was always there— behind him, or before, or on either side. There had always been the shadowed corner, the dark place into which he dared not look, but from which something seemed always to be watching him—and Paul had done things that were not pretty to watch, he knew.

But now he had a curious sense of relief, as though he had at last thrown down the gauntlet to the thing in the corner.

Yet it was but a day since he had been sulking in the traces; but yesterday afternoon that he had been sent to the bank with Denny & Carson's deposit, as usual—but this time he was instructed to leave the book to be balanced. There was above two thousand dollars in cheques, and nearly a thousand in the bank notes which he had taken from the book and quietly transferred to his pocket. At the bank he had made out a new deposit slip. His nerves had been steady enough to permit of his returning to the office, where he had finished his work and asked for a full day's holiday tomorrow, Saturday, giving a perfectly reasonable pretext. The bank book, he knew, would not be returned before Monday or Tuesday, and his father would be out of town for the next week. From the time he slipped the bank notes into his pocket until he boarded the night train for New York, he had not known a moment's hesitation.

How astonishingly easy it had all been; here he was, the thing done; and this time there would be no awakening, no figure at the

top of the stairs. He watched the snow flakes whirling by his window
until he fell asleep.

When he awoke, it was four o'clock in the afternoon. He bounded
up with a start; one of his precious days gone already! He spent
nearly an hour in dressing, watching every stage of his toilet carefully
in the mirror. Everything was quite perfect; he was exactly the
kind of boy he had always wanted to be.

When he went downstairs, Paul took a carriage and drove up
Fifth avenue toward the Park. The snow had somewhat abated;
carriages and tradesmen's wagons were hurrying soundlessly to and
fro in the winter twilight; boys in woollen mufflers were shovelling
off the doorsteps; the avenue stages made fine spots of colour against
the white street. Here and there on the corners whole flower gardens
blooming behind glass windows, against which the snowflakes stuck
and melted; violets, roses, carnations, lilies of the valley—somehow
vastly more lovely and alluring that they blossomed thus unnatu-
rally in the snow. The Park itself was a wonderful stage winter-piece.

When he returned, the pause of the twilight had ceased, and the
tune of the streets had changed. The snow was falling faster, lights
streamed from the hotels that reared their many stories fearlessly
up into the storm, defying the raging Atlantic winds. A long, black
stream of carriages poured down the avenue, intersected here and
there by other streams, tending horizontally. There were a score of
cabs about the entrance of his hotel, and his driver had to wait.
Boys in livery were running in and out of the awning stretched across
the sidewalk, up and down the red velvet carpet laid from the door
to the street. Above, about, within it all, was the rumble and roar,
the hurry and toss of thousands of human beings as hot for pleasure
as himself, and on every side of him towered the glaring affirmation
of the omnipotence of wealth.

The boy set his teeth and drew his shoulders together in a spasm
of realization; the plot of all dramas, the text of all romances, the
nerve-stuff of all sensations was whirling about him like the snow
flakes. He burnt like a fagot in a tempest.

When Paul came down to dinner, the music of the orchestra
floated up the elevator shaft to greet him. As he stepped into the
thronged corridor, he sank back into one of the chairs against the
wall to get his breath. The lights, the chatter, the perfumes, the

bewildering medley of colour—he had, for a moment, the feeling of not being able to stand it. But only for a moment; these were his own people, he told himself. He went slowly about the corridors, through the writing-rooms, smoking-rooms, reception-rooms, as though he were exploring the chambers of an enchanted palace, built and peopled for him alone.

When he reached the dining-room he sat down at a table near a window. The flowers, the white linen, the many-coloured wine glasses, the gay toilettes of the women, the low popping of corks, the undulating repetitions of the *Blue Danube* from the orchestra, all flooded Paul's dream with bewildering radiance. When the roseate tinge of his champagne was added—that cold, precious, bubbling stuff that creamed and foamed in his glass—Paul wondered that there were honest men in the world at all. This was what all the world was fighting for, he reflected; this was what all the struggle was about. He doubted the reality of his past. Had he ever known a place called Cordelia Street, a place where fagged looking business men boarded the early car? Mere rivets in a machine they seemed to Paul—sickening men, with combings of children's hair always hanging to their coats, and the smell of cooking in their clothes. Cordelia Street—Ah, that belonged to another time and country! Had he not always been thus, had he not sat here night after night, from as far back as he could remember, looking pensively over just such shimmering textures, and slowly twirling the stem of a glass like this one between his thumb and middle finger? He rather thought he had.

He was not in the least abashed or lonely. He had no especial desire to meet or to know any of these people; all he demanded was the right to look on and conjecture, to watch the pageant. The mere stage properties were all he contended for. Nor was he lonely later in the evening, in his loge at the Opera. He was entirely rid of his nervous misgivings, of his forced aggressiveness, of the imperative desire to show himself different from his surroundings. He felt now that his surroundings explained him. Nobody questioned the purple; he had only to wear it passively. He had only to glance down at his dress coat to reassure himself that here it would be impossible for anyone to humiliate him.

He found it hard to leave his beautiful sitting-room to go to bed that night, and sat long watching the raging storm from his turret window. When he went to sleep, it was with the lights turned on in his bedroom; partly because of his old timidity, and partly so that, if he should wake in the night, there would be no wretched moment of doubt, no horrible suspicion of yellow wall-paper, or of Washington and Calvin above his bed.

On Sunday morning the city was practically snowbound. Paul breakfasted late, and in the afternoon he fell in with a wild San Francisco boy, a freshman at Yale, who said he had run down for a "little flyer" over Sunday. The young man offered to show Paul the night side of the town, and the two boys went off together after dinner, not returning to the hotel until seven o'clock the next morning. They had started out in the confiding warmth of a champagne friendship, but their parting in the elevator was singularly cool. The freshman pulled himself together to make his train, and Paul went to bed. He awoke at two o'clock in the afternoon, very thirsty and dizzy, and rang for ice-water, coffee, and the Pittsburgh papers.

On the part of the hotel management, Paul excited no suspicion. There was this to be said for him, that he wore his spoils with dignity and in no way made himself conspicuous. His chief greediness lay in his ears and eyes, and his excesses were not offensive ones. His dearest pleasures were the grey winter twilights in his sitting-room; his quiet enjoyment of his flowers, his clothes, his wide divan, his cigarette, and his sense of power. He could not remember a time when he had felt so at peace with himself. The mere release from the necessity of petty lying, lying every day and every day, restored his self-respect. He had never lied for pleasure, even at school; but to make himself noticed and admired, to assert his difference from other Cordelia Street boys; and he felt a good deal more manly, more honest, even, now that he had no need for boastful pretensions, now that he could, as his actor friends used to say, "dress the part." It was characteristic that remorse did not occur to him. His golden days went by without a shadow, and he made each as perfect as he could.

On the eighth day after his arrival in New York, he found the whole affair exploited in the Pittsburgh papers, exploited with a wealth of detail which indicated that local news of a sensational nature was at a low ebb. The firm of Denny & Carson announced that the boy's father had refunded the full amount of his theft, and that they had no intention of prosecuting. The Cumberland minister had been interviewed, and expressed his hope of yet reclaiming the motherless lad, and Paul's Sabbath-school teacher declared that she would spare no effort to that end. The rumour had reached Pittsburgh that the boy had been seen in a New York hotel, and his father had gone East to find him and bring him home.

Paul had just come in to dress for dinner; he sank into a chair, weak in the knees, and clasped his head in his hands. It was to be worse than jail, even; the tepid waters of Cordelia Street were to close over him finally and forever. The grey monotony stretched before him in hopeless, unrelieved years;—Sabbath-school, Young People's Meeting, the yellow-papered room, the damp dish-towels; it all rushed back upon him with sickening vividness. He had the old feeling that the orchestra had suddenly stopped, the sinking sensation that the play was over. The sweat broke out on his face, and he sprang to his feet, looked about him with his white, conscious smile, and winked at himself in the mirror. With something of the childish belief in miracles with which he had so often gone to class, all his lessons unlearned, Paul dressed and dashed whistling down the corridor to the elevator.

He had no sooner entered the dining-room and caught the measure of the music than his remembrance was lightened by his old elastic power of claiming the moment, mounting with it, and finding it all sufficient. The glare and glitter about him, the mere scenic accessories had again, and for the last time, their old potency. He would show himself that he was game, he would finish the thing splendidly. He doubted, more than ever the existence of Cordelia Street, and for the first time he drank his wine recklessly. Was he not, after all, one of these fortunate beings? Was he not still himself, and in his own place? He drummed a nervous accompaniment to the music and looked about him, telling himself over and over that it had paid.

He reflected drowsily, to the swell of the violin and the chill sweetness of his wine, that he might have done it more wisely. He might have caught an outbound steamer and been well out of their clutches before now. But the other side of the world had seemed too far away and too uncertain then; he could not have waited for it; his need had been too sharp. If he had to choose over again, he would do the same thing tomorrow. He looked affectionately about the dining-room, now gilded with a soft mist. Ah, it had paid indeed!

Paul was awakened next morning by a painful throbbing in his head and feet. He had thrown himself across the bed without undressing, and had slept with his shoes on. His limbs and hands were lead heavy, and his tongue and throat were parched. There came upon him one of those fateful attacks of clear-headedness that never occurred except when he was physically exhausted and his nerves hung loose. He lay still and closed his eyes and let the tide of realities wash over him.

His father was in New York; "stopping at some joint or other," he told himself. The memory of successive summers on the front stoop fell upon him like a weight of black water. He had not a hundred dollars left; and he knew now, more than ever, that money was everything, the wall that stood between all he loathed and all he wanted. The thing was winding itself up; he had thought of that on his first glorious day in New York, and had even provided a way to snap the thread. It lay on his dressing-table now; he had got it out last night when he came blindly up from dinner—but the shiny metal hurt his eyes, and he disliked the look of it, anyway.

He rose and moved about with a painful effort, succumbing now and again to attacks of nausea. It was the old depression exaggerated; all the world had become Cordelia Street. Yet somehow he was not afraid of anything, was absolutely calm; perhaps because he had looked into the dark corner at last, and knew. It was bad enough, what he saw there; but somehow not so bad as his long fear of it had been. He saw everything clearly now. He had a feeling that he had made the best of it, that he had lived the sort of life he was meant to live, and for half an hour he sat staring at the revolver. But he told himself that was not the way, so he went downstairs and took a cab to the ferry.

When Paul arrived at Newark, he got off the train and took another cab, directing the driver to follow the Pennsylvania tracks out of the town. The snow lay heavy on the roadways and had drifted deep in the open fields. Only here and there the dead grass or dried weed stalks projected, singularly black, above it. Once well into the country, Paul dismissed the carriage and walked, floundering along the tracks, his mind a medley of irrelevant things. He seemed to hold in his brain an actual picture of everything he had seen that morning. He remembered every feature of both his drivers, the toothless old woman from whom he had bought the red flowers in his coat, the agent from whom he had got his ticket, and all of his fellow-passengers on the ferry. His mind, unable to cope with vital matters near at hand, worked feverishly and deftly at sorting and grouping these images. They made for him a part of the ugliness of the world, of the ache in his head, and the bitter burning on his tongue. He stooped and put a handful of snow into his mouth as he walked, but that, too, seemed hot. When he reached a little hillside, where the tracks ran through a cut some twenty feet below him, he stopped and sat down.

The carnations in his coat were drooping with the cold, he noticed; their red glory over. It occurred to him that all the flowers he had seen in the show windows that first night must have gone the same way, long before this. It was only one splendid breath they had, in spite of their brave mockery at the winter outside the glass. It was a losing game in the end, it seemed, this revolt against the homilies by which the world is run. Paul took one of the blossoms carefully from his coat and scooped a little hole in the snow, where he covered it up. Then he dozed awhile, from his weak condition, seeming insensible to the cold.

The sound of an approaching train woke him, and he started to his feet, remembering only his resolution, and afraid lest he should be too late. He stood watching the approaching locomotive, his teeth chattering, his lips drawn away from them in a frightened smile; once or twice he glanced nervously sidewise, as though he were being watched. When the right moment came, he jumped. As he fell, the folly of his haste occurred to him with merciless clearness, the vastness of what he had left undone. There flashed through his brain, clearer than ever before, the blue of Adriatic water, the yellow of Algerian sands.

He felt something strike his chest,—his body was being thrown swiftly through the air, on and on, immeasurably far and fast, while his limbs gently relaxed. Then, because the picture making mechanism was crushed, the disturbing visions flashed into black, and Paul dropped back into the immense design of things.

PART FOUR

BRAIN DISORDERS

The neuroses, psychoses, and character disorders are distortions of personality considered to be functional or psychogenic in origin. This implies that the primary etiology of these conditions lies in early faulty social relationships and in the vicissitudes of anxiety. There are many other abnormal conditions, however, which arise out of disturbances in the central nervous system and most particularly the brain.

The form and severity of impairment resulting from organic pathology depends on several factors. First, the specific form of damage, whether infection, trauma, degeneration, malignant growth, or toxic action, must be considered along with the extent of damage. Secondly, the premorbid personality of the individual should be carefully examined as this will have important consequences for the course and prognosis of the disorder. This simply means that a well-integrated person will be better able to cope with his new disability than will an individual with a neurotic or psychotic predisposition. In these latter types, the inevitable temporary disorganization of personality brought about by even a mild brain disturbance may spiral into a full-fledged neurotic or psychotic behavior pattern.

Epilepsy and senility, represented in the selections of Dostoevski and Swift, are forms of what are known as the chronic brain disorders. These are the more or less irreversible organic pathological conditions in which brain tissue has been permanently destroyed, resulting in impaired cognitive and emotional functioning. Syphilis and the congenital brain anamalies (microcephaly, hydrocephaly, and others) are other forms of such chronic disorders.

There are also conditions known as acute brain disorders, involving relatively temporary and reversible tissue damage, as in sudden physical trauma, alcoholic intake, and various infections.

Another form of organic disability is mental retardation. Increasing interest is currently being focussed on this problem, although the condition itself has long been recognized. There are more than five million retarded persons in the United States at this time, but the problem of classifying their condition is still unresolved. Some systems utilize IQ ratings, some focus on educability and adjustment potential, still others concern themselves with etiology. Most important, however, is that retardation is no longer a family stigma which must be hidden and denied as in Porter's *He;* and, as with the other disorders we have discussed, once out in the open and recognized, methods of prevention and treatment can be developed.

Epilepsy

Epilepsy represents an abnormal brain condition which gives rise to convulsions of varying degrees of intensity, as well as to disorders of consciousness. Epileptic conditions have long been observed and described, and their classification is well delineated. There are four chief forms.

The first is the dramatic *grand mal* attack, characterized by violent convulsions and subsequent loss of consciousness.

The *petit mal* seizure is a milder, often unnoticed, disturbance of consciousness in which the individual experiences a transient blackout.

During *psychomotor seizures* no convulsive activity occurs, but rather a loss of consciousness without the cessation of organized behavior. In other words, the person is no longer in touch with reality, yet he is able to carry on some degree of organized behavior. During this time his behavior may be bizarre or impulsive and violent.

Jacksonian seizures are marked by very limited convulsive activity in a distinct and isolated part of the body—such as an eye twitch or a spasm of the upper arm—which then spreads to neighboring muscle systems.

In terms of etiology, it is clear that the epileptic seizures are a result of disturbances in the brain's electrical activity, a fact long attested to by abnormal findings on the EEG (electroencephalogram). These abnormalities are tied to certain personality traits, although the notion of a single "epileptic personality" is still open to question. Often the epileptic individual, who lives under the threat of a sudden loss of control, appears to be prone to emotional outbursts, to be querulous and morose, and to be generally distractible and stubborn. All of these traits can be seen as responses to the real difficulty in adapting which the epileptic faces.

Dostoevsky, who himself suffered from a severe seizure disorder, presents in Prince Myshkin a magnificient portrait of the epileptic's struggle with self-control. In these passages from *The Idiot*, the development of Myshkin's *grand mal* seizure is followed from an initial stage of restless impatience through a period of heightened excitement to the climax on the stairs with its wild cry and furious loss of control. The premonitory symptoms, called the aura, which means "wind before the storm," are ominously noted by Dostoevsky—"The storm was certainly gathering, though slowly. It was beginning to thunder far away. The air had become very sultry. . . ."

THE IDIOT

Kolya had not made his appearance at half-past three, nor even at four. Myshkin went out and walked away mechanically. At the beginning of summer in Petersburg there are sometimes exquisite days—bright, still and hot. By good fortune this day was one of those rare days. For some time Myshkin wandered aimlessly. He knew the town very little. He stood still sometimes in squares, on bridges, or at cross roads facing certain houses; once he went into a confectioner's to rest. Sometimes he began watching the passers-by with great interest; but most of the time he scarcely noticed the people in the street, nor where he was going. He was painfully strained and restless, and at the same time he felt an extraordinary craving for solitude. He longed to be alone and to give himself up quite passively to this agonising emotion without seeking to escape from it. He loathed the thought of facing the questions that were surging in his heart and his mind. "Am I to blame for all this?" he muttered to himself, almost unconscious of his own words.

Towards six o'clock he found himself at the railway station of the Tsarskoe Syelo line. Solitude had soon become unbearable; a new warm impulse seized upon his heart, and for one moment the darkness in which his soul was steeped was lighted up by a ray of brightness. He took a ticket to Pavlovsk and was in impatient haste to get off; but, of course, he was pursued by something, and that something

Fyodor Dostoevsky, from The Idiot, *tr. by Constance Garnett. New York: Bantam Books, 1958.*

was a reality and not a fancy, as he was perhaps inclined to imagine. He had almost taken his seat in the train, when he suddenly flung the ticket he had only just taken on the floor and went back out of the station, pondering and confused. Some time later in the street he seemed suddenly to recall something; he seemed suddenly to grasp something very strange, something that had long worried him. He suddenly realised that he had been doing something which he had been doing for a long time, though he had not been aware of it till that minute. For some hours previously, even at "The Scales," and even before he went there, he had at intervals begun suddenly looking for something. He would forget it for a long while, half an hour at a time, and then begin looking about him again uneasily.

But he had no sooner observed in himself this morbid and till then quite unconscious impulse, when there flashed upon his mind another recollection which interested him extremely. He remembered that, at the moment when he became aware that he was absorbed in looking for something, he was standing on the pavement before a shop window, examining with great interest the goods exposed in it. He felt he must find out whether he really had stood before that shop window just now, five minutes, perhaps, before; whether he hadn't dreamed it; whether he wasn't mistaken. Did that shop really exist with the goods in its window? He certainly felt specially unwell that day, almost as he used in the past when an attack of his old disease was coming on. He knew that a such times he used to be exceptionally absent-minded, and often mixed up things and people, if he did not look at them with special strained attention. But there was another special reason why he wanted to find out whether he really had been standing then before that shop. Among the things in the shop window was one thing he had looked at, he had even mentally fixed the price of it at sixty kopecks. He remembered that in spite of his absent-mindedness and agitation. If, then, that shop existed and that thing really was in the window, he must have stopped simply to look at that thing. So it must have interested him so much that it attracted his attention, even at the time when he was in such distress and confusion, just after he had come out of the railway station. He walked almost in anguish, looking to the right and his heart beat with uneasy impatience. But here was the shop, he had found it at last! He had been five hundred paces from it when he had felt impelled to turn back. And there was the article worth sixty kopecks. "It would be certainly sixty kopecks, it's not worth more," he repeated now and laughed. But his laughter was hysterical; he felt very wretched. He remembered clearly now that just when he had been standing here before this window he had suddenly turned round, as he had done that morning when he caught Rogozhin's eyes fixed upon him. Making certain that he was not mistaken (though he had felt quite sure of it before), he left the shop and walked quickly away from it. He must certainly think it all over. It was clear now that it had not been his fancy at the station either, that something real must have happened to him, and that it must be overcome again by a sort of insuperable inner loathing: he did not want to think anything out, and he did not; he fell to musing on something quite different.

He remembered among other things that he always had one minute just before the epileptic fit (if it came on while he was awake), when suddenly in the midst of sadness, spiritual darkness and oppression, there seemed at moments a flash of light in his brain, and with extraordinary impetus all his vital forces suddenly began working at their highest tension. The sense of life, the consciousness of self, were multiplied ten times at these moments which passed like a flash of lightning. His mind and his heart were flooded with extraordinary light; all his uneasiness, all his doubts, all his anxieties were relieved at once; they were all merged in a lofty calm, full of serene, harmonious joy and hope. But these moments, these flashes, were only the prelude of that final second (it was never more than a second) with which the fit began. That second was, of course, unendurable. Thinking of that moment later, when he was all right again, he often said to himself that all these gleams and flashes of the highest sensation of life and self-consciousness, and therefore also of the highest form of existence, were nothing but disease, the interruption of the normal conditions; and if so, it was not at all the highest form of being, but on the contrary must be reckoned the lowest. And yet he came at last to an extremely paradoxical conclusion. "What if it is disease?" he decided at last. "What does it matter that it is an abnormal intensity, if the result, if the minute of sensation, remembered and analysed afterwards in health, turns out to be the acme of harmony and beauty, and gives a feeling, unknown and undivined till then, of completeness, of proportion, of reconciliation, and of ecstatic devotional merging in the highest synthesis of life?" These vague expressions seemed to him very comprehensible, though too weak. That it really was "beauty and worship," that it really was the "highest synthesis of life" he could not doubt, and could not admit the possibility of doubt. It was not as though he saw abnormal and unreal visions of some sort at that moment, as from hashish, opium, or wine, destroying the reason and distorting the soul. He was quite capable of judging of that when the attack was over. These moments were only an extraordinary quickening of self-consciousness—if the condition was to be expressed in one word—and at the same time of the direct sensation of existence in the most intense degree. Since at that second, that is at the very last conscious moment before the fit, he had time to say to himself clearly and consciously, "Yes, for this moment one might give one's whole life!" then without doubt that moment was really worth the whole of life. He did not insist on the dialectical part of his argument, however. Stupefaction, spiritual darkness, idiocy stood before him conspicuously as the consequence of these "higher moments"; seriously, of course, he could not have disputed it. There was undoubtedly a mistake in his conclusion—that is, in his estimate of that minute, but the reality of the sensation somewhat perplexed him. What was he to make of that reality? For the very thing had happened; he actually had said to himself at that second, that, for the infinite happiness he had felt in it, that second really might well be worth the whole of life. "At that moment," as he told Rogozhin one day in Moscow at the time when they used to meet there, "at that moment I seem somehow to understand the extraordinary saying that *there shall be no more time.* Probably," he added, smiling, "this is the very second which was not long enough for the water to be spilt out of Mahomet's pitcher, though the epileptic prophet had time to gaze at all the habitations of Allah."

. . . It was sultry and there was a feeling in the air like a foreboding of a thunderstorm in the distance. His present contemplative mood had a certain charm for him. His mind and memory seemed to fasten upon every external object about him, and he found pleasure in it. He was yearning all the while to forget something in the present, something grave; but at the first glance about him he was aware again at once of his gloomy thought, the thought he was so longing to get away from. He recalled that he had talked at dinner to the waiter at the restaurant of a very strange murder which had excited much talk and sensation. But he had no sooner recollected it than something strange happened to him again.

An extraordinary, overwhelming desire, almost a temptation, suddenly paralyzed his will. He got up from the seat, walked straight from the Garden towards the Petersburg Side. Not long ago he had asked a passerby on the bank of the Neva to point out to him across the river the Petersburg Side. It was pointed out to him, but he had not gone there then. And in any case it would have been useless to go that day, he knew it. He had long had the address; he could easily find the house of Lebedyev's relation; but he knew almost for certain that he would not find her at home. "She certainly is gone to Pavlovsk, or Kolya would have left word at 'The Scales,' as he had agreed." So if he went there now, it was certainly not with the idea of seeing her. A gloomy, tormenting curiosity of another sort allured him now. A sudden new idea had come into his mind.

But it was enough for him that he had set off and that he knew where he was going; though a minute later he was walking along again almost unconscious of his surroundings. Further consideration of his "sudden idea" became all at once intensely distasteful to him, almost impossible. He stared with painfully strained attention at every object that met his eye: he gazed at the sky, at the Neva. He spoke to a little boy he met Perhaps his epileptic condition was growing more and more acute. The storm was certainly gathering, though slowly. It was beginning to thunder far away. The air had become very sultry. . . .

The gateway, which was always dark, was particularly dark at that moment; the storm-cloud had crept over the sky and engulfed the evening light, and at the very moment that Myshkin approached the house the storm broke and there was a downpour. He was just at the entrance of the gateway when he moved on abruptly after his momentary halt. And he suddenly saw in the half dark under the gateway close to the stairs a man. The man seemed to be waiting for something, but he vanished at once. Myshkin had only caught a glimpse of him and could not see him distinctly and could not have told for certain who he was. Besides, numbers of people might be passing here; it was a hotel and people were continually running in and out. But he suddenly felt a complete and overwhelming conviction that he recognised the man and that it was certainly Rogozhin.

A moment after, Myshkin rushed after him up the stairs. His heart sank. "Everything will be decided now," he repeated to himself with strange conviction.

The staircase up which Myshkin ran from the gateway led to the corridors of the first and second floors, on which were the rooms of the hotel. As in all old houses, the staircase was of stone, dark and narrow, and it turned round a thick stone column. On the first half-landing there was a hollow like a niche in the column, not more than half a yard wide and nine inches deep. Yet there was room for a man to stand there. Dark as it was, Myshkin, on reaching the half-landing, at once discovered that a man was hiding in the niche. Myshkin suddenly wanted to pass by without looking to the right. He had taken one step already, but he could not resist turning round.

Those two eyes, *the same two eyes*, met his own. The man hidden in the niche had already moved one step from it. For one second they stood facing one another and almost touching. Suddenly Myshkin seized him by the shoulders and turned him back towards the staircase, nearer to the light; he wanted to see his face more clearly.

Rogozhin's eyes flashed and a smile of fury contorted his face. His right hand was raised and something gleamed in it; Myshkin did not think of checking it. He only remembered that he thought he cried out, "Parfyon, I don't believe it!" Then suddenly something seemed torn asunder before him; his soul was flooded with intense *inner* light. The moment lasted perhaps half a second, yet he clearly and consciously remembered the beginning, the first sound of the fearful scream which broke of itself from his breast and which he could not have checked by any effort. Then his consciousness was instantly extinguished and complete darkness followed.

It was an epileptic fit, the first he had had for a long time. It is well known that epileptic fits come on quite suddenly. At the moment the face is horribly distorted, especially the eyes. The whole body and the features of the face work with convulsive jerks and contortions. A terrible, indescribable scream that is unlike anything else breaks from the sufferer. In that scream everything human seems obliterated and it is impossible, or very difficult, for an observer to realise and admit that it is the man himself screaming. It seems indeed as though it were some one else screaming from within the man. That is how many people at least have described their impression. The sight of a man in an epileptic fit fills many people with positive and unbearable horror, in which there is a certain element of the uncanny. It must be supposed that some such feeling of sudden horror, together with the other terrible sensations of the moment, had suddenly paralysed Rogozhin and so saved Myshkin from the knife with which he would have stabbed him. Then before he had time to grasp that it was a fit, seeing that Myshkin had staggered away from him and fallen backwards downstairs, knocking his head violently against the stone step, Rogozhin flew headlong downstairs, avoiding the prostrate figure, and, not knowing what he was doing, ran out of the hotel.

Struggling in violent convulsions, the sick man slipped down the steps, of which there were about fifteen, to the bottom of the staircase. Very soon, not more than five minutes later, he was noticed and a crowd collected. A pool of blood by his head raised the doubt whether the sick man had hurt himself, or whether there had been some crime. It was soon recognised, however, that it was a case of epilepsy; one of the people at the hotel recognised Myshkin as having arrived that morning. The difficulty was luckily solved by a fortunate circumstance.

Kolya Ivolgin, who had promised to be back at "The Scales" at four and had instead gone to Pavlovsk, had on a sudden impulse refused to dine at Madame Epanchin's, had come back to Petersburg and hurried to "The Scales," where he had turned up about seven o'clock. Learning from the note that Myshkin had left for him that the latter was in town, he hastened to find him at the address given in the note. Being informed in the hotel that Myshkin had gone out, he went downstairs to the restaurant and waited for him there, drinking tea and listening to the organ. Happening to overhear that some one had had a fit, he was led by a true presentiment to run out to the spot and recognised Myshkin. Suitable steps were taken at once. Myshkin was carried to his room. Though he regained consciousness, he did not fully come to himself for a long time. A doctor who was sent for to look at his injured head said there was not the least danger, and ordered a lotion. An hour later, when Myshkin began to be able to understand pretty well what was going on, Kolya took him in a covered carriage from the hotel to Lebedyev's. Lebedyev received the sick man with bows and extraordinary warmth. For his sake he hastened his removal, and three days later they were all at Pavlovsk.

Senility

In an era when the promise of an ever-increasing life span has moved from the realm of science fiction to that of scientific investigation, the biological, sociological, and psychological changes brought about by aging have become of greater concern than ever before.

In general, aging involves a decrease in flexibility and adaptability, impairment of cognitive functioning, physiological deterioration, and a wide variety of social status changes. This physical and mental decline is often accompanied by the development or exacerbation of emotional problems. These may take the form of withdrawal, depression, paranoid thinking, excitability, labile emotionality, or any of the other indices of psychopathology. As in all brain disorders, the emergent symptomatology will be related to the premorbid personality of the person.

These passages taken from Swift's *Gulliver's Travels* savagely, yet somewhat regretfully, catalogue the changes which accompany senescence. Along the way Swift's mordant wit mocks man's exalted fantasies about eternal life. His corrosive images echo Shakespeare's commentary on the final age of man:

> Last scene of all,
> That ends this strange eventful history,
> Is second childishness, and mere oblivion,
> Sans teeth, sans eyes, sans taste, sans everything.

Jonathan Swift

GULLIVER'S TRAVELS

One day in much good company I was asked by a person of quality, whether I had seen any of their *Struldbrugs*, or *Immortals*. I said I had not, and desired he would explain to me what he meant by such an appellation applied to a mortal creature. He told me, that sometimes, though very rarely, a child happened to be born in a family with a red circular spot in the forehead, directly over the left eyebrow, which was an infallible mark that it should never die. The spot, as he described it, was about the compass of a silver threepence, but in the course of time grew larger, and changed its colour; for at twelve years old it became green, so continued till five and twenty, then turned to a deep blue; at five and forty it grew coal black, and as large as an English shilling, but never admitted any further alteration. He said these births were so rare, that he did not believe there could be above eleven hundred *struldbrugs* of both sexes in the whole kingdom, of which he computed about fifty in the metropolis, and among the rest a young girl born about three years ago. That these productions were not peculiar to any family, but a mere effect of chance; and the children of the *struldbrugs* themselves were equally mortal with the rest of the people.

I freely own myself to have been struck with inexpressible delight upon hearing this account, and the person who gave it me happening to understand the Balnibarbian language, which I spoke very well, I could not forbear breaking out into expressions perhaps a little too

---

Jonathan Swift, from Gulliver's Travels. *New York: Random House, 1931.*

extravagant. I cried out as in a rapture: Happy nation where every child hath at least a chance for being immortal! Happy people who enjoy so many living examples of ancient virtue, and have masters ready to instruct them in the wisdom of all former ages! but, happiest beyond all comparison are those excellent *struldbrugs*, who being born exempt from that universal calamity of human nature, have their minds free and disengaged, without the weight and depression of spirits caused by the continual apprehension of death. I discovered my admiration that I had not observed any of these illustrious persons at court; the black spot on the forehead being so remarkable a distinction, that I could not have easily overlooked it; and it was impossible that his Majesty, a most judicious prince, should not provide himself with a good number of such wise and able counsellors. Yet perhaps the virtue of those reverend sages was too strict for the corrupt and libertine manners of a court. And we often find by experience that young men are too opinionative and volatile to be guided by the sober dictates of their seniors. However, since the King was pleased to allow me access to his royal person, I was resolved upon the very first occasion to deliver my opinion to him on this matter freely and at large, by the help of my interpreter; and whether he would please to take my advice or no, yet in one thing I was determined, that his Majesty having frequently offered me an establishment in this country, I would with great thankfulness accept the favour, and pass my life here in the conversation of those superior beings the *struldbrugs*, if they would please admit me.

The gentleman to whom I addressed my discourse, because (as I have already observed) he spoke the language of Balnibarbi, said to me with a sort of a smile, which usually ariseth from pity to the ignorant, that he was glad of any occasion to keep me among them, and desired my permission to explain to the company what I had spoke. He did so, and they talked together for some time in their own language, whereof I understood not a syllable, neither could I observe by their countenances what impression my discourse had made on them. After a short silence, the same person told me that his friends and mine (so he thought fit to express himself) were very much pleased with the judicious remarks I had made on the great happiness and advantages of immortal life; and they were desirous to know in a particular manner, what scheme of living I should have formed to myself, if it had fallen to my lot to have been born a *struldbrug*.

I answered, it was easy to be eloquent on so copious and delightful a subject, especially to me who have been often apt to amuse myself with visions of what I should do if I were a king, a general, or a great lord; and upon this very case I had frequently run over the whole system how I should employ myself and pass the time if I were sure to live for ever.

That if it had been my good fortune to come into the world a *struldbrug*, as soon as I could discover my own happiness by understanding the difference between life and death, I would first resolve by all arts and methods whatsoever to procure myself riches. In the pursuit of which by thrift and management, I might reasonably expect, in about two hundred years to be the wealthiest man in the kingdom. In the second place, I would from my earliest youth apply myself to the study of arts and sciences, by which I should arrive in time to excel all others in learning. Lastly, I would carefully record every action and event of consequence that happened in the public, impartially draw the characters of the several successions of princes and great ministers of state, with my own observations on every point. I would exactly set down the several changes in customs, language, fashions of dress, diet and diversions. By all which acquirements, I should be a living treasury of knowledge and wisdom, and certainly become the oracle of the nation.

I would never marry after threescore, but live in an hospitable manner, yet still on the saving side. I would entertain myself in forming and directing the minds of hopeful young men, by convincing them from my own remembrance, experience and observation, fortified by numerous examples, of the usefulness of virtue in public and private life. But my choice and constant companions should be a set of my own immortal brotherhood, among whom I would elect a dozen from the most ancient down to my own contemporaries. Where any of these wanted fortunes, I would provide them with convenient lodges round my own estate, and have some of them always at my table, only mingling a few of the most valuable among you mortals, whom length of time would harden me to lose with little or no reluctance, and treat your posterity after the same manner; just as a man diverts himself with the annual succession of pinks and tulips in his garden, without regretting the loss of those which withered the preceding year.

These *struldbrugs* and I would mutually communicate our observations and memorials through the course of time, remark the several gradations by which corruption steals into the world, and oppose it in every step, by giving perpetual warning and instruction to mankind; which, added to the strong influence of our own example, would probably prevent that continual degeneracy of human nature so justly complained of in all ages.

Add to all this the pleasure of seeing the various revolutions of states and empires, the changes in the lower and upper world, ancient cities in ruins, and obscure villages become the seats of kings. Famous rivers lessening into shallow brooks, the ocean leaving one coast dry, and overwhelming another; the discovery of many countries yet unknown. Barbarity overrunning the politest nations, and the most barbarous become civilized. I should then see the discovery of the longitude, the perpetual motion, the universal medicine, and many other great inventions brought to the utmost perfection.

What wonderful discoveries should we make in astronomy, by outliving and confirming our own predictions, by observing the progress and returns of comets, with the changes of motion in the sun, moon, and stars.

I enlarged upon many other topics, which the natural desire of endless life and sublunary happiness could easily furnish me with. When I had ended, and the sum of my discourse had been interpreted as before, to the rest of the company, there was a good deal of talk among them in the language of the country, not without some laughter at my expense. At last the same gentleman who had been my interpreter said he was desired by the rest to set me right in a few mistakes, which I had fallen into through the common imbecility of human nature, and upon that allowance was less answerable for them. That this breed of *struldbrugs* was peculiar to their country, for there were no such people either in Balnibarbi or Japan, where he had the honour to be ambassador from his Majesty, and found the natives in both those kingdoms very hard to believe that the fact was possible; and it appeared from my astonishment when he first mentioned the matter to me, that I received it as a thing wholly new, and scarcely to be credited. That in the two kingdoms above mentioned, where during his residence he had conversed very much, he observed long life to be the universal desire and wish of mankind. That whoever had one foot in the grave was sure to hold back the other as strongly as he could. That the oldest had still hopes of living one day longer, and looked on death as the greatest evil, from which nature always prompted him to retreat; only in this island of Luggnagg the appetite for living was not so eager, from the continual example of the *struldbrugs* before their eyes.

That the system of living contrived by me was unreasonable and unjust, because it supposed a perpetuity of youth, health, and vigour, which no man could be so foolish to hope, however extravagant he may be in his wishes. That the question therefore was not whether a man would choose to be always in the prime of youth, attended with prosperity and health, but how he would pass a perpetual life under all the usual disadvantages which old age brings along with it. For although few men will avow their desires of being immortal upon such hard conditions, yet in the two kingdoms before mentioned of Balnibarbi and Japan, he observed that every man desired to put off death for some time longer, let it approach ever so late; and he rarely heard of any man who died willingly, except he were incited by the extremity of grief or torture. And he appealed to me whether in those countries I had travelled as well as my own, I had not observed the same general disposition.

After this preface he gave me a particular account of the *struldbrugs* among them. He said they commonly acted like mortals, till about thirty years old, after which by degrees they grew melancholy and dejected, increasing in both till they came to fourscore. This he learned from their own confession; for otherwise there not being above two or three of that species born in an age, they were too few to form a general observation by. When they came to fourscore years, which is reckoned the extremity of living in this country, they had not only all the follies and infirmities of other old men, but many more which arose from the dreadful prospect of never dying. They were not only opinionative, peevish, covetous, morose, vain, talkative, but uncapable of friendship, and dead to all natural affection, which never descended below their grandchildren. Envy and impotent desires are their prevailing passions. But those objects against which their envy seems principally directed, are the vices of the younger sort, and the deaths of the old. By reflecting on the former, they find themselves cut off from all possibility of pleasure; and whenever they see a funeral, they lament and repine that others have gone to a harbour of rest, to which they themselves never can hope to arrive. They have no remembrance of anything but what they learned and observed in their youth and middle age, and even that is very imperfect. And for the truth or particulars of any fact, it is safer to depend on common traditions than upon their best recollections. The least miserable among them appear to be those who turn to dotage, and entirely lose their memories; these meet with more pity and assistance, because they want many bad qualities which abound in others.

If a *struldbrug* happen to marry one of his own kind, the marriage is dissolved of course by the courtesy of the kingdom, as soon as the younger of the two comes to be fourscore. For the law thinks it a reasonable indulgence, that those who are condemned without any fault of their own to a perpetual continuance in the world, should not have their misery doubled by the load of a wife.

As soon as they have completed the term of eighty years, they are looked on as dead in law; their heirs immediately succeed to their estates, only a small pittance is reserved for their support, and the poor ones are maintained at the public charge. After that period they are held incapable of any employment of trust or profit, they cannot purchase lands or take leases, neither are they allowed to be witnesses in any cause, either civil or criminal, not even for the decision of meers and bounds.

At ninety they lose their teeth and hair, they have at that age no distinction of taste, but eat and drink whatever they can get, without relish or appetite. The diseases they were subject to still continue without increasing or diminishing. In talking they forget the common appellation of things, and the names of persons, even of those who are their nearest friends and relations. For the same reason they never can amuse themselves with reading, because their memory will not serve to carry them from the beginning of a sentence to the end; and by this defect they are deprived of the lony entertainment whereof they might otherwise be capable.

The language of this country being always upon the flux, the *struldbrugs* of one age do not understand those of another, neither are they able after two hundred years to hold any conversation (farther than by a few general words) with their neighbours the mortals; and thus they lie under the disadvantage of living like foreigners in their own country.

This was the account given me of the *struldbrugs*, as near as I can remember. I afterwards saw five or six of different ages, the youngest not above two hundred years old, who were brought to me at several times by some of my friends; but although they were told that I was a great traveller, and had seen all the world, they had not the least curiosity to ask me a question; only desired I would give them *slumskudask*, or a token of remembrance, which is a modest way of begging, to avoid the law that strictly forbids it, because they are provided for by the public, although indeed with a very scanty allowance.

They are despised and hated by all sorts of people; when one of them is born, it is reckoned ominous, and their birth is recorded very particularly; so that you may know their age by consulting the registry, which however hath not been kept above a thousand years past, or at least hath been destroyed by time or public disturbances. But the usual way of computing how old they are, is by asking them what kings or great persons they can remember, and then consulting history, for infallibly the last prince in their mind did not begin his reign after they were fourscore years old.

They were the most mortifying sight I ever beheld, and the women more horrible than the men. Besides the usual deformities in extreme old age, they acquired an additional ghastliness in proportion to their number of years, which is not to be described; and among half a dozen, I soon distinguished which was the eldest, although there was not above a century or two between them.

The reader will easily believe, that from what I had heard and seen, my keen appetite for perpetuity of life was much abated. I grew heartily ashamed of the pleasing visions I had formed, and thought no tyrant could invent a death into which I would not run with pleasure from such a life. The King heard of all that had passed between me and my friends upon this occasion, and rallied me very pleasantly, wishing I would send a couple of *struldbrugs* to my own country, to arm our people against the fear of death; but this it seems is forbidden by the fundamental laws of the kingdom, or else I should have been well content with the trouble and expense of transporting them.

I could not but agree that the laws of this kingdom, relating to the *struldbrugs*, were founded upon the strongest reasons, and such as any other country would be under the necessity of enacting in the like circumstances. Otherwise, as avarice is the necessary consequent of old age, those immortals would in time become proprietors of the whole nation, and engross the civil power, which, for want of abilities to manage, must end in the ruin of the public.

Mental Retardation

With the establishment of the President's Committee on Mental Health and Mental Retardation in 1961, increasing attention has been focussed on mental retardation problems, both causation and treatment. Although precise figures are difficult to accumulate, it is estimated that there are some 5 million retardates in the United States, making it clearly a national problem.

Many forms of retardation exist and much confusion still blankets the field in terms of definitions and classificatory schemes. Based on intelligence test scores there are 4 levels of retardation generally agreed upon—these with IQ's below 20 who will never be able to function without total care; those with IQ's between 20 and 35 who can be helped to develop at least the skills necessary to protect themselves; the moderate cases with IQ's between 36 and 52 who can certainly be trained to maintain themselves in an occupation; and the mildly retarded individuals of IQ's from 53 to 68 who are capable of achieving some reasonable level of social and occupational adequacy.

What is clear is that these individuals, once isolated and forgotten, are often capable of sustaining themselves given the proper attention and training. This is hard work, but even harder is the work one must often do in counseling the parents of a retardate who may still look upon the child as a sign of familial disgrace and inadequacy and who experience many ambivalent feelings about him. These conflicting parental attitudes are poignantly expressed in Katherine Anne Porter's "He."

Katherine Anne Porter

HE

Life was very hard for the Whipples. It was hard to feed all the hungry mouths, it was hard to keep the children in flannels during the winter, short as it was: "God knows what would become of us if we lived north," they would say: keeping them decently clean was hard. "It looks like our luck won't never let up on us," said Mr. Whipple, but Mrs. Whipple was all for taking what was sent and calling it good, anyhow when the neighbors were in earshot. "Don't ever let a soul hear us complain," she kept saying to her husband. She couldn't stand to be pitied. "No, not if it comes to it that we have to live in a wagon and pick cotton around the country," she said, "nobody's going to get a chance to look down on us."

Mrs. Whipple loved her second son, the simple-minded one, better than she loved the other two children put together. She was forever saying so, and when she talked with certain of her neighbors, she would even throw in her husband and her mother for good measure.

"You needn't keep on saying it around," said Mr. Whipple, "you'll make people think nobody else has any feelings about Him but you."

"It's natural for a mother," Mrs. Whipple would remind him. "You know yourself it's more natural for a mother to be that way. People don't expect so much of fathers, some way."

Katherine Anne Porter, "*He*," *in* Flowering Judas and Other Stories. *New York: Harcourt Brace, 1963.*

This didn't keep the neighbors from talking plainly among themselves. "A Lord's pure mercy if He should die," they said. "It's the sins of the fathers," they agreed among themselves. "There's bad blood and bad doings somewhere, you can bet on that." This behind the Whipples' backs. To their faces everybody said, "He's not so bad off. He'll be all right yet. Look how He grows!"

Mrs. Whipple hated to talk about it, she tried to keep her mind off it, but every time anybody set foot in the house, the subject always came up, and she had to talk about Him first, before she could get on to anything else. It seemed to ease her mind. "I wouldn't have anything happen to Him for all the world, but it just looks like I can't keep Him out of mischief. He's so strong and active, He's always into everything; He was like that since He could walk. It's actually funny sometimes, the way He can do anything; it's laughable to see Him up to His tricks. Emly has more accidents; I'm forever tying up her bruises, and Adna can't fall a foot without cracking a bone. But He can do anything and not get a scratch. The preacher said such a nice thing once when he was here. He said, and I'll remember it to my dying day, 'The innocent, walk with God—that's why He don't get hurt.'" Whenever Mrs. Whipple repeated these words, she always felt a warm pool spread in her breast, and the tears would fill her eyes, and then she could talk about something else.

He did grow and He never got hurt. A plank blew off the chicken house and struck Him on the head and He never seemed to know it. He had learned a few words, and after this He forgot them. He didn't whine for food as the other children did, but waited until it was given Him; He ate squatting in the corner, smacking and mumbling. Rolls of fat covered Him like an overcoat, and He could carry twice as much wood and water as Adna. Emly had a cold in the head most of the time—"she takes that after me," said Mrs. Whipple—so in bad weather they gave her the extra blanket off His cot. He never seemed to mind the cold.

Just the same, Mrs. Whipple's life was a torment for fear something might happen to Him. He climbed the peach trees much better than Adna and went skittering along the branches like a monkey, just a regular monkey. "Oh, Mrs. Whipple, you hadn't ought to let Him do that. He'll lose His balance sometime. He can't rightly know what He's doing."

Mrs. Whipple almost screamed out at the neighbor. "He *does* know what He's doing! He's as able as any other child! Come down out of there, you!" When He finally reached the ground she could hardly keep her hands off Him for acting like that before people, a grin all over His face and her worried sick about Him all the time.

"It's the neighbors," said Mrs. Whipple to her husband. "Oh, I do mortally wish they would keep out of our business. I can't afford to let Him do anything for fear they'll come nosing around about it. Look at the bees, now. Adna can't handle them, they sting him up so; I haven't got time to do everything, and now I don't dare let Him. But if He gets a sting He don't really mind."

"It's just because He ain't got sense enough to be scared of any-thing," said Mr. Whipple.

"You ought to be ashamed of yourself," said Mrs. Whipple, "talking that way about your own child. Who's to take up for Him if we don't, I'd like to know? He sees a lot that goes on, He listens to things all the time. And anything I tell Him to do He does it. Don't never let anybody hear you say such things. They'd think you fa-vored the other children over Him."

"Well, now I don't, and you know it, and what's the use of getting all worked up about it? You always think the worst of everything. Just let Him alone, He'll get along somehow. He gets plenty to eat and wear, don't He?" Mr. Whipple suddenly felt tired out. "Any-how, it can't be helped now."

Mrs. Whipple felt tired too, she complained in a tired voice. "What's done can't never be undone, I know that good as anybody; but He's my child, and I'm not going to have people say anything. I get sick of people coming around saying things all the time."

In the early fall Mrs. Whipple got a letter from her brother saying he and his wife and two children were coming over for a little visit next Sunday week. "Put the big pot in the little one," he wrote at the end. Mrs. Whipple read this part out loud twice, she was so pleased. Her brother was a great one for saying funny things. "We'll just show him that's no joke," she said, "we'll just butcher one of the sucking pigs."

"It's a waste and I don't hold with waste the way we are now," said Mr. Whipple. "That pig'll be worth money by Christmas."

"It's a shame and a pity we can't have a decent meal's vittles once in a while when my own family comes to see us," said Mrs. Whipple.

"I'd hate for his wife to go back and say there wasn't a thing in the house to eat. My God, it's better than buying up a great chance of meat in town. There's where you'd spend the money!"

"All right, do it yourself then," said Mr. Whipple. "Christamighty, no wonder we can't get ahead!"

The question was how to get the little pig away from his ma, a great fighter, worse than a Jersey cow. Adna wouldn't try it: "That sow'd rip my insides out all over the pen." "All right, old fraidy," said Mrs. Whipple, "*He's* not scared. Watch *Him* do it." And she laughed as though it was all a good joke and gave Him a little push towards the pen. He sneaked up and snatched the pig right away from the teat and galloped back and was over the fence with the sow raging at His heels. The little black squirming thing was screeching like a baby in a tantrum, stiffening its back and stretching its mouth to the ears. Mrs. Whipple took the pig with her face stiff and sliced its throat with one stroke. When He saw the blood He gave a great jolting breath and ran away. "But He'll forget and eat plenty, just the same," thought Mrs. Whipple. Whenever she was thinking, her lips moved making words. "He'd eat it all if I didn't stop Him. He'd eat up every mouthful from the other two if I'd let Him."

She felt badly about it. He was ten years old now and a third again as large as Adna, who was going on fourteen. "It's a shame, a shame," she kept saying under her breath, "and Adna with so much brains!"

She kept on feeling badly about all sorts of things. In the first place it was the man's work to butcher; the sight of the pig scraped pink and naked made her sick. He was too fat and soft and pitiful-looking. It was simply a shame the way things had to happen. By the time she had finished it up, she almost wished her brother would stay at home.

Early Sunday morning Mrs. Whipple dropped everything to get Him all cleaned up. In an hour He was dirty again, with crawling under fences after a possum, and straddling along the rafters of the barn looking for eggs in the hayloft. "My Lord, look at you now after all my trying! And here's Adna and Emly staying so quiet. I get tired trying to keep you decent. Get off that shirt and put on another, people will say I don't half dress you!" And she boxed Him on the ears, hard. He blinked and blinked and rubbed His head, and His face hurt Mrs. Whipple's feelings. Her knees began to tremble, she had to sit down while she buttoned His shirt. "I'm just all gone before the day starts."

The brother came with his plump healthy wife and two great roaring hungry boys. They had a grand dinner, with the pig roasted to a crackling in the middle of the table, full of dressing, a pickled peach in his mouth and plenty of gravy for the sweet potatoes.

"This looks like prosperity all right," said the brother; "you're going to have to roll me home like I was a barrel when I'm done."

Everybody laughed out loud; it was fine to hear them laughing all at once around the table. Mrs. Whipple felt warm and good about it. "Oh, we've got six more of these; I say it's as little as we can do when you come to see us so seldom."

He wouldn't come into the dining room, and Mrs. Whipple passed it off very well. "He's timider than my other two," she said, "He'll just have to get used to you. There isn't everybody He'll make up with, you know how it is with some children, even cousins." Nobody said anything out of the way.

"Just like my Alfy here," said the brother's wife. "I sometimes got to lick him to make him shake hands with his own grand-mammy."

So that was over, and Mrs. Whipple loaded up a big plate for Him first, before everybody. "I always say He ain't to be slighted, no matter who else goes without," she said, and carried it to Him herself.

"He can chin Himself on the top of the door," said Emly, helping along.

"That's fine, He's getting along fine," said the brother.

They went away after supper. Mrs. Whipple rounded up the dishes, and sent the children to bed and sat down and unlaced her shoes. "You see?" she said to Mr. Whipple. "That's the way my whole family is. Nice and considerate about everything. No out-of-the-way remarks—they *have* got refinement. I get awfully sick of people's remarks. Wasn't that pig good?"

Mr. Whipple said, "Yes, we're out three hundred pounds of pork, that's all. It's easy to be polite when you come to eat. Who knows what they had in their minds all along?"

"Yes, that's like you," said Mrs. Whipple. "I don't expect anything else from you. You'll be telling me next that my own brother will be saying around that we made Him eat in the kitchen! Oh, my God!" She rocked her head in her hands, a hard pain started in the very middle of her forehead. "Now it's all spoiled, and everything was so nice and easy. All right, you don't like them and you never did—all right, they'll not come here again soon, never you mind! But they *can't* say He wasn't dressed every lick as good as Adna—oh, honest, sometimes I wish I was dead!"

"I wish you'd let up," said Mr. Whipple. "It's bad enough as it is."

It was a hard winter. It seemed to Mrs. Whipple that they hadn't ever known anything but hard times, and now to cap it all a winter like this. The crops were about half of what they had a right to expect; after the cotton was in it didn't do much more than cover the grocery bill. They swapped off one of the plow horses, and got cheated, for the new one died of the heaves. Mrs. Whipple kept thinking all the time it was terrible to have a man you couldn't depend on not to get cheated. They cut down on everything, but Mrs. Whipple kept saying there are things you can't cut down on, and they cost money. It took a lot of warm clothes for Adna and Emly, who walked four miles to school during the three-months session. "He sets around the fire a lot, He won't need so much," said Mr. Whipple. "That's so," said Mrs. Whipple, "and when He does the outdoor chores He can wear your tarpaullion coat. I can't do no better, that's all."

In February He was taken sick, and lay curled up under His blanket looking very blue in the face and acting as if He would choke. Mr. and Mrs. Whipple did everything they could for Him for two days, and then they were scared and sent for the doctor. The doctor told them they must keep Him warm and give Him plenty of milk and eggs. "He isn't as stout as He looks, I'm afraid," said the doctor. "You've got to watch them when they're like that. You must put more cover onto Him, too."

"I just took off His big blanket to wash," said Mrs. Whipple, ashamed. "I can't stand dirt."

"Well, you'd better put it back on the minute it's dry," said the doctor, "or He'll have pneumonia."

Mr. and Mrs. Whipple took a blanket off their own bed and put His cot in by the fire. "They can't say we didn't do everything for Him," she said, "even to sleeping cold ourselves on His account."

When the winter broke He seemed to be well again, but He walked as if His feet hurt Him. He was able to run a cotton planter during the season.

"I got it all fixed up with Jim Ferguson about breeding the cow next time," said Mr. Whipple. "I'll pasture the bull this summer and give Jim some fodder in the fall. That's better than paying out money when you haven't got it."

"I hope you didn't say such a thing before Jim Ferguson," said Mrs. Whipple. "You oughtn't to let him know we're so down as all that."

"Godamighty, that ain't saying we're down. A man is got to look ahead sometimes. *He* can lead the bull over today. I need Adna on the place."

At first Mrs. Whipple felt easy in her mind about sending Him for the bull. Adna was too jumpy and couldn't be trusted. You've got to be steady around animals. After He was gone she started thinking, and after a while she could hardly bear it any longer. She stood in the lane and watched for Him. It was nearly three miles to go and a hot day, but He oughtn't to be so long about it. She shaded her eyes and stared until colored bubbles floated in her eyeballs. It was just like everything else in life, she must always worry and never know a moment's peace about anything. After a long time, she saw Him turn into the side lane, limping. He came on very slowly, leading the big hulk of an animal by a ring in the nose, twirling a little stick in His hand, never looking back or sideways, but coming on like a sleep-walker with His eyes half shut.

Mrs. Whipple was scared sick of bulls; she had heard awful stories about how they followed on quietly enough, and then suddenly pitched on with a bellow and pawed and gored a body to pieces. Any second now that black monster would come down on Him, my God, He'd never have sense enough to run.

She mustn't make a sound nor a move; she mustn't get the bull started. The bull heaved his head aside and horned the air at a fly. Her voice burst out of her in a shriek, and she screamed at Him to come on, for God's sake. He didn't seem to hear her clamor, but kept on twirling His switch and limping on, and the bull lumbered along behind him as gently as a calf. Mrs. Whipple stopped calling and ran towards the house, praying under her breath: "Lord, don't let anything happen to Him. Lord, you *know* people will say we oughtn't to have sent Him. You *know* they'll say we didn't take care of Him. Oh, get Him home, safe home, safe home, and I'll look out for Him better! Amen."

She watched from the window while He led the beast in, and tied him up in the barn. It was no use trying to keep up, Mrs. Whipple couldn't bear another thing. She sat down and rocked and cried with her apron over her head.

From year to year the Whipples were growing poorer and poorer. The place just seemed to run down of itself, no matter how hard they worked. "We're losing our hold," said Mrs. Whipple. "Why can't we do like other people and watch for our best chances? They'll be calling us poor white trash next."

"When I get to be sixteen I'm going to leave," said Adna. "I'm going to get a job in Powell's grocery store. There's money in that. No more farm for me."

"I'm going to be a schoolteacher," said Emly. "But I've got to finish the eighth grade, anyhow. Then I can live in town. I don't see any chances here."

"Emly takes after my family," said Mrs. Whipple. "Ambitious every last one of them, and they don't take second place for anybody."

When fall came Emly got a chance to wait on table in the railroad eating-house in the town near by, and it seemed such a shame not to take it when the wages were good and she could get her food too, that Mrs. Whipple decided to let her take it, and not bother with school until the next session. "You've got plenty of time," she said. "You're young and smart as a whip."

With Adna gone too, Mr. Whipple tried to run the farm with just Him to help. He seemed to get along fine, doing His work and part of Adna's without noticing it. They did well enough until Christmas time, when one morning He slipped on the ice coming up from the barn. Instead of getting up He thrashed round and round, and when Mr. Whipple got to Him, He was having some sort of fit.

They brought Him inside and tried to make Him sit up, but He blubbered and rolled, so they put Him to bed and Mr. Whipple rode to town for the doctor. All the way there and back he worried about where the money was to come from: it sure did look like he had about all the troubles he could carry.

From then on He stayed in bed. His legs swelled up double their size, and the fits kept coming back. After four months, the doctor said, "It's no use, I think you'd better put Him in the County Home for treatment right away. I'll see about it for you. He'll have good care there and be off your hands."

"We don't begrudge Him any care, and I won't let Him out of my sight," said Mrs. Whipple. "I won't have it said I sent my sick child off among strangers."

"I know how you feel," said the doctor. "You can't tell me anything about that, Mrs. Whipple. I've got a boy of my own. But you'd better listen to me. I can't do anything more for Him, that's the truth."

Mr. and Mrs. Whipple talked it over a long time that night after they went to bed. "It's just charity," said Mrs. Whipple, "that's what we've come to, charity! I certainly never looked for this."

"We pay taxes to help support the place just like everybody else," said Mr. Whipple, "and I don't call that taking charity. I think it would be fine to have Him where He'd get the best of everything . . . and besides, I can't keep up with these doctor bills any longer."

"Maybe that's why the doctor wants us to send Him—he's scared he won't get his money," said Mrs. Whipple.

"Don't talk like that," said Mr. Whipple, feeling pretty sick, "or we won't be able to send Him."

"Oh, but we won't keep Him there long," said Mrs. Whipple. "Soon's He's better, we'll bring Him right back home."

"The doctor has told you and told you time and again He can't ever get better, and you might as well stop talking," said Mr. Whipple.

"Doctors don't know everything," said Mrs. Whipple, feeling almost happy. "But anyhow, in the summer Emly can come home for a vacation, and Adna can get down for Sundays: we'll all work together and get on our feet again, and the children will feel they've got a place to come to."

All at once she saw it full summer again, with the garden going fine, and new white roller shades up all over the house, and Adna and Emly home, so full of life, all of them happy together. Oh, it could happen, things would ease up on them.

They didn't talk before Him much, but they never knew just how much He understood. Finally the doctor set the day and a neighbor who owned a double-seated carryall offered to drive them over. The hospital would have sent an ambulance, but Mrs. Whipple couldn't stand to see Him going away looking so sick as all that. They wrapped Him in blankets, and the neighbor and Mr. Whipple lifted Him into the back seat of the carryall beside Mrs. Whipple, who had on her black shirtwaist. She couldn't stand to go looking like charity.

"You'll be all right, I guess I'll stay behind," said Mr. Whipple. "It don't look like everybody ought to leave the place at once."

"Besides, it ain't as if He was going to stay forever," said Mrs. Whipple to the neighbor. "This is only for a little while."

They started away, Mrs. Whipple holding to the edges of the blankets to keep Him from sagging sideways. He sat there blinking and blinking. He worked His hands out and began rubbing His nose with His knuckles, and then with the end of the blanket. Mrs. Whipple couldn't believe what she saw; He was scrubbing away big tears that rolled out of the corners of His eyes. He sniveled and made a gulping noise. Mrs. Whipple kept saying, "Oh, honey, you don't feel so bad, do you? You don't feel so bad, do you?" for He seemed to be accusing her of something. Maybe He remembered that time she boxed His ears, maybe He had been scared that day with the bull, maybe He had slept cold and couldn't tell her about it; maybe He knew they were sending Him away for good and all because they were too poor to keep Him. Whatever it was, Mrs. Whipple couldn't bear to think of it. She began to cry, frightfully, and wrapped her arms tight around Him. His head rolled on her shoulder: she had loved Him as much as she possibly could, there were Adna and Emly who had to be thought of too, there was nothing she could do to make up to Him for His life. Oh, what a mortal pity He was ever born.

They came in sight of the hospital, with the neighbor driving very fast, not daring to look behind him.

PART FIVE

THERAPY

Therapy is a helping relationship, and all the many forms of therapy which have been devised aim toward the same goal: to enable the patient to achieve a better social and emotional adjustment. The two main classes of therapy are known as the somatotherapies and psychotherapy.

Under the former rubric fall the procedures of chemotherapy, shock therapy, and psychosurgery, methods with a long history rooted in the ancients' use of drugs and primitive surgical techniques. Tranquilizers, insulin and electroshock treatments, and various forms of brain surgery are the most common modern forms of these somatotherapies. All of these, as the generic name implies, attempt to influence the patient's mental difficulties through physical manipulation.

There are similarly many forms of psychotherapy or the treatment of emotional disturbances through psychological methods. Names such as psychoanalysis, group therapy, play therapy, and family therapy all designate a form of the so-called "talking cure." All styles of psychotherapy involve a set of typical factors which, taken together, spell out the process of therapy.

At the outset, an individual suffering some form of psychological distress comes together in a relationship with a helping person in the form of a therapist. This relationship involves a series of more or less formal "contracts" as to where and when the contact is to take place, why it has been sought (which involves the goals of the patient), and how it is to proceed.

Gradually an atmosphere develops in which the patient comes to perceive that he is in the presence of an accepting, concerned person in whom he can have confidence and who will make every effort to understand him and his difficulty. Once this stage of rapport is achieved the patient can begin to express, in all their intensity and confusion, his emotional feelings and concerns. Having released or ventilated these emotions, patient and therapist can now begin to explore both the present status and the roots of these feelings and attitudes, seeking to understand where and how in the person's life history they became twisted and distorted. As the patient gropes towards putting his conflicts into new perspective, his behavior and feelings become more comprehensible and less dominated by childish modes of perceiving and reacting. At this point, the patient has gained insight and the process of relearning begins in earnest. The person tentatively attempts a new approach to people and crises and comes to the realization that he is capable of handling himself and dealing with what happens to him in a more mature and constructive manner. As these changes take firm hold, the relationship is terminated.

It might be appropriate to close this discussion with a summary statement by one of the finest of psychotherapists, the late Frieda Fromm-Reichmann, who described therapy as:

... communication between two people through spoken words, gesture, and attitude, the psychiatrist and the psychiatric patient, with the goal that both may learn to understand the troublesome aspects of the patient's life and bring them and their hidden causes to the patient's awareness, so that his living may be facilitated and his difficulties in living may be alleviated, if not eliminated.[1]

---

[1] Frieda Fromm-Reichmann. Remarks on the philosophy of mental disorder. In Dexter M. Bullard (ed.), *Psychoanalysis and Psychotherapy*. Chicago: Univ. of Chicago Press, 1959, pp. 3-46.

The Relationship of Past and Present

Proust's dissection of the process of recall and his portrayal of the infinite, delicate ties of past and present experience stand as a good introduction to our therapy readings. Proust, like the patient in therapy, is attempting to comprehend the partial images and feelings which have arisen in a current experience, and he quickly comes to realize that "it is plain that the object of my quest, the truth, lies not in the cup but in myself," that is, in his own unconscious.

His journey is a very important analogue to psychotherapy. In the beginning there is the life situation which sets off the questioning and concern. This is followed by a resonance, an unfocussed feeling state that, somewhere within oneself, lie the clues to understanding what has occurred. Slowly a chain of associations begins to move from present to past, all aiming to break open the repressions which maintain the memories in the darkness of the unconscious. Finally, recognition and insight come and one's current life is firmly linked to past experience with a sense of completeness and closure.

Marcel Proust

SWANN'S WAY

Many years had elapsed during which nothing of Combray, save what was comprised in the theatre and the drama of my going to bed there, had any existence for me, when one day in winter, as I came home, my mother, seeing that I was cold, offered me some tea, a thing I did not ordinarily take. I declined at first, and then, for no particular reason, changed my mind. She sent out for one of those short, plump little cakes called 'petites madeleines,' which look as though they had been moulded in the fluted scallop of a pilgrim's shell. And soon, mechanically, weary after a dull day with the prospect of a depressing morrow, I raised to my lips a spoonful of the tea in which I had soaked a morsel of the cake. No sooner had the warm liquid, and the crumbs with it, touched my palate than a shudder ran through my whole body, and I stopped, intent upon the extraordinary changes that were taking place. An exquisite pleasure had invaded my senses, but individual, detached, with no suggestion of its origin. And at once the vicissitudes of life had become indifferent to me, its disasters innocuous, its brevity illusory—this new sensation having had on me the effect which love has of filling me with a precious essence; or rather this essence was not in me, it was myself. I had ceased now to feel mediocre, accidental, mortal. Whence could it have come to me, this all-powerful joy? I was

Marcel Proust, from Swann's Way, *in* Remembrance of Things Past, *tr. by C. K. Scott Moncrieff. New York: Random House, 1956.*

conscious that it was connected with the taste of tea and cake, but that it infinitely transcended those savours, could not, indeed, be of the same nature as theirs. Whence did it come? What did it signify? How could I seize upon and define it?

I drink a second mouthful, in which I find nothing more than in the first, a third, which gives me rather less than the second. It is time to stop; the potion is losing its magic. It is plain that the object of my quest, the truth, lies not in the cup but in myself. The tea has called up in me, but does not itself understand, and can only repeat indefinitely with a gradual loss of strength, the same testimony; which I, too, cannot interpret, though I hope at least to be able to call upon the tea for it again and to find it there presently, intact and at my disposal, for my final enlightenment. I put down my cup and examine my own mind. It is for it to discover the truth. But how? What an abyss of uncertainty whenever the mind feels that some part of it has strayed beyond its own borders; when it, the seeker, is at once the dark region through which it must go seeking, where all its equipment will avail it nothing. Seek? More than that: create. It is face to face with something which does not so far exist, to which it alone can give reality and substance, which it alone can bring into the light of day.

And I begin again to ask myself what it could have been, this unremembered state which brought with it no logical proof of its existence, but only the sense that it was a happy, that it was a real state in whose presence other states of consciousness melted and vanished. I decide to attempt to make it reappear. I retrace my thoughts to the moment at which I drank the first spoonful of tea. I find again the same state, illumined by no fresh light. I compel my mind to make one further effort, to follow and recapture once again the fleeting sensation. And that nothing may interrupt it in its course I shut out every obstacle, every extraneous idea, I stop my ears and inhibit all attention to the sounds which come from the next room. And then, feeling that my mind is growing fatigued without having any success to report, I compel it for a change to enjoy that distraction which I have just denied it, to think of other things, to rest and refresh itself before the supreme attempt. And then for the second time I clear an empty space in front of it. I place in position before my mind's eye the still recent taste of that first mouthful, and I feel something start within me, something that leaves its resting-place and attempts to rise, something that has been embedded like an anchor at a great depth; I do not know yet what it is, but I can feel it mounting slowly; I can measure the resistance, I can hear the echo of great spaces traversed.

Undoubtedly what is thus palpitating in the depths of my being must be the image, the visual memory which, being linked to that taste, has tried to follow it into my conscious mind. But its struggles are too far off, too much confused; scarcely can I perceive the colourless reflection in which are blended the uncapturable whirling medley of radiant hues, and I cannot distinguish its form, cannot invite it, as the one possible interpreter, to translate to me the evidence of its contemporary, its inseparable paramour, the taste of cake soaked in tea; cannot ask it to inform me what special circumstance is in question, of what period in my past life.

Will it ultimately reach the clear surface of my consciousness, this memory, this old, dead moment which the magnetism of an identical moment has travelled so far to importune, to disturb, to raise up out of the very depths of my being? I cannot tell. Now that I feel nothing, it has stopped, has perhaps gone down again into its darkness, from which who can say whether it will ever rise? Ten times over I must essay the task, must lean down over the abyss. And each time the natural laziness which deters us from every difficult enterprise, every work of importance, has urged me to leave the thing alone, to drink my tea and to think merely of the worries of to-day and of my hopes for to-morrow, which let themselves be pondered over without effort or distress of mind.

And suddenly the memory returns. The taste was that of the little crumb of madeleine which on Sunday mornings at Combray (because on those mornings I did not go out before church-time), when I went to say good day to her in her bedroom, my aunt Léonie used to give me, dipping it first in her own cup of real or of lime-flower tea. The sight of the little madeleine had recalled nothing to my mind before I tasted it; perhaps because I had so often seen such things in the interval, without tasting them, on the trays in pastry-cooks' windows, that their image had dissociated itself from those Combray days to take its place among others more recent; perhaps because of those memories, so long abandoned and put out of mind, nothing now survived, everything was scattered; the forms of things, including that of the little scallop-shell of pastry, so richly sensual under its severe, religious folds, were either obliterated or had been so long dormant as to have lost the power of expansion which would have allowed them to resume their place in my consciousness. But when from a long-distant past nothing subsists, after the people are dead, after the things are broken and scattered, still, alone, more fragile, but with more vitality, more unsubstantial, more persistent, more faithful, the smell and taste of things remain poised a long time, like souls, ready to remind us, waiting and hoping for their moment, amid the ruins of all the rest; and bear unfaltering, in the tiny and almost impalpable drop of their essence, the vast structure of recollection.

And once I had recognized the taste of the crumb of madeleine soaked in her decoction of lime-flowers which my aunt used to give me (although I did not yet know and must long postpone the discovery of why this memory made me so happy) immediately the old grey house upon the street, where her room was, rose up like the scenery of a theatre to attach itself to the little pavilion, opening on to the garden, which had been built out behind it for my parents (the isolated panel which until that moment had been all that I could see); and with the house the town, from morning to night and in all weathers, the Square where I was sent before luacheon, the streets along which I used to run errands, the country ronds we took when it was fine. And just as the Japanese amuse themselves by filling a porcelain bowl with water and steeping in it little crumbs of paper which until then are without character or form, but, the moment they become wet, stretch themselves and bend, take on colour and distinctive shape, become flowers or houses or people, permanent and recognisable, so in that moment all the flowers in our garden and in M. Swann's park, and the water-lilies on the Vivonne and the good folk of the village and their little dwellings and the parish church and the whole of Combray and of its surroundings, taking their proper shapes and growing solid, sprang into being, town and gardens alike, from my cup of tea. . . .

Free Association

The method of free association is the cornerstone of psychoanalytic treatment. Developed by Freud to supplant the use of hypnosis in therapy, it is designed to reduce the patient's conscious control over what he says and thus allow previously repressed material to emerge. The patient is admonished to say whatever comes into his mind no matter how absurd, trivial, or scandalous it might appear. Through the analysis of this stream of associations the therapist is better able to understand the material which lies outside the awareness of the patient, in a dissociated state.

The earliest practitioner of this method, however, turns out not to have been Freud. In this hilarious excerpt from Aristophanes' *The Clouds*,[1] Socrates utilizes free association to try and calm as well as to bring self-knowledge to Strepsiades, who is having a difficult time with his son. The scene, marvelously enough, is complete with a couch!

---

[1] For an extended discussion of these passages see S. Halpern. Free association in 423 B.C. *Psychoanalytic Rev.*, 1963, *50*, 69-86.

Aristophanes

THE CLOUDS

SOCRATES [*coming out*]   By Respiration, the Breath of Life! By Chaos! By the Air! I have never seen a man so gross, so inept, so stupid, so forgetful. All the little quibbles, which I teach him, he forgets even before he has learnt them. Yet I will not give it up, I will make him come out here into the open air. Where are you, Strepsiades? Come, bring your couch out here.

STREPSIADES [*from within*]   But the bugs will not allow me to bring it.

SOCRATES   Have done with such nonsense! place it there and pay attention.

STREPSIADES [*coming out, with the bed*]   Well, here I am.

SOCRATES   . . . Come, lie down there.

STREPSIADES   What for?

SOCRATES   Ponder awhile over matters that interest you.

STREPSIADES   Oh! I pray you, not there! but, if I must lie down and ponder, let me lie on the ground.

SOCRATES   That's out of the question. Come! on the couch!

STREPSIADES [*as he lies down*]   What cruel fate! What a torture the bugs will this day put me to!

[SOCRATES *turns aside.*]

CHORUS [*singing*]   Ponder and examine closely, gather your thoughts together, let your mind turn to every side of things; if you

Aristophanes, from The Clouds, *in* The Complete Greek Drama, *W. J. Oates and Eugene O'Neill, Jr.* (eds.). *New York: Random House, 1938.*

meet with a difficulty, spring quickly to some other idea; above all, keep your eyes away from all gentle sleep.

STREPSIADES [*singing*]   Ow, Wow, Wow, Wow is me! . . .

CHORUS [*singing*]   What ails you? why do you cry so?

STREPSIADES   Oh! I am a dead man! Here are these cursed Corinthians advancing upon me from all corners of the couch; they are biting me, they are gnawing at my sides, they are drinking all my blood, they are yanking off my balls, they are digging into my arse, they are killing me!

LEADER OF THE CHORUS   Not so much wailing and clamour, if you please.

STREPSIADES   How can I obey? I have lost my money and my complexion, my blood and my slippers, and to cap my misery, I must keep awake on this couch, when scarce a breath of life is left in me.

[*A brief interval of silence ensues.*]

SOCRATES   Well now! what are you doing? are you reflecting?

STREPSIADES   Yes, by Posidon!

SOCRATES   What about?

STREPSIADES   Whether the bugs will entirely devour me.

SOCRATES   May death seize you, accursed man! [*He turns aside again.*]

STREPSIADES   Ah! it has already.

SOCRATES   Come, no giving way! Cover up your head; the thing to do is to find an ingenious alternative.

STREPSIADES   An alternative! ah! I only wish one would come to me from within these coverlets!

[*Another interval of silence ensues.*]

SOCRATES   Wait! let us see what our fellow is doing! Ho! you, are you asleep?

STREPSIADES   No, by Apollo!

SOCRATES   Have you got hold of anything?

STREPSIADES   No, nothing whatever.

SOCRATES   Nothing at all?

STREPSIADES   No, nothing except my tool, which I've got in my hand.

SOCRATES   Aren't you going to cover your head immediately and ponder?

STREPSIADES   On what? Come, Socrates, tell me.

SOCRATES   Think first what you want, and then tell me.

STREPSIADES   But I have told you a thousand times what I want. Not to pay any of my creditors.

SOCRATES   Come, wrap yourself up; concentrate your mind, which wanders too lightly; study every detail, scheme and examine thoroughly.

STREPSIADES   Alas! Alas!

SOCRATES   Keep still, and if any notion troubles you, put it quickly aside, then resume it and think over it again.

STREPSIADES   My *dear* little Sorcates!

SOCRATES   What is it, old greybeard?

STREPSIADES   I have a scheme for not paying my debts.

SOCRATES   Let us hear it.

STREPSIADES   Tell me, if I purchased a Thessalian witch, I could make the moon descend during the night and shut it, like a mirror, into a round box and there keep it carefully. . . .

SOCRATES   How would you gain by that?

STREPSIADES   How? why, if the moon did not rise, I would have no interest to pay.

SOCRATES   Why so?

STREPSIADES   Because money is lent by the month.

SOCRATES   Good! but I am going to propose another trick to you. If you were condemned to pay five talents, how would you manage to quash that verdict? Tell me.

STREPSIADES   How? how? I don't know, I must think.

SOCRATES   Do you always shut your thoughts within yourself? Let your ideas fly in the air, like a may-bug, tied by the foot with a thread.

STREPSIADES   I have found a very clever way to annul that conviction; you will admit that much yourself.

SOCRATES   What is it?

STREPSIADES   Have you ever seen a beautiful, transparent stone at the druggists' with which you may kindle fire?

SOCRATES   You mean a crystal lens.

STREPSIADES   That's right. Well, now if I placed myself with this stone in the sun and a long way off from the clerk, while he was writing out the conviction, I could make all the wax, upon which the words were written, melt.

SOCRATES   Well thought out, by the Graces!

STREPSIADES   Ah! I am delighted to have annulled the decree that was to cost me five talents.

SOCRATES   Come, take up this next question quickly.

STREPSIADES   Which?

SOCRATES   If, when summoned to court, you were in danger of losing your case for want of witnesses, how would you make the conviction fall upon your opponent?

STREPSIADES   That's very simple and easy.

SOCRATES   Let me hear.

STREPSIADES   This way. If another case had to be pleaded before mine was called, I should run and hang myself.

SOCRATES   You talk rubbish!

STREPSIADES   Not so, by the gods! if I were dead, no action could lie against me.

SOCRATES   You are merely beating the air. Get out! I will give you no more lessons.

STREPSIADES [*imploringly*]   Why not? Oh! Socrates! in the name of the gods!

SOCRATES   But you forget as fast as you learn. Come, what was the thing I taught you first? Tell me.

STREPSIADES   Ah! let me see. What was the first thing? What was it then? Ah! that thing in which we knead the bread, oh! my god! what do you call it?

SOCRATES   Plague take the most forgetful and silliest of old addle-pates!

STREPSIADES   Alas! what a calamity! what will become of me? I am undone if I do not learn how to ply my tongue. Oh! Clouds! give me good advice.

The Doctor-Patient Relationship

The cornerstone of all psychotherapy is the relationship of patient and therapist, and no one has better described the qualities of the good therapist than Nathaniel Hawthorne in this brief excerpt from *The Scarlet Letter*. In his description, Hawthorne stresses such important variables as empathy, understanding, and the doctor role, and suggests a goal for which all therapists strive—"then, at some inevitable moment, will the soul of the sufferer be dissolved, and flow forth in a dark, but transparent stream, bringing all its mysteries into the daylight."

Nathaniel Hawthorne

THE SCARLET LETTER

Thus Roger Chillingworth scrutinized his patient carefully, both as he saw him in his ordinary life, keeping an accustomed pathway in the range of thoughts familiar to him, and as he appeared when thrown amidst other moral scenery, the novelty of which might call out something new to the surface of his character. He deemed it essential, it would seem, to know the man, before attempting to do him good. Wherever there is a heart and an intellect, the diseases of the physical frame are tinged with the peculiarities of these. In Arthur Dimmesdale, thought and imagination were so active, and sensibility so intense, that the bodily infirmity would be likely to have its groundwork there. So Roger Chillingworth—the man of skill, the kind and friendly physician—strove to go deep into his patient's bosom, delving among his principles, prying into his recollections, and probing everything with a cautious touch, like a treasure-seeker in a dark cavern. Few secrets can escape an investigator, who has opportunity and license to undertake such a quest, and skill to follow it up. A man burdened with a secret should especially avoid the intimacy of his physician. If the latter possess native sagacity, and a nameless something more,—let us call it intuition; if he show no intrusive egotism, nor disagreeably prominent characteristics of his own: if he have the power, which must be born with him, to bring his mind into such affinity with his patient's, that this last shall

Nathaniel Hawthorne, from The Scarlet Letter. *New York: Rinehart, 1958.*

unawares have spoken what he imagines himself only to have thought; if such revelations be received without tumult, and acknowledged not so often by an uttered sympathy as by silence, an inarticulate breath, and here and there a word, to indicate that all is understood; if to these qualifications of a confidant be joined the advantages afforded by his recognized character as a physician,— then, at some inevitable moment, will the soul of the sufferer be dissolved, and flow forth in a dark, but transparent stream, bringing all its mysteries into the daylight.

SELECTED
BIBLIOGRAPHIES

For the reader who wishes to delve further into the fascinating borderland between psychopathology and literature, we present below a selected bibliography in two parts. The first contains a list of authors and some of their works which present literary renderings of various psychopathological conditions. For some authors we have listed several selections, while for others only a reference to a collection of stories is presented. In this latter category fall such diverse authors as Gogol, William James, Melville, and Hawthorne. The interested reader, we feel, may profitably consult any of the writings of these men from the viewpoint of abnormal psychology. For additional materials of this kind, the reader is referred to the *Short Story Index* compiled by Estelle A. Fidell and Esther V. Flory (New York: H. W. Wilson), which classifies short stories under such headings as *Mental Illness, Homosexuality*, and *Neuroses;* the *Fiction Catalogue*, edited by Estelle A Fidell (New York: H. W. Wilson), which deals similarly with novels; and the *Play Index*, edited by Estelle A. Fidell and Dorothy M. Peake (New York: H. W. Wilson), which likewise indexes pertinent dramatic material. Other excellent sources for further leads are the always-interesting journal *Literature and Psychology*, edited by Leonard Manheim and Morton Kaplan, and the strongly psychoanalytic journal, *American Imago*, both of which focus on the interrelationship between psychology and literature.

The second section of this bibliography is devoted to a selection of critical writings in the area of psychopathology and literature. We include as well some more general articles on the psychological analysis of literature. Those seeking a more comprehensive listing of references, covering a far broader range of phenomena, should consult Norman Kiell's monumental bibliographies, *Psychoanalysis, Psychology and Literature: A Bibliography* (Madison, Wisc.: Univ. Wisc. Press, 1963) and *Psychiatry and Psychology in the Visual Arts and Aesthetics: A Bibliography* (Madison, Wisc.: Univ. Press, 1965). In addition, critical essays can be found in the above-mentioned scholarly journals and, on occasion, in various psychiatric and psychoanalytic journals, particularly *The American Journal of Psychiatry, Psychoanalytic Review, Psychiatry,* and *The International Journal of Psychoanalysis.*

Psychopathology and Literature:
Further Readings

Aeschylus. *The Complete Greek Tragedies*. Vol. 1. Chicago: Univ. Chicago Press, 1959.

Agee, J. *A Death in the Family*. New York: McDowell, Obolensky, 1957.

Aiken, C. *Among the Lost People*. New York: Scribner's, 1934.

———— *Blue Voyage*. New York: Scribner's, 1927.

Akutagawa, R. *Rashomon and Other Stories*. New York: Bantam, 1959.

Anderson, S. *Winesburg, Ohio*. New York: Boni & Liveright, 1919.

Andreyev, L. *The Seven That Were Hanged and Other Stories*. New York: Random House, 1958.

Aswell, M. L. *The World Within*. New York: Whittlesey House, 1947.

Augustine, Saint. *Confessions*. New York: Dutton, 1950.

Balchin, N. *Mine Own Executioner*. New York: Houghton-Mifflin, 1949.

Baldwin, J. *Giovanni's Room*. New York: Signet, 1959.

Balzac, H. de. *Père Goriot and Eugénie Grandet*. New York: Modern Library, 1946.

———— *The Short Novels of Balzac*. New York: Dial Press, 1948.

Barea, A. "The scissors." In *Horizon Stories*. New York: Vanguard, 1946.

Bassing, E. *Home Before Dark*. New York: Random House, 1957.

Bedel, M. *Jerome*. New York: Viking Press, 1928.

Bellow, S. *The Adventures of Augie March*. New York: Viking Press, 1953.

———— *Herzog*. London: Weidenfeld & Nicolson, 1965.

———— *The Last Analysis*. New York: Viking Press, 1965.

Benson, S. "Little woman." In *Short Stories from the New Yorker*. New York: Simon & Schuster, 1940.

Bergman, I. *Four Screen Plays of Ingmar Bergman*. New York: Simon & Schuster, 1960.

Bierce, A. *In the Midst of Life*. New York: Modern Library, 1927.

Blankfort, M. *The Juggler*. Boston: Little, Brown, 1952.

Bottome, P. *Private Worlds*. New York: Houghton, 1934.

Bowen, E. *Death of the Heart*. New York: Knopf, 1939.

Bowles, P. *Delicate Prey and Other Stories*. New York: Random House, 1950.

Boyle, K. "Rest cure." In *The First Lover, and Other Stories*. New York: Smith & Haas, 1933.

Brand, M. *The Outward Room*. New York: Simon & Schuster, 1937.

Brontë, E. J. *Wuthering Heights*. New York: Macmillan, 1960.

Brown, W. *Monkey on My Back*. New York: Greenberg, 1953.

Büchner, G. "Woyzeck." In Eric Bentley (Ed.) *The Modern Theatre*, Vol. 1. New York: Anchor, 1955.

Caldwell, E. *God's Little Acre*. New York: Modern Library, 1934.

Camus, A. *The Stranger*. New York: Knopf, 1946.

Capote, T. *The Grass Harp and a Tree of Night, and Other Stories*. New York: Signet, 1956.

Caragiale, I. L. "The Easter Torch." In K. Bercovici (Ed.) *Best Short Stories of the World*. New York: Stratford, 1917.

Casanova, G. *The Memoirs of Jacques Casanova de Seingalt. . .* London: Navarre Soc. Ltd., 1922.

Chekhov, A. *The Bet, and Other Stories*. Boston: J. W. Luce, 1915.

———— *The Black Monk, and Other Stories*. New York: Frederick A. Stokes, 1915.

———— *Chekhov: The Major Plays*. New York: New American Library, 1964.

Coates, R. M. "The fury." In *Short Stories from the New Yorker*. New York: Simon & Schuster, 1940.

———— *Wisteria Cottage*. New York: Harcourt Brace, 1948.

Collier, J. *Fancies and Goodnights*. New York: Doubleday, 1951.

Conrad, J. *Heart of Darkness*, and *The Secret Sharer*. New York: Signet, 1950.

Crane, S. "The open boat." In *Twenty Stories by Stephen Crane*. New York: Knopf, 1940.

Dawson, J. *The Ha-Ha*. Boston: Little, Brown & Co., 1961.

De Assis, M. *Epitaph of a Small Winner*. New York: Noonday Press, 1956.

———— *The Psychiatrist, and Other Stories*. Berkeley, Calif.: Univ. of Calif. Press, 1963.

Dennis, N. *Cards of Identity*. New York: Vanguard, 1955.

Denzer, P. *Episode*. New York: Dutton, 1954.

Dostoevsky, F. *The Brothers Karamazov*. New York: Modern Library, 1950.

———— *Crime and Punishment*. New York: Norton, 1964.

———— "Notes from underground." In *Three Short Novels of Dostoyevsky*. New York: Dell, 1960.

———— *The Possessed*. New York: Dell, 1961.

Dowdy, C. *Weep for My Brother*. Garden City, N. Y.: Doubleday, 1950.

Durrell, L. *The Alexandria Quartet*. New York: Dutton, 1960.

Elliott, G. P. "Among the dangs." In *Nelson Algren's Own Book of Lonesome Monsters*. New York: Lancer Books, 1962.

Ellison, R. *Invisible Man*. New York: Random House, 1952.

Engstrand, S. *The Sling and the Arrow*. New York: Creative Age Press, 1947.

Faulkner, W. "A Rose for Emily." In *Collected Stories*. New York: Random House, 1950.

———— *The Sound and the Fury*. New York: Random House, 1946.

Fitzgerald, F. S. *The Great Gatsby*. New York: Scribner's, 1925.

———— *Tender Is the Night*. New York: Scribner's, 1933.

Flaubert, G. *Madame Bovary*. New York: Random House, 1957.

Ford, J. "Perkin Warbeck." In *John Ford; five plays*. New York: Hill & Wang, 1957.

Forster, E. M. *A Passage to India*. New York: Harcourt, Brace & Co., 1924.

Fowles, J. *The Collector*. Boston: Little, Brown & Co., 1963.

Frame, J. *Faces in the Water*. New York: Braziller, 1961.

———— *Scented Gardens for the Blind*. New York: Braziller, 1964.

Frankau, G. *Michael's Wife*. New York: Dutton, 1948.

Frisch, M. *I'm Not Stiller*. New York: Vintage Books, 1962.

Frost, R. "A servant to servants." In *Collected Poems*. New York: Holt, 1939.

Genet, J. *Our Lady of the Flowers*. New York: Grove Press, 1963.

Gibson, W. *The Cobweb*. New York: Knopf, 1954.

Gide, A. *The Immoralist*. New York: Knopf, 1930.

Goethe, J. W. von. *Faust*. New York: Oxford Univ. Press, 1954.

Gogol, N. *Tales of Good and Evil*. New York: Doubleday, 1957.

Golding, W. *The Lord of the Flies*. New York: Coward-McCann, 1962.

Gorky, M. "The lower depths." In *Seven Plays of Maxim Gorky*. New Haven: Yale Univ. Press, 1945.

Green, H. *Back*. New York: Viking Press, 1946.

Green, J. *The Closed Garden*. New York: Harper, 1928.

———— *The Dark Journey*. New York: Harper, 1929.

Grubb, D. *The Night of the Hunter*. New York: Harper & Bros., 1953.

Hall, R. *The Well of Loneliness.* New York: Covici, 1928.

Hamsun, K. *Hunger.* New York: Grosset & Dunlap, 1920.

Hauptmann, G. "Flagman Thiel." In Bennett Cerf (Ed.) *Great German Short Novels.* New York: Modern Library, 1933.

Hawthorne, N. *Hawthorne's Short Stories.* New York: Vintage Books, 1955.

Heller, J. *Catch-22.* New York: Simon & Schuster, 1961.

Hellman, L. "The Children's Hour." In *Four Plays by Lillian Hellman.* New York: Modern Library, 1940.

Hesse, H. *Magister Luoi.* New York: Holt, 1949.

—— *Steppenwolf.* New York: Holt, 1929.

Hoffmann, E. T. A. *Hoffmann's Strange Stories.* Boston: Burnham Bros., 1855.

—— *The Serapion Brethren.* London: Bell, 1892.

Holmes, O. W. *The Psychiatric Novels of Oliver Wendell Holmes.* Clarence P. Oberndorf (Ed.) New York: Columbia Univ. Press, 1946.

Howard, S. *The Silver Cord.* New York: Scribner's 1927.

Humphrey, W. "Sister." In *The Last Husband, and Other Stories.* New York: Lippincott, 1962.

Huxley, A. *After Many a Summer Dies the Swan.* New York: Harper, 1939.

—— *Point Counter Point.* New York: Doubleday, 1928.

—— "The rest cure." In *Brief Candles.* New York: Doubleday, 1930.

Ibsen, H. *Eleven Plays of Henrik Ibsen.* New York: Modern Library, 1935.

Inge, W. *Picnic.* New York: Random House, 1953.

Jackson, C. *The Lost Weekend.* New York: Noonday Press, 1960.

James, H. *The Short Stories of Henry James.* New York: Random House, 1945.

Janeway, E. *The Question of Gregory.* Garden City, N.Y.: Doubleday, 1949.

Joyce, J. *Ulysses.* New York: Random House, 1946.

Kafka, F. *The Castle.* New York: Knopf, 1954.

—— *Selected Short Stories of Franz Kafka.* New York: Modern Library, 1952.

—— *The Trial.* New York: Knopf, 1957.

Keilson, H. *The Death of the Adversary.* New York: Orion Press, 1962.

Kesey, K. *One Flew over the Cuckoo Nest.* New York: Viking Press, 1962.

Koestler, A. *Arrival and Departure.* New York: Macmillan, 1943.

Kramm, J. *The Shrike.* New York: Random House, 1952.

Lagerlof, S. *The Emperor of Portugallia.* Garden City, N.Y. Doubleday, Page & Co, 1916.

—— "The fallen king." In *Modern Swedish Short Stories.* London: Cape, 1934.

———— *Jerusalem.* New York: Doubleday, 1916.

Landolfi, T. *Gogol's Wife & Other Stories.* New York: New Directions, 1961.

Laurents, A. *A Clearing in the Woods.* New York: Random House, 1956.

Lawrence, D. H. *The Complete Short Stories.* London: Heinemann, 1957.

———— *Sons and Lovers.* London: Duckworth, 1913.

Levin, M. *Compulsion.* New York: Pocket Books, 1959.

Lewisohn, L. *The Case of Mr. Crump.* New York: J. Henderson, 1930.

Lind, J. *Soul of Wood and Other Stories.* New York: Grove Press, 1965.

Lipsky, E. *The Kiss of Death.* New York: New American Library, 1947.

London, J. "Told in the drooling ward." In *Turtles of Tasman.* New York: Macmillan, 1916.

Lorca, F. G. "Yerma." In *Three Tragedies of Federico García Lorca.* New York: New Directions, 1955.

Lovecraft, H. P. "The outsider." In *Best Supernatural Stories of H.P. Lovecraft.* New York: World, 1944.

Maier, H. *Undertow.* New York: Doubleday, 1945.

Mailer, N. *An American dream.* New York: Dial Press, 1965.

———— *The Deer Park.* New York: Putnam, 1955.

Malamod, B. *The Assistant.* New York: Farrar, Straus & Cudahy, 1957.

Mann, H. *Little Superman.* New York: Creative Age Press, 1945.

Mann, T. *Doctor Faustus.* New York: Knopf, 1948.

———— *The Magic Mountain.* New York: Knopf, 1961.

———— *Stories of Three Decades.* New York: Modern Library, 1936.

March, W. *The Bad Seed.* New York: Rinehart, 1954.

Maugham, S. *Best Short Stories.* New York: Modern Library, 1957.

Maupassant, G. de. *The Complete Short Stories of Guy de Maupassant.* New York: W. J. Black, 1903.

Mauriac, F. *Therese; A Portrait in Four Parts.* New York: Farrar, Straus, 1951.

McCarthy, M. *The Company She Keeps.* New York: Dell, 1955.

McCullers, C. *The Ballad of the Sad Cafe.* New York: Houghton-Mifflin, 1941.

———— *The Heart Is a Lonely Hunter.* New York: Houghton-Mifflin, 1940.

———— *The Member of the Wedding.* New York: Houghton-Mifflin, 1946.

———— *Reflections in a Golden Eye.* New York: Houghton-Mifflin, 1941.

Melville, H. *Billy Budd.* Cambridge, Harvard Univ. Press, 1948.

———— *The Complete Short Stories of Herman Melville.* New York: Random House, 1949.

———— *Moby Dick.* New York: Random House, 1950.

Middleton, T. "Women Beware Women." In *Old English Plays.* London: 1916.

Miller, A. *Collected Plays*. New York: Viking Press, 1957.
Molière, J. B. P. *Plays*. New York: Modern Library, 1924.
Morgan, C. *The Price of Salt*. New York: Coward-McCann, 1952.

Nabokov, V. *Lolita*. New York: Putnam, 1955.
——— *Nabokov's Dozen*. Garden City, N.Y.: Doubleday, 1958.
Nin, Anais. *Under a Glass Bell, and Other Stories*. New York: Dutton, 1948.

O'Connor, F. *A Good Man Is Hard to Find*. New York: Signet, 1956.
O'Neill, E. *Long Day's Journey into Night*. New Haven: Yale Univ. Press, 1956.
——— *The Plays of Eugene O'Neill* (3 vols.) New York: Random House, 1948.

Parker, D. *Laments for the Living*. New York: Viking Press, 1930.
Percy, W. *The Moviegoer*. New York: Knopf, 1961.
Peretz, I. L. "Mad. Talmudist." In Irving Howe & Eliezer Greenberg (Eds.), *Treasury of Yiddish Stories*. New York: Viking, 1954.
Peters, F. *The World Next Door*. New York: Farrar, Straus & Co., 1949.
Pirandello, L. *Naked Masks*. New York: Dutton: 1957.
——— *One, None and a Hundred Thousand*. New York: Dutton, 1933.
——— *Short Stories*. New York: Oxford Univ. Press, 1965.
Poe, E. A. *Tales of Edgar Allan Poe*. New York: Random House, 1944.
Proust, M. *Remembrance of Things Past*. (2 vols.) New York: Random House, 1934.

Rilke, R. M. *The Notebooks of Malte Laurids Brigge*. New York: Norton, 1949.
Roth, H. *Call It Sleep*. New York: Avon, 1964.
Roth, P. *Letting Go*. New York: Random House, 1962.
Rubin, T. *Lisa and David*. New York: Macmillan, 1961.

Sade, M. de. *Marquis de Sade*. New York: Grove, 1965.
Salinger, J. D. *The Catcher in the Rye*. Boston: Little, Brown & Co., 1951.
——— *Nine Stories*. Boston: Little, Brown & Co., 1953.
Sartre, J. P. *Nausea*. Norfolk, Conn.: New Directions, 1949.
Schnitzler, A. *Flight into Darkness*. New York: Simon & Schuster, 1931.
——— *Reigen, the Affairs of Anatol and Other Plays*. New York: Modern Library, 1933.
Schulberg, B. *What Makes Sammy Run?* New York: Random House, 1941.
Scott, N. *The Story of Mrs. Murphy*. New York: Dutton, 1947.
Shakespeare, W. *Complete Works*. New York: Harper, 1960.
Shrodes, C., J. Van Gundy, and R. W. Husband. *Psychology through Literature*. New York: Oxford Univ. Press, 1943.

Sologub, F. *The Little Demon*. London: New English Library, 1962.

Sophocles. *Sophocles. The Seven Plays in English Verse*. London: Oxford Univ. Press, 1928.

Soubiran, A. *Bedlam*. New York: Putnam, 1957.

Stendhal (Marie-Henri Beyle). *The Red and the Black*. New York: Boni & Liveright, 1926.

Stevenson, R. L. "Dr. Jekyll and Mr. Hyde." In *The Merry Men, and Other Tales and Fables*. New York: Scribner's, 1921.

Still, J. "Mrs. Razor." In Hollis S. Summers (Ed.) *Kentucky Story*. Louisville: Univ. Kentucky Press, 1954.

Strindberg, A. *Six Plays of Strindberg*. New York: Anchor Books, 1955.

Svevo, I. *Confessions of Zeno*. New York: Knopf, 1958.

———— *A Life*. New York: Knopf, 1963.

Swallow, A. (Ed.) *Anchor in the Sea*. Denver, Colo.: Alan Swallow, 1957.

Symons, A. J. A. *The Quest for Corvo*. New York: Macmillan, 1934.

Telfer, D. *The Caretakers*. New York: Simon & Schuster, 1959.

Tolstoy, L. *Anna Karenina*. New York: Modern Library, 1950.

———— *The Death of Ivan Ilyitch, and Other Stories*. New York: Dodd, Mead & Co., 1927.

———— *The Kreutzer Sonata*. Boston: B. R. Tucker, 1890.

Traven, B. *The Treasure of the Sierra Madre*. New York: Knopf, 1935.

Tolstoy, L. *War and Peace*. New York: Modern Library, 1931.

Unamuno, M. de. "Abel Sanchez." In Leo Hamalian & Edmond Volpe (Eds.) *Ten Modern Short Novels*. New York: Putnam, 1958.

Vidal, G. *The City & the Pillar*. New York: Dutton, 1948.

Ward, M. J. *The Snake Pit*. New York: Random House, 1946.

Wells, H. G. *Mr. Blettsworthy on Rampole Island*. Garden City, N.Y.: Doubleday, 1928.

Welty, E. " Why I live at the P. O. " In *Curtain of Green*. New York: Doubleday, 1941.

Werfel, F. "The officer puppet." In W. Burnett (Ed.), *Seas of God*. New York: Lippincott, 1944.

Wertham, F. *Dark Legend*. New York: Doubleday, 1949.

West, J. "The child's day." In A. Swallow (Ed.) *Anchor in the Sea*, Denver, Colo.: Alan Swallow, 1947.

West, N. *The Day of the Locust*. New York: New Directions, 1939.

———— *Miss Lonelyhearts*. New York: New Directions, 1933.

West, R. *The Return of the Soldier*. New York: Century Co., 1918.

Wheelis, A. *The Seeker*. New York: Random House, 1960.

White, E. B. "The door." In *Short Stories from the New Yorker*. New York: Simon & Schuster, 1940.

Whitman, W. *Leaves of Grass*. New York: Modern Library, 1921.

Wilde, O. *The Picture of Dorian Gray*. New York: Modern Library, 1926.

Williams, T. *Cat on a Hot Tin Roof*. New York: New Directions, 1955.

——— *The Glass Menagerie*. New York: New Directions, 1949.

Williams, W. C. *The Farmers' Daughters*. New York: New Directions, 1961.

Wilson, E. *Memoirs of Hecate County*. New York: Farrar, Straus, 1959.

Winters, Y. "The brink of darkness." In Swallow, A. (Ed.) *Anchor in the Sea*. Denver, Colo.: Alan Swallow, 1947.

Wolfe, T. "God's lonely man." In *The Hills Beyond*. New York: Harper, 1941.

——— *Of Time and the River*. New York: Grosset & Dunlap, 1935.

Woolf, V. *To the Lighthouse*. New York: Harcourt, Brace & Co., 1927.

——— *Mrs. Dalloway*. New York: Modern Library, 1928.

——— "The new dress." In *Haunted House and Other Stories*. New York: Harcourt, Brace & Co., 1940.

——— *Orlando*. New York: Harcourt, Brace & Co., 1928.

Wouk, H. *The Caine Mutiny*. Garden City, N.Y.: Doubleday, 1951.

Wright, R. *Native Son*. New York: Harper & Bros., 1940.

Zola, E. *The Human Beast*. New York: United Book Guild, 1948.

Psychopathology and Literature: Critical Writings

Abenheimer, K. M. On narcissism—including an analysis of Shakespeare's *King Lear. Brit. J. med. Psychol.*, 1945, *20*, 322-329.

Adler, C. A. Richard III—his significance as a study in criminal life-style. *Int. J. indiv. Psychol.*, 1936, *2*, 55-60.

Akmakjian, H. Psychoanalysis and the future of literary criticism. *Psychoanal. Psychoan. Rev.* 1962, *49*, 3-28.

Albrecht, M. C. Psychological motives in the fiction of Julian Green. *J. Pers.*, 1948, *16*, 278-303.

Allport, G. W. The study of personality by the intuitive method. An experiment in teaching from *The Locomotive-God. J. abn. soc. Psychol.*, 1929, *24*, 14-27.

———— Personality: a problem for science or a problem for art? *Revista de Psihologie*, 1938, *1*, 488-502.

Altus, W. D. Sexual role, the short story, and the writer. *J. Psychol.*, 1959, *47*, 37-40.

Anderson, F. A. Psychopathological glimpses of some Biblical characters. *Psychoan. Rev.*, 1927, *14*, 56-70.

Arden, E. Hawthorne's "Case of Arthur D." *Amer. Imago*, 1961, *18*, 45-55.

Armstrong, E. A. *Shakespeare's Imagination: A Study of the Psychology of Association and Inspiration.* Lincoln, Nebraska: Univ. Nebraska Press, 1963.

Arrowsmith, W. Literature and the uses of anxiety. *Western Human. Rev.*, 1956, *10*, 325-335.

Askew, M. W. Literature and the psychotherapist. *Psychoanal. Psychoan. Rev.*, 1958, *45*, 102-112.

———— Catharsis and modern tragedy. *Psychoanal. Psychoan. Rev.*, 1961, *48*, 81-88.

Atkin, I. Smerdyakov: a review of an amoral epileptic. *J. ment. Sci.*, 1929, *75*, 263-266.

——— Raskolnikov: the study of a criminal. *J. criminal Psychopathol.*, 1943, *5*, 255-280.

Babb, L. Abnormal psychology in John Ford's *Perkin Warbeck*. *Mod. lang. Notes*, 1936, *51*, 234-237.

——— Love melancholy in the Elizabethan and early Stuart drama. *Bull. hist. Med.*, 1943, *13*, 117-132.

Bachelard, G. *The Psychoanalysis of Fire*. Boston: Beacon Press, 1964.

Bain, R. Man is the measure: writing, neurotic and normal. *Sociometry*, 1944, *7*, 332-337.

Barrett, W. Writers and madness. *Partisan Rev.*, 1947, *14*, 5-22.

Basler, R. P. *Sex, Symbolism, and Psychology in Literature*. New Brunswick, N.J.: Rutgers Univ. Press, 1948.

Beharriell, F. J. Freud's debt to literature. *Psychoanal.*, 1957, *4-5*, 18-30.

Bergler, E. Proust and the "torture theory" of love. *Amer. Imago*, 1953, *10*, 265-288.

——— Little Dorrit and Dickens' intuitive knowledge of psychic masochism. *Amer. Imago*, 1957, *14*, 371-388.

——— D. H. Lawrence's *The Fox* and the psychoanalytic theory on Lesbianism. *J. nerv. ment. Dis.* 1958, *126*, 488-491.

Bodkin, M. *Archetypal Patterns in Poetry. Psychological Studies in Imagination.* New York: Oxford Univ. Press, 1934.

Bonaparte, M. *The Life and Works of Edgar Allen Poe, A Psychoanalytic Interpretation.* (2 vols.) London: Imago Publ. Co., 1949.

Bragman, L. J. The case of Ludwig Lewisohn. *Amer. J. Psychiat.*, 1931, *11*, 319-331.

——— The case of Arthur Symons. The psychopathology of a man of letters. *Brit. J. med. Psychol.*, 1932, *12*, 346-362.

——— The case of Algernon Charles Swinburne: a study in sadism. *Psychoan. Rev.*, 1934, *21*, 51-74.

——— The case of John Ruskin. A study in cyclothymia. *Amer. J. Psychiat.*, 1935, *91*, 1137-1159.

——— The case of John Aldington Symonds. A study in aesthetic homosexuality. *Amer. J. Psychiat.*, 1936, *92*, 375-398.

——— The case of Dante Gabriel Rossetti. *Amer. J. Psychiat.*, 1936, *92*, 1111-1122.

——— The case of Floyd Dell. A study in the psychology of adolescence. *Amer. J. Psychiat.*, 1937, *93*, 1401-1411.

Brenner, A. B. The fantasies of W. S. Gilbert. *Psychoan. Quart.*, 1952, *21*, 373-401.

Brink, L., and S. E. Jelliffe. Emil Kraepelin, psychiatrist and poet. *J. nerv. ment. Dis.*, 1933, *77*, 134-152, 274-282.

Brod, M. Kafka: father and son. *Partisan Rev.*, 1938, *4*, 21-28.

Brown, D. F. Veil of Tanit: the personal significance of a woman's adornment to Gustave Flaubert. *Romanic Rev.*, 1943, 34, 196-210.

Bruner, J. S. Freud and the image of man. *Partisan Rev.*, 1957, *23*, 340-347.

Buck, S. The uses of madness. *Tenn. stud. in Lit.*, 1958, *3*, 63-71.

Burchell, S. C. Dostoevski and the sense of guilt. *Psychoan. Rev.*, 1930, *17*, 195-207.

Burke, K. Freud—and the analysis of poetry. *Amer. J. Sociol.*, 1939, *45*, 391-417.

———— The thinking of the body. *Psychoan. Rev.*, 1963, *50*, 25-68.

Buxbaum, E. The role of detective stories in a child analysis. *Psychoan. Quart.*, 1941, *10*, 373-381.

Cady, E. H. The neuroticism of William Dean Howells. *Publ. mod. lang. Assoc.*, 1946, *61*, 229-238.

Cargill, O. Henry James as Freudian pioneer. *Chicago Rev.*, 1956, *10*, 13-29.

Carrère, J. *Degeneration in the Great French Masters: Rousseau, Chateaubriand, Balzac, Stendhal, Sand, Musset, Baudelaire, Flaubert, Verlaine, Zola.* New York: Brentano's, 1922.

Cassity, J. H. Psychopathological glimpses of Lord Byron. *Psychoan. Rev.*, 1925, *12*, 397-413.

Cleckley, H. *The Caricature of Love: A Discussion of Social, Psychiatric and Literary Manifestations of Pathologic Sexuality.* New York: Ronald, 1957.

Coleman, S. M. Phantom double: its psychological significance with special reference to de Maupassant and Dostoevsky. *Brit. J. med. Psychol.*, 1934, *14*, 254-273.

———— August Strindberg: the autobiographies. *Psychoan. Rev.*, 1936, *23*, 248-273.

Colum, M. M. The psychopathic novel. *Forum*, 1934, *91*, 219-223.

Coriat, I. H. *The Hysteria of Lady Macbeth.* New York: Moffat, Yard, 1912.

———— The sadism in Oscar Wilde's *Salome*. *Psychoan. Rev.*, 1914, *1*, 257-259.

———— Anal-erotic character traits in Shylock. *Int. J. Psychoanal.*, 1921, *2*, 354-360.

Crawford, N. A. Literature and the psychopath. *Psychoan. Rev.*, 1923, *10*, 440-446.

Crick, J. Thomas Mann and psycho-analysis: the turning point. *Lit. Psychol.*, 1960, *10*, 45-55.

Davie, T. M. Hamlet's "madness." *J. ment. Sci.*, 1942, *88*, 449-450.

Davis, D. B. *Homicide in American Fiction, 1798-1860: A Study in Social Values.* Ithaca, N.Y.: Cornell Univ. Press, 1957.

Delay, J. *The Youth of Andre Gide.* Chicago: Univ. Chicago Press, 1963.

Deutsch, F. Artistic expression and neurotic illness. I. The respiratory neurosis of Charles Kingsley. *The Water Babies* and *Anton Locke's* dream. *Amer. Imago*, 1947, *4*, 64-102.

Deutsch, H. Don Quixote and Don Quixotism. *Psychoan. Quart.*, 1937, *6*, 215-222.

Deveraux, G. Why Oedipus killed Lais; a note on the complementary Oedipus complex in Greek drama. *Int. J. Psychoanal.*, 1953, *34*, 132-141.

Donnelly, J. Incest, ingratitude, and insanity. *Psychoan. Rev.*, 1953, *40*, 149-155.

Draper, J. W. "Kate the curst." *J. nerv. ment. Dis.*, 1939, *89*, 757-764.

———— Lady Macbeth. *Psychoan. Rev.*, 1941, *28*, 479-486.

Ebin, D. (Ed.) *The Drug Experience.* New York: Orion Press, 1961.

Edel, L. Notes on the use of psychological tools in literary scholarship. *Lit. Psychol.*, 1951, *1*, 1-3.

Edgar, I. Shakespeare's psychopathological knowledge: a study in criticism and interpretation. *J. abn. soc. Psychol.*, 1935, *30*, 70-83.

Eissler, K. R. The function of details in the interpretation of works of literature. *Psychoan. Quart.*, 1959, *28*, 1-20.

Emery, J. P. Othello's epilepsy. *Psychoanal. Psychoan. Rev.*, 1959, *46*, 30-32.

Ewing, F. C. *Hamlet: An Analytic and Psychological Study.* Boston: Stratford, 1934.

Faber, M. D. Two studies in self-aggression in Shakespearian tragedy. *Lit. Psychol.*, 1964, *14*, 80-96.

Farnell, F. J. Erotism as portrayed in literature. *Int. J. Psychoanal.*, 1920, *1*, 396-413.

Feldman, A. B. Othello's obsessions. *Amer. Imago*, 1952, *9*, 147-164.

———— Othello in reality. *Amer. Imago*, 1954, *11*, 147-179.

———— Fifty years of the psychoanalysis of literature: 1900-1950. *Lit. Psychol.*, 1955, *5*, 40-42, 54-64.

———— Imaginary incest: a study of Shakespeare's *Pericles. Amer. Imago*, 1955, *12*, 117-155.

———— Zola and the riddle of sadism. *Amer. Imago*, 1956, *13*, 415-425.

———— The yellow malady: short studies of five tragedies of jealousy. *Lit. Psychol.*, 1956, *6*, 38-42.

Fiedler, L. A. *Love and Death in the American Novel.* New York: Criterion Press, 1960.

———— *No! In Thunder*, Boston: Beacon Press, 1960.

Fingarette, H. Orestes: paradigm hero and central motif of contemporary ego psychology. *Psychoan. Rev.*, 1963, *50*, 87-111.

Florance, E. C. The neurosis of Raskolnikov: a study in incest and murder. *Arch. crim. Psychodynamics*, 1955, *1*, 344-396.

Foster, J. H. *Sex Variant Women in Literature*. New York: Vantage Press, 1956.

Fraiberg, L. *Psychoanalysis and American Literary Criticism*. Detroit: Wayne State Univ. Press. 1960.

———— Kafka and the dream. *Partisan Rev.*, 1956, *23*, 47-69.

Freedman, B. Italo Svevo; a psychoanalytic novelist. *Psychoan. Rev.*, 1931, *18*, 434-438.

Freud, S. Psychopathic characters on the stage. *Psychoan. Quart.*, 1942, *11*, 459-464.

———— "Dostoevsky and parricide." In *Collected Papers*, *Vol. V*. London: Hogaith, 1950.

———— *On Creativity and the Unconscious*. (Benjamin Nelson, Ed.) New York: Harper Bros., 1958.

Friedlander, K. Charlotte Brontë: a study of a masochistic character. *Int. J. Psychoanal.*, 1943, *24*, 45-54.

Fruhock, W. M. Thomas Wolfe: of time and neurosis. *Southwest Rev.*, 1948, *33*, 349-360.

Garraty, J. A. The interrelations of psychology and biography. *Psychol. Bull.*, 1954, *51*, 569-582.

Gellert, R. A survey of the treatment of the homosexual in some plays. *Encore*, 1961, *8*, 29 39.

Glaser, F. B. The case of Franz Kafka. *Psychoan. Rev.*, 1964, *51*, 99-121.

Glicksberg, C. I. Forms of madness in literature, *Arizona Quart.*, 1956, *55*, 153-162.

———— Depersonalization in the modern drama. *Personalist.*, 1958, *39*, 158-169.

———— To be or not to be: the literature of suicide. *Queen's Quart.*, 1960, *68*, 384-395.

Goodheart, E. Freud and Lawrence. *Psychoanal. Psychoan. Rev.*, 1960, *47*, 56-64.

Goodman, P. The psychological revolution and the writer's life-view. *Psychoan. Rev.*, 1963, *50*, 17-24.

Gordon, K. Meredith as psychologist. *J. Psychol.*, 1939, 7, 317-322.

Gorer, G. *The Life and Ideas of the Marquis de Sade*. London: Peter Owens, 1953.

Grant, V. W. Paranoid dynamics: a case study. *Amer. J. Psychiat.*, 1956, *113*, 143-148.

Greenacre, P. The mutual adventures of Jonathan Swift and Lemuel Gulliver: a study in pathography. *Psychoan. Quart.*, 1955, *24*, 20-62.

―――― *Swift and Carroll: A Psychoanalytic Study of Two Lives.* New York: Inter. Univ. Press, 1955.

Greene, T. M. Anxiety and the search for meaning. *Texas Quart.*, 1958, *1*, 172-191.

Greenwald, H., and A. Krich. *The Prostitute in Literature.* New York: Ballantine Books, 1960.

Guerard, A. J. The brink of darkness. *Sequoia*, 1961, *6*, 25-30.

Hallman, R. J. *Psychology of Literature: A Study of Alienation and Tragedy.* New York: Philosophical Library, 1961.

Halpern, S. Free association in 423 B. C.: Socrates in *The Clouds* of Aristophanes. *Psychoan. Rev.*, 1963, *50*, 69-86.

Hecht, M. B. Uncanniness, yearning, and Franz Kafka's works. *Amer. Imago*, 1952, *9*, 45-55.

Heilman, R. B. Charlotte Brontë, reason and the moon. *19th Cent. Fict.*, 1960, *14*, 283-302.

Heiserman, A., and J. E. Miller. J. D. Salinger: some crazy cliff. *Western Human. Rev.*, 1956, *10*, 129-137.

Heller, L., and A. Keller. Hamlet's parents: the dynamic formulation of a tragedy. *Amer. Imago*, 1960, *17*, 413-421.

Heller, P. The masochistic rebel in German literature. *J. aesth. art. Crit.*, 1953, *11*, 198-213.

Hepburn, J. G. Disarming and uncanny visions: Freud's "The Uncanny" with regard to form and content in stories by Sherwood Anderson and D. H. Lawrence. *Lit. Psychol.*, 1959, *9*, 9-12.

Hesse, H. Artist and psychoanalyst. *Psychoan. Rev.*, 1963, *50*, 5-10.

Hoffman, F. J. *Freudianism and the Literary Mind.* Baton Rouge: Louisiana State Univ. Press, 1945.

―――― Grace, violence, and self: death and modern literature. *Virginia Quart. Rev.*, 1958, *34*, 439-454.

Holland, N. N. Hobbling with Horatio; or the uses of literature. *Hudson Rev.*, 1959-60, *12*, 549-557.

Howe, I. The book of the grotesque. *Partisan Rev.*, 1951, *18*, 32-40.

Hyman, S. E. "Psychoanalysis and the Climate of Tragedy, "in Benjamin Nelson (Ed.), *Freud and the Twentieth Century.* New York: Meridian Books, 1957.

Jeffreys, H. Ibsen's Peer Gynt: a psychoanalytic study. *Psychoan. Rev.*, 1924, *11*, 361-402.

Jelliffe, S. E., and L. Brink. Alcoholism and the phantasy life in Tolstoi's *Redemption*. *New York Med. J.*, 1919, *109*, 92-97.

————, and ———— *Psychoanalysis and the drama*, New York: Nerv. ment. Dis. Publ., 1922.

Jofen, J. B. Two mad heroines. A study of the mental disorders of Ophelia in *Hamlet* and Margarete in *Faust*. *Lit. Psychol.*, 1961, *11*, 70-77.

Jones, A. E. Mark Twain and sexuality. *Publ. mod. lang. Assoc.*, 1956, *51*, 595-616.

Jones, E. *Hamlet and Oedipus*. New York: Doubleday Anchor, 1954.

Kanzer, M. Dostoyevsky's matricidal impulses. *Psychoan. Rev.*, 1948, *35*, 115-125.

———— The central theme in Shakespeare's works. *Psychoan. Rev.*, 1951, *38*, 1-16.

———— Autobiographical aspects of the writer's imagery. *Int. J. Psychoanal.*, 1959, *40*, 52-58.

———— Imagery in King Lear. *Amer. Imago*, 1965, *22*, 3-13.

Kaplan, D. M. Homosexuality and American theatre: a psychoanalytic comment. *Tulane Drama Rev.*, 1965, *9*, 25-55.

Karpman, B. *The Kreutzer Sonata:* a problem in latent homosexuality and castration. *Psychoan. Rev.*, 1938, *24*, 20-48.

———— Neurotic traits of Jonathan Swift as revealed by *Gulliver's Travels*. *Psychoan. Rev.*, 1942, *29*, 26-54, 165-184.

Katz, J. Balzac and Wolfe: a study of self-destructive overproductivity. *Psychoanal.*, 1957, *5*, 3 20.

Kaufmann, F. W., and W. S. Taylor. Literature as adjustment. *J. abn. soc. Psychol.*, 1936, *31*, 229-234.

Kenney, W. D. Dr. Johnson and the psychiatrists. *Amer. Imago*, 1960, *17*, 75-82.

Kiell, N. *The Adolescent through Fiction*. New York: Inter. Univ. Press, 1959.

Kiely, R. The craft of despondency—the traditional novelists. *Daedalus*, 1963, *92*, 220-237.

Kirschbaumer, L. Poetry in schizophrenia and other psychoses. *J. nerv. ment. Dis.*, 1940, *91*, 141-156.

Klaf, F. S. "Night Song"—Nietzsche's poetic insight into the psychotic process. *Psychoanal. Psychoan. Rev.*, 1959, *46*, 80-84.

Kohlberg, L. Psychological analysis and literary forms: a study of the doubles in Dostoevsky. *Daedalus*, 1963, *92*, 345-362.

Kohut, H. *Death in Venice* by Thomas Mann: a story about the disintegration of artistic sublimation. *Psychoan. Quart.*, 1957, *26*, 206-228.

Kris, E. *Psychoanalytic Explorations in Art*. New York: Inter. Univ. Press, 1952.

Kubie, L. S. *God's Little Acre* by Erskine Caldwell. *Psychoan. Quart.*, 1934, *3*, 328-333.
———— *Neurotic Distortion of the Creative Process.* New York: Noonday Press, 1961.

Ladell, R. G. M. The neurosis of Dr. Samuel Johnson. *Brit. J. med. Psychol.*, 1929, *9*, 314-323.
Lapp, J. C. Watcher betrayed and the fatal woman: some recurring patterns in Zola. *Publ. mod. lang. Assoc.*, 1959, *74*, 276-284.
Leites, N. Trends in affectlessness. *Amer. Imago*, 1947, *4*, 89-112.
———— Trends in moral temper. *Amer. Imago*, 1948, *5*, 3-37.
Lesser, S. O. Freud and Hamlet again. *Amer. Imago*, 1955, *12*, 207-220.
———— The function of form in narrative art. *Psychiatry*, 1955, *18*, 51-63.
———— Tragedy, comedy and the esthetic experience. *Lit. Psychol.*, 1956, *6*, 131-139.
———— *Fiction and the Unconscious.* Boston: Beacon Press, 1957.
———— The role of unconscious understanding in Flaubert and Dostoevsky. *Daedalus*, 1963, *92*, 363-382.
Lewis, N. D. C. Some theriomorphic symbolisms and mechanisms in ancient literature and dreams. *Psychoan. Rev.*, 1963-64, *50*, 5-26.
Lowenthal, L. *Literature and the Image of Man. Sociological Studies of the European Drama and Novel, 1600-1900.* Boston: Beacon Press, 1957.
Lynes, C., Jr. Proust and Albertine: on the limits of autobiography and of psychological truth in the novel. *J. aesth. art Crit.*, 1952, *10*, 328-337.

McCullen, J. T. Madness and isolation of characters in Elizabethan and early Stuart drama. *Stud. Philol.*, 1951, *48*, 206-218.
McCurdy, H. G. Literature and personality. *Char. Pers.*, 1939, *7*, 300-308.
———— Analysis of the novels of D. H. Lawrence. *Char. Pers.*, 1940, *8*, 181-203, 311-322.
———— A study of the novels of Charlotte and Emily Brontë as an expression of their personalities. *J. Pers.*, 1947, *16*, 109-152.
———— Literature as a resource in personality study: theory and methods. *J. aesth. art Crit.*, 1949, *8*, 42-46.
MacCurdy, J. T. Concerning Hamlet and Orestes. *J. abn. Psychol.*, 1919, *13*, 250-260.
McLenden, W. L. Giradoux and the split personality. *Publ. mod. lang. Assoc.*, 1958, *53*, 573-584.
Malin, I. *Psychoanalysis and American Fiction.* New York: Dutton, 1965.
Manheim, E. B. Pandora's box: persistent fantasies in themes in the plays of Jean Anouilh. *Lit. Psychol.*, 1958, *8*, 6-10.

Manheim, L. F. Thanatos: the death instinct in Dickens' later novels. *Psychoanal. Psychoan. Rev.*, 1960, *47*, 17-31.

Mann, T. Freud and the future. *Int. J. Psychoanal.*, 1956, *37*, 106-115.

Mavron, C. *Introduction to the Psychoanalysis of Mallarme.* Berkeley: Univ. Calif. Press, 1963.

Mendel, S. Hamletian man. *Arizona Quart.*, 1960, *16*, 223-236.

Menninger, C. F. The insanity of Hamlet. *Menninger Quart.*, 1952, *6*, 1-8.

Mileck, J. "Hesse and Psychology." In *Hermann Hesse and His Critics.* Chapel Hill: Univ. North Carolina Press, 1958.

Miller, M. L. *Nostalgia: A Psychoanalytic Study of Marcel Proust.* Boston: Houghton-Mifflin, 1956.

Moore, J. B. Carson McCullers: The heart is a timeless hunter. *20th cent. Lit.*, 1965, *11*, 76-81.

Moore, T. V. A study in sadism: the life of Algernon Charles Swinburne. *Char. Pers.*, 1937, *6*, 1-15.

Morris, R. The novel as catharsis. *Psychoan. Rev.*, 1944, *31*, 88-104.

Mortimer, R. Dostoevski and the dream. *Mod. Philol.*, 1956, *54*, 106-116.

Mott, F. J. Drama and the evocation of unconscious images. *J. clin. psychopath. Psychother.*, 1946, *7*, 783-793.

Mowrer, O. H. "The Life and Work of Edgar Allan Poe—a Study in Conscience Killing." In *Learning Theory and Personality Dynamics; Selected Papers.* New York: Ronald, 1950.

Moynihan, J. The hero's guilt, the case of *Great Expectations. Essays in Criticism*, 1960, *10*, 60-79.

Muir, K. Madness in *King Lear. Shakespeare Survey*, 1960, *13*, 72-80.

Nelson, B. Hesse and Jung: two newly recovered letters. *Psychoan. Rev.*, 1963, *50*, 11-16.

———— Sartre, Genet, Freud, *Psychoan. Rev.*, 1963, *50*, 155-171.

Niederland, W. G. The first application of psychoanalysis to a literary work. *Psychoan. Quart.*, 1960, *29*, 228-235.

Novotny, P. A poetic corroboration of psychoanalysis. *Amer. Imago*, 1965, *22*, 40-46.

Nydes, J. Creativity and psychotherapy. *Psychoanal. Psychoan. Rev.*, 1962, *49*, 29-33.

Oberndorf, C. P. Oliver Wendell Holmes—a precursor of Freud. *J. nerv. ment. Dis.*, 1941, *93*, 759-764.

———— Psychic determinism of Holmes and Freud. *J. nerv. ment. Dis.*, 1943, *98*, 184-188.

———— *The Psychiatric Novels of Oliver Wendell Holmes.* New York: Columbia Univ. Press, 1946.

O'Brien, J. Albertine the ambiguous: notes on Proust's transposition of sexes. *Publ. mod. lang. Assoc.*, 1949, *64*, 933-952.

O'Brien-Moore, A. *Madness in Ancient Literature*. New York: Steckert, 1933.

Ong, W. J. Swift on the mind: the myth of asepsis. *Mod. lang. Quart.*, 1954, *15*, 208-221.

Ordon, M. Unconscious contents in *Bahnwärter Thiel*. *Germanic Rev.*, 1951, *26*, 223-229.

Overholser, W. Shakespeare's psychiatry—and after. *Shakespeare Quart.*, 1959, *19*, 335-352.

Partridge, G. E. Psychopathological study of Jean-Nicholas-Arthur Rimbaud. *Psychoan. Rev.*, 1930, *17*, 401-425.

Paschall, D. M. *The Vocabulary of Mental Aberration in Roman Comedy and Petronius*. Philadelphia: Ling. Soc. Amer., 1939.

Pauncz, A. Psychopathology of Shakespeare's *King Lear:* exemplification of the Lear complex (a new interpretation). *Amer. Imago*, 1952, *9*, 57-78.

——— The Lear complex in world literature. *Amer. Imago*, 1954, *11*, 51-83.

Pederson-Krag, G. Detective stories and the primal scene. *Psychoan. Quart.*, 1949, *18*, 207-214.

Peters, E. Herman Hesse, The psychological implications of his writings. *German life Letters*, 1948, *1*, 209-214.

Petrullo, H. B. The neurotic hero of *Typee*. *Amer. Imago*, 1955, *12*, 317-323.

Phillips, W. (Ed.) *Art and Psychoanalysis*. New York: Criterion, 1957.

Pickford, R. W. *Déjà vu* in Proust and Tolstoy. *German life Letters*, 1950, *3*, 90-100.

Piper, W. Sources and processes in the writing of fiction. *Amer. J. Psychol.*, 1931, *43*, 188-201.

Plank, R. The reproduction of psychosis in science fiction. *Int. record Med.*, 1954, *167*, 407-421.

——— Portraits of fictitious psychiatrists. *Amer. Imago*, 1956, *13*, 259-267.

Plottke, P. Individual psychology in the analysis of literature: Dr. Jekyll and Mr. Hyde. *Indiv. Psychol. Bull.*, 1951, *9*, 9-17.

Praz, M. *The Romantic Agony*. New York: Oxford Univ. Press, 1951.

——— Poe and psychoanalysis. *Sewanee Rev.*, 1960, *68*, 375-389.

Proudfit, I. The big round world. A psychiatric study of Louis Stevenson. *Psychoan. Rev.*, 1936, *23*, 121-148.

Rank, O. *Art and Artist; Creative Urge and Personality Development*. New York: Knopf, 1932.

Ravich, R. A. Shakespeare and psychiatry. *Lit. Psychol.*, 1964, *14*, 97-105.

Read, H. Lost leader; or, the psychopathology of reaction in the arts. *Sewanee Rev.*, 1955, *63*, 551-566.

Regensteiner, H. The obsessive personality in Jakof Wassermann's novel. *Der Fall Maurizuis*. *Lit. Psychol.*, 1964, *14*, 106-115.

Reid, B. L. Smollett's healing journey.*Virginia Quart. Rev.*, 1965, *41*, 549-570.

Reik, T. *The Secret Self. Psychoanalytic Experiences in Life and Literature*. New York: Farrar, Straus & Young, 1952.

Rein, D. M. *S. Weir Mitchell as a Psychiatric Novelist*. New York: Inter. Univ. Press, 1952.

———— Orestes and Electra in Greek literature. *Amer. Imago*, 1954, *11*, 33-50.

———— Conrad Aiken and psychoanalysis. *Psychoan. Rev.*, 1955, *42*, 402-411.

Ribner, I. Lear's madness in the nineteenth century. *Shakespeare Assoc. Bull.*, 1947, *22*, 117-129.

Richardson, M. Psychoanalysis of ghost stories. *20th Cent. Fic.*, 1959, *166*, 419-431.

Riviere, J. The unconscious phantasy of an inner world reflected in examples from English literature. *Int. J. Psychoanal.*, 1952, *33*, 160-172.

———— The inner world in Ibsen's *Master Builder*. *Int. J. Psychoanal.*, 1952, *33*, 173-180.

Robertson, J. W. *Edgar A. Poe: A Psychopathic Study*. New York: Putnam, 1922.

Rogers, R. The beast in Henry James. *Amer. Imago*, 1956, *13*, 427-454.

Rom, P. Goethe on psychotherapy. *J. indiv. Psychol.*, 1963, *19*, 182-184.

Rosenfield, C. "Men of a smaller growth": a psychological analysis of William Golding's *Lord of the Flies*. *Lit. Psychol.*, 1961, *11*, 93-101.

———— The shadow within: the conscious and unconscious use of the "double." *Daedalus*, 1963, *92*, 326-344.

Rosenzweig, S. The ghost of Henry James: a study in thematic apperception. *Char. Pers.*, 1943, *12*, 79-100.

———— A Savoyard note on the Freudian theory of manic-depressive psychosis. *Psychoan. Rev.*, 1944, *31*, 336-339.

Sachs, H. *The Creative Unconscious: Studies in the Psychoanalysis of Art* (*2nd Ed.*) Cambridge, Mass.: Sci-Art, 1951.

Schatia, V. Peer Gynt—a study of insecurity. *Psychoan. Rev.*, 1938, *25*, 49-52.

———— Hedda Gabler's doll's house. *Psychoan. Rev.*, 1939, *9*, 33-38.

———— *The Master Builder:* a case of involutional psychosis. *Psychoan. Rev.*, 1940, *27*, 311-318.

Schilder, P. Psychoanalytic remarks on Alice in Wonderland and Lewis Carroll. *J. nerv. ment. Dis.*, 1938, 87, 159-168.

Schroeter, J. Willa Cather and the professor's house. *Yale Rev.*, 1965, *54*, 494-512.

Seidenberg, R., and E. Papathomaopoulos. Sophocles' Ajax—a morality for madness. *Psychoan. Quart.*, 1961, *30*, 404-412.

Seidlin, O. Hermann Hesse: the exorcism of the demon. *Symposium*, 1950, *4*, 325-348.

Seitzman, D. Salinger's "Franny": homoerotic imagery. *Amer. Imago*, 1965, *22*, 57-76.

Seyppel, J. H. The animal theme and totemism in Franz Kafka. *Amer. Imago*, 1956, *13*, 69-93.

Shapiro, S. A. Othello's Desdemona. *Lit. Psychol.*, 1964, *14*, 56-60.

———— Henry Green's *Back:* the presence of the past. *Critique*, 1965, 7, 87-96.

Sharpe, E. F. From *King Lear* to *The Tempest*. *Int. J. Psychoanal.*, 1946, *27*, 19-30.

Shengold, L. Chekhov and Schreber: vicissitudes of a certain kind of father-son relationship. *Int. J. Psychoanal.*, 1961, *42*, 431-438.

Shoben, E. J. Jr. A clinical view of the tragic. *Lit. Psychol.*, 1964, *14*, 23-34.

Shrodes, C. Bibliotherapy: an application of psychoanalytic theory. *Amer. Imago*, 1960, *17*, 311-319.

Shumaker, W. *Literature and the Irrational: A Study in Anthropological Backgrounds*. Englewood Cliffs, N. J.: Prentice-Hall, 1960.

Sievers, W. D. *Freud on Broadway*. New York: Hermitage House, 1955.

Silverberg, W. V. Notes on *The Iceman Cometh*. *Psychiatry*, 1947, *10*, 27-29.

Slochower, H. Incest in *The Brothers Karamazov*. *Amer. Imago*, 1959, *16*, 127-145.

Smith, G. R. Iago the paranoiac. *Amer. Imago*, 1959, *16*, 155-167.

Smith, S. S., and A. Isotoff. The abnormal from within: Doestoevsky. *Psychoan. Rev.*, 1935, *22*, 361-391.

Snodgrass, W. D. Crime for punishment: the tenor of part one. *Hudson Rev.*, 1960, *13*, 202-253.

Solomon, E. The incest theme in *Wuthering Heights*. *19th Century Fic.*, 1959, *14*, 80-83.

Somerville, H. *Madness in Shakespearian Tragedy*. London: Richards, 1930.

Squires, P. C. Fyodor Dostoevsky: a psychopathological sketch. *Psychoan. Rev.*, 1937, *24*, 365-388.

———— Jean Paul Friedrich Richter: a psychoanalytic portraiture. *Psychoan. Rev.*, 1939, *26*, 191-218.

———— The clairpsychism of Strindberg. *Psychoan. Rev.*, 1942, *29*, 50-70.

Stafford, J. The psychological novel. *Kenyon Rev.*, 1948, *10*, 214-227.

Stavrov, C. N. The neurotic heroine in Tennessee Williams. *Lit. Psychol.* 1955, *5*, 26-34.

Steinberg, A. H. Hardness, light and psychiatry in *Tender Is the Night*. *Lit. Psychol.*, 1953, *3*, 3-8.

Steinberg, E. R. The stream-of-consciousness novelist: an inquiry into the relation of consciousness and language. *ETC*, 1960, *17*, 423-439.

Sterba, E. The school boy suicide in André Gidé's novel *The Counterfeiters*. *Amer. Imago*, 1951, *8*, 307-320.

Stern, E. S., and W. H. Whiles. Three Ganser states and Hamlet. *J. Ment, Sci.*, 1942, *88*, 134-141.

Stewart, H. Jocasta's crimes. *Int. J. Psychoanal.*, 1961, *42*, 424-430.

Stragnell, G. A psychopathological study of Ferenc Molnar's *Liliom*. *Psychoan. Rev.*, 1922, *9*, 40-49.

———— A psychopathological study of Kunt Hamsun's *Hunger*. *Psychoan. Rev.*, 1922, *9*, 198-217.

Suits, C. The role of the horses in "a voyage to the Houyhnhms" *Univ. Toronto Quart.*, 1965, *34*, 118-132.

Tarachow, S. Psychoanalytic observations on *The Medium* and *The Telephone* by Gian-Carlo Menotti. *Psychoan. Rev.*, 1949, *36*, 376-384.

Talbert, E. L. The modern novel and the response of the reader. *J. abn. soc. Psychol.*, 1932, *26*, 409-414.

Taylor, J. R. The case of William Blake: creation, regression and pathology. *Psychoan. Rev.*, 1963, *50*, 139-154.

Taylor, W. S., and E. Culler. The problem of *The Locomotive-God*. *J. abn. soc. Psychol.*, 1929, *24*, 342-399.

Thayer, L. D., and N. H. Pronko. Some psychological factors in the reading of fiction. *J. genet. Psychol.*, 1958, *93*, 113-117.

Thrift, I. E. Religion and madness. The case of William Cowper. *Psychoan. Rev.*, 1926, *13*, 312-317.

Tibbetts, A. M. Nathanael West's *The Dream Life of Balso Snell*. *Stud. short Fict.*, 1965, *2*, 105-112.

Tilley, W. The idiot boy in Mississippi: Faulkner's *The Sound and the Fury*. *Amer. J. ment. Def.*, 1955, *59*, 374-377.

Tymms, R. Alternation of personality in the dramas of Heinrich von Kleist and Zacharias Weiner. *Mod. lang. Rev.*, 1942, *37*, 64-73.

Ubben, J. H. Heredity and alcoholism in the life and works of Theodor Storm. *German Quart.*, 1955, *28*, 231-236.

Ullman, M. A note on *The Threepenny Opera*. *Amer. J. Psychol.*, 1959, *13*, 429-435.

Upvall, A. *August Strindberg. A Psychoanalytic Study with Special Reference to the Oedipus Complex*. Boston: Badger, 1920.

Velikovsky, I. Tolstoy's *Kreutzer Sonata* and unconscious homosexuality. *Psychoan. Rev.*, 1937, *24*, 18-25.

Veszy-Wagner, L. Orestes the delinquent: the inevitability of parricide. *Amer. Imago*, 1961, *18*, 371-381.

Vredenburgh, J. The character of the incest object: a study of alternation between narcissism and object choice. *Amer. Imago*, 1957, *14*, 45-52.

―――― Further contributions to a study of the incest object. *Amer. Imago*, 1959, *16*, 263-268.

Waelder, R. *Psychoanalytic Avenues to Art*. New York: Inter. Univ. Press, 1965.

Wasserstrom, W. In Gertrude's closet. *Yale Rev.*, 1958, *48*, 245-265.

Watkins, W. B. C. *Perilous Balance. The Tragic Genius of Swift, Johnson and Steine*. Princeton: Princeton Univ. Press, 1939.

Webster, P. D. Arrested individuation or the problem of Joseph K. and Hamlet. *Amer. Imago*, 1948, *5*, 225-245.

―――― A critical examination of Franz Kafka's *The Castle*. *Amer. Imago*, 1951, *8*, 35-60.

―――― Franz Kafka's *In the Penal Colony*: a psychoanalytic interpretation. *Amer. Imago*, 1956, *13*, 399-407.

―――― Franz Kafka's *Metamorphosis* as death and resurrection fantasy. *Amer. Imago*, 1959, *16*, 349-365.

Wegrocki, H. G. Masochistic motives in the literary and graphic art of Bruno Schultz. *Psychoan. Rev.*, 1936, *23*, 154-164.

Weiss, D. Oedipus in Nottingham. *Lit. Psychol.*, 1957, 7, 33-42.

―――― D. H. Lawrence's great circle: from "Sons and Lovers" to "Lady Chatterley." *Psychoan. Rev.*, 1963, *50*, 112-138.

Weissman, P. Conscious and unconscious autobiographical dramas of Eugene O'Neill. *J. Amer. Psychoanalytic Assoc.*, 1957, *5*, 432-460.

―――― Psychopathological characters in current drama. A study of a trio of heroines. *Amer. Imago*, 1960, *17*, 272-288.

―――― *Creativity in the Theater*. New York: Basic Books, 1965.

Wells, F. L. Hölderlin: greatest of schizophrenics. *J. abn. soc. Psychol.*, 1946, *41*, 199-206.

Wertham, F. The matricidal impulse: critique of Freud's interpretation of *Hamlet*. *J. criminal. Psychopathol.*, 1941, *2*, 455-464.

―――― An unconscious determinant in *Native Son*. *J. clin. Pathology*, 1944-45, *6*, 111-115.

―――― The road to Rapollo: a psychiatric study. *J. abn. soc. Psychol.*, 1949, *3*, 585-600.

White, G. M. *A Passage to India*: an analysis and revaluation. *Publ. mod. lang. Assoc.*, 1953, *48*, 641-657.

White, J. S. Georg Buechner or the suffering through the father. *Amer. Imago*, 1952, *9*, 365-427.

White, W. Father and son: some comments on Hemingway's psychology. *Dalhousie Rev.*, 1952, *31*, 276-284.

Wile, I. S. Some Shakespearian characters in the light of present-day psychologies. *Psychiatric Quart.*, 1942, *16*, 62-90.

Williamson, A. The divided image: the quest for identity in the works of Djuna Barnes. *Critique*, 1965, *1*, 58-74.

Wilmer, H. Psychiatrist on Broadway. *Amer. Imago*, 1955, *12*, 157-178.

Wilson, R. N. Literature, society, and personality. *J. aesth. art Crit.*, 1952, *10*, 297-309.

———— Literary experience and personality. *J. aesth. art Crit.*, 1956, *15*, 47-57.

Wisdom, J. O. The lust for power in Hedda Gabler. *Psychoan. Rev.*, 1944, *31*, 419-437.

Wittkower, R., and M. Wittkower. *Born under Saturn: The Character and Conduct of Artists; A Documented History from Antiquity to the French Revolution.* New York: Random House, 1963.

Wolberg, L. R. *The Divine Comedy* of Dante. *Psychoan. Rev.*, 1943, *30*, 33-46.

Wood, A. B. Psychodynamics through literature. *Amer. Psychologist*, 1955, *10*, 32-33.

Wood, M. M. *Paths of Loneliness.* New York: Columbia Univ. Press, 1953.

Woods, A. H. Syphilis in Shakespeare's tragedy of *Timon of Athens*. *Amer. J. Psychiat.*, 1934, *91*, 95-107.

Wright, C. Katherine Mansfield and the "secret smile." *Lit. Psychol.*, 1955, *5*, 44-48.

Wyatt, F. Analysis of a popular novel. *Amer. Psychologist*, 1947, *2*, 280-281.

———— Some comments on the use of symbols in the novel. *Lit. Psychol.*, 1954, *4*, 15-23.

Yale French Studies. Proust. 1965, *34*, whole.

Zangwill, O. L. A case of paramnesia in Nathaniel Hawthorne. *Char. Pers.* 1945, *13*, 245-260.

Zilboorg, G. The discovery of the Oedipus complex—episodes from Marcel Proust. *Psychoan. Quart.*, 1939, *8*, 279-302.

Zuk, G. H. A note on Richard's anxiety dream. *Amer. Imago*, 1957, *14*, 37-39.

Selected Abbreviations of Journals Used

Amer. Imago American Imago
Amer. J. ment. Def. American Journal of Mental Deficiency
Amer. J. Psychiat. American Journal of Psychiatry
Amer. J. Sociol. American Journal of Sociology
Amer. Psychologist American Psychologist
Arch. crim. Psychodynamics Archives of Criminal Psychodynamics
Brit. J. med. Psychol. British Journal of Medical Psychology
Bull. hist. Med. Bulletin of the History of Medicine
Char. Pers. Character and Personality
Indiv. Psychol. Bull. Individual Psychology Bulletin
Int. J. indiv. Psychol. International Journal of Individual Psychology
Int. J. Psychoanal. International Journal of Psycho-analysis
Int. record Med. International Record of Medicine
J. abn. Psychol. Journal of Abnormal Psychology
J. abn. soc. Psychol. Journal of Abnormal and Social Psychology
J. aesth. art Crit. Journal of Aesthetics and Art Criticism
J. Amer. psychoanalytic Assoc. Journal of the American Psychoanalytic Association
J. clin. Pathology Journal of Clinical Pathology
J. criminal. Psychopathol. Journal of Criminal Psychopathology
J. genet. Psychol. Journal of Genetic Psychology
J. indiv. Psychol. Journal of Individual Psychology
J. ment. Sci. Journal of Mental Science
J. nerv. ment. Dis. Journal of Nervous and Mental Disease
J. Pers. Journal of Personality

J. Psychol.   Journal of Psychology
Lit. Psychol.   Literature and Psychology
Mod. lang. Notes   Modern Language Notes
Mod. lang. Quart.   Modern Language Quarterly
Mod. Philol.   Modern Philology
New York Med. J.   New York Medical Journal
Psychoanal.   Psychoanalysis
Psychoanal. Psychoan. Rev.   Psychoanalysis and the Psychoanalytic Review
Psychoan. Quart.   Psychoanalytic Quarterly
Psychoan. Rev.   Psychoanalytic Review
Psychol. Bull.   Psychological Bulletin
Publ. mod. lang. Assoc.   Publications of the Modern Language Association
Stud. Philol.   Studies in Philology
Stud. short Fict.   Studies of Short Fiction
Tenn. stud. in Lit.   Tennessee Studies in Literature
Western Human. Rev.   Western Humanities Review